VECTORS AND ANALYTIC GEOMETRY

VECTORS AND
ANALYTIC GEOMETRY

Israel H. Rose

HUNTER COLLEGE

PRINDLE, WEBER & SCHMIDT, INCORPORATED

Boston, Massachusetts   London   Sydney

Preface

There is some feeling in the mathematical community today that a course in analytic geometry (more or less of the classical type so useful in the study of calculus, but reflecting recent changes in school mathematics and including a treatment of vectors) might well serve once more to bridge the gap between high school and college mathematics. This book has been written for such a course to be given in either the freshman year of college or the senior year of high school, following at least three years of high school mathematics.

Since vectors play an increasingly important role in both pure and applied mathematics, and since they are furthermore intrinsically bound up with analytic geometry, it makes very good sense to include a study of vectors in a course in analytic geometry. However, I think it makes even better sense to arrange things so that the analytic geometry follows the vector theory and is founded upon it. That is what I have done in this book. This development seems to me to be the natural one, and from it one gains the usual advantages of doing what comes naturally. In particular, multiplicity of cases may be avoided, results in different dimensions may be unified, both statements and proofs may be simplified, and one is led, in an entirely unforced way, to the definition and study of important concepts of linear algebra (for example, linear independence of vectors).

The temptation was strong to go further in the direction of linear algebra in this book—to include, for example, a treatment of matrix algebra and linear transformations, so that some of the analytic geometry beyond that of lines and planes in two and three dimensions might receive the benefit of a vector treatment also. But to do so, and keep the course within reasonable bounds, would have necessitated the omission of some of the classical topics I have included, and would have changed the character of this book. I have therefore been satisfied here to restrict the vector treatment of analytic geometry essentially to the study of lines and planes in Cartesian coordinate systems, only crossing the threshold of linear algebra to supply what I think is a good foundation and motivation for that subject.

I freely admit (anticipating criticism on this score) that a course including more linear algebra and less of the customary analytic geometry would be a good idea; indeed, I have in mind writing such a book. But that would be a different book and for a different course.

With respect to the relation of this book to the "new mathematics", I have used some of its concepts and terms, but only where I thought they would be helpful, and there they have been explained. No previous knowledge of this sort is assumed, but the student who has some knowledge of modern school mathematics will find it helpful in reading this book. Others will find, in the pages that follow, an opportunity to learn some of the terms, concepts, and points of view of the "new mathematics" in a context in which they are actually useful.

I hope that this book, in its treatment of groups, vector spaces and the like will enable the student to see the important role that *structure* plays in mathematics, and so gain a better insight into the nature of mathematics at an earlier stage than he has in the past. *Proof* also receives more stress in this book than is usual at this level, but the instructor will find that considerable latitude still exists with respect to the attention and time that may be devoted to proof in the course. For example, the book contains a considerable number of problems that are actually statements to be proved— certainly more than can be proved in a three hour course. A large number of these problems are statements to be *illustrated* and proved. For the most part these are statements about vectors (all, or almost all, in Chapters 2 and 3) that can be seen fairly intuitively to be true. It is suggested, therefore, that *all* of the problems that ask for an illustration and proof be assigned, but that the student be required to prove only a selected number of these.

The format of the proofs is somewhat novel in that there are included numbered question marks, representing reasons (occasionally statements), to be supplied by the reader. Answers to most of these queries may be found in the answer section. Generally, each such answer simply identifies by letter and number some statement in the text, necessitating further search on the part of the student seeking the answer. It is hoped that the student will be diverted from rote memorization and will gain in understanding by thus participating in the process of proof.

The book, including some of the optional material, may be taught in a three hour, one semester course (but please note my remarks above on the assignment of problems involving proofs). All of the material in the book may be taught in a four hour, one semester course.

I wish to thank John Wiley and Sons, Inc., publishers of my earlier books *A Modern Introduction to College Mathematics* and *Algebra: An Introduction to Finite Mathematics* for permission to use modifications of portions of those books in the pages that follow.

ISRAEL H. ROSE

Contents

Chapter 4.   *Algebraic Graphs in E2'*

Chapter 5.   *Quadratic Graphs in E2'*

Chapter 6.   *Transcendental Graphs, Parametric Equations,*
and Polar Coordinates

VECTORS AND ANALYTIC GEOMETRY

Chapter 1

The Foundations

1a. WHAT IS ANALYTIC GEOMETRY?

Early in the seventeenth century, a Frenchman with something of a reputation for laziness described geometry as "greatly fatiguing the imagination." He further complained that the beautiful deductive proofs that geometers prized so greatly were "of avail rather in the communication of what we already know . . . than in the investigation of the unknown," But he later wrote, "I believed that I could borrow all that was best both in Geometrical Analysis and in Algebra, and correct all the defects of the one by the help of the other."

No better description of analytic geometry exists. In the year 1637, in an appendix to a philosophical tract, this Frenchman carried out his project with brilliant success. His name was René Descartes.

"Geometrical analysis" or "geometry" is well known to us as the study of points and of figures made up of points. The "Algebra" to which Descartes referred is also familiar. It has to do primarily with certain numbers (now called real numbers), how they behave when added and multiplied, certain relations among them (for example, $=$, $<$, $>$), and related concepts. We shall have, of course, a great deal to say about both of these components of analytic geometry. We shall begin with the real numbers.

But before we begin, the reader is advised that he will miss a great deal if he does not delve into the historical and human background of the mathematics he is about to study. Histories of mathematics, encyclopedias, and books on the nature of mathematics should be looked into, but especially recommended is *Men of Mathematics*, by E. T. Bell (Simon and Schuster, 1937), which is available in an inexpensive paperback edition.

1

1b. THE REAL NUMBERS: ADDITIVE PROPERTIES

In this section and in the next two, we shall summarize and give names to a number of well-known facts about the real numbers, and briefly consider some of their important implications.

First we remind the reader that he has often made use of the following fact: The points of a straight line may be labeled with numbers in such a way that if A, B are points on that line, with number labels a, b respectively, then the distance between the points A and B [which we shall denote $\mathrm{dis}(A, B)$] is equal to the nonnegative difference between the numbers a and b.

(*Note:* Henceforth, we shall often refer to "the point a" when we mean "the point labeled a"; also, "line" will mean "straight line" unless otherwise noted.)

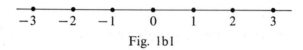

Fig. 1b1

For example, in Fig. 1b1 we see a representation of part of a line partially so labeled; and we see that $\mathrm{dis}(2, -1) = 2 - (-1) = 3$ and that $\mathrm{dis}(2, 2) = 2 - 2 = 0$. [The unit of distance is, of course, $\mathrm{dis}(0, 1)$.]

The line so labeled is often called a *scaled line* or a *number line*. *The real numbers may be thought of as the numbers that are used to label all the points of a scaled line.* (It is this concrete representation of real numbers by means of points on a line that led to the name *real*. They were so named in contrast with *imaginary* numbers, which for a long time had no pictorial representation.)

We shall assume that the reader is familiar with the well-known partition of the "set" (i.e., the collection) of all real numbers into the following three "subsets" (when we say that a set A is a *subset* of a set B, we mean that each element of A is an element of B).

(i) The *positive* real numbers (those that lie to the right of 0 on the usual representation of a horizontal scaled line; those that are greater than 0.)

(ii) The *negative* real numbers (those that lie to the left of 0 on the usual representation of a horizontal scaled line; those that are less then 0.)

(iii) The set whose only element is 0.

Note that 0 is neither positive nor negative. In fact, no two of the sets (i), (ii), (iii) have any element in common. We express this fact by saying that the sets (i), (ii), (iii) are *disjoint*.

Now we proceed to list and give names to a number of familiar properties of real numbers. (We shall find it convenient to make use of the symbol "$\in$" to mean "belongs to," "belonging to," "is an element of," etc.). If S is the set of all real numbers, we shall assume that the following statements are true.

1b1. If a, $b \in S$, then there exists a unique element of S, called "the sum of a and b," that we denote $a + b$. (When we say "$+$ is *closed* in S" or "S is *closed* under $+$," we mean that statement 1b1 holds true.)

1b2. If a, b, $c \in S$, then $(a + b) + c = a + (b + c)$. ("$+$ is *associative* in S.")

1b3. There exists an element $0 \in S$ (called an *additive identity*) such that, for each $a \in S$, $a + 0 = a$ and $0 + a = a$. ("$+$ is *identive* in S.")

1b4. For each $a \in S$, there exists an element $-a \in S$ (called an *additive inverse of* a) such that $a + (-a) = 0$ and $(-a) + a = 0$. ("$+$ is *inversive* in S.")

We sum up statements 1b1–1b4 by saying S^+ *is a group* (read "S under $+$ is a group"). A great many statements may now be proved to be logical consequences of statements 1b1–1b4. (They form the content of the branch of mathematics called *group theory*.) The importance of the concept of a group lies in the fact that every one of these logical consequences applies to each particular group that may be encountered—and exceedingly many groups actually are encountered in mathematics.

We now list just a few of the statements that are true about groups. Since this is not a course in group theory, we shall not lay great stress on proving these statements, but shall for the most part accept them, just as we have extensively accepted them, pretty much on an intuitive basis, in our earlier work with real numbers. We shall, however, prove just one of them, by way of example, leaving the proofs of the others as optional problems.

(*Note:* From now on, a question mark followed by a numeral, or sometimes simply a question mark, will indicate a question to be answered or a statement to be justified by the reader. Answers may be found at the end of this book.)

1b5. The additive identity of a group S^+ is unique.

Proof: Let 0_1, 0_2 be additive identities in S. We wish to prove that $0_1 = 0_2$. But, on the one hand, $0_1 + 0_2 = 0_1$ (since $0_1 \in S$, and 0_2 is an additive identity in S); and on the other, $0_1 + 0_2 = 0_2$ (?). Therefore (by a property of equality) $0_1 = 0_2$. $\|$

(Note that we use a double vertical line to indicate the end of a proof or solution.)

1b6. If $a \in$ group S^+, then the additive inverse of a is unique. (*Hint for proof:* $[(-a)_1 + a] + (-a)_2 = (-a)_1 + [a + (-a)_2]$.)

1b7. In a group S^+, $-0 = 0$.

1b8. If $a \in$ group S^+, then $-(-a) = a$.

1b9. If $a, b, c \in$ group S^+ and $a + b = a + c$ (or $b + a = c + a$), then $b = c$.

1b10. If $a, b \in$ group S and $a + b = 0$, then $a = -b$ and $b = -a$.

1b11 (Definition). Suppose $a, b, c, \ldots \in$ group S^+ (the three dots are read "and so on"). Then we define $a + b + c = (a + b) + c, a + b + c + d = [(a + b) + c] + d$, etc.

1b12. Suppose $a, b, c, d \in$ group S^+. Then

$$a + b + c + d = [a + (b + c)] + d = (a + b) + (c + d) = \cdots.$$

1b13 (Definition). Suppose that $a, b, c, \ldots \in$ group S^+. Then we define $a - b = a + (-b), a + b - c = a + b + (-c), a - b - c + d = a + (-b) + (-c) + d$, etc.

1b14. Suppose $a, b \in$ group S^+. Then (i) $a - b = 0$ if and only if $a = b$, (ii) $a - a = 0$, (iii) $-(a - b) = b - a$.

We now add another assumption to the assumptions 1b1–1b4. If S is the set of all real numbers, we assume also:

1b15. If $a, b \in S$, then $a + b = b + a$. ("+ is *commutative* in S.")

1b16 (Definition). Group S^+ is said to be *commutative* or *abelian* (after the Norwegian mathematician, Niels Henrik Abel, 1802–1829) if and only if + is commutative in S.

1b17. Suppose that $a, b, c, \ldots \in$ abelian group S^+. Then (i) $a + b + c = a + c + b = b + a + c = \ldots$; (ii) $-(a + b) = -a - b$, etc.; (iii) if $a - b + c + d = 0$, then $a = b - c - d, b = a + c + d$, etc.; (iv) if $a + b = c + d$, then $(a - c) + (b - d) = 0, d = a + b - c$, etc.; (v) if $b + a = a + c$, then $b = c$; etc.

1c.   THE REAL NUMBERS: MULTIPLICATIVE PROPERTIES

If S is the set of all real numbers, we shall assume that the following six statements are true.

1c1. $\cdot$ is closed in S (i.e., if $a, b \in S$, then there exists a unique element of S, called *the product of a and b*, that we denote $a \cdot b$ or ab).

1c2. $\cdot$ is associative in S (i.e., ?).

1c3. $\cdot$ is identive in S (i.e., ?), and the multiplicative identity of S is different from its additive identity.

1c4. $\cdot$ is inversive *in the set of nonzero elements of S* (i.e., ?).

1c5. $\cdot$ is commutative in S (i.e., ?).

1c6. If $a, b, c \in S$, then $a(b + c) = ab + ac$. (We call this statement the *distributive law*, or we say "$\cdot$ is distributive over $+$ in S.")

We sum up statements 1b1–1b4, 1b15, and 1c1–1c6 by saying $S^{+\cdot}$ *is a field* (read "S under $+$ and $\cdot$ is a field"). Most often we abbreviate this statement simply to "S is a field."

Among the many logical consequences of our field assumptions, we emphasize the following. (*Note:* $\neq$ is read "is unequal to"; $\notin$ is read "does not belong to"; etc.)

1c7. Suppose $a, b, c, d, e, f \in$ field S and $v, w, x \in$ field S. Then (i) $a(-v) = (-a)v = -(av)$; (ii) $(-a)(-v) = av$; (iii) $a(v - w) = av - aw$, and $(a - b)r = av - bv$; (iv) if $av = bv$, then $(a - b)v = 0$; (v) if $av + bw = cv + dw$, then $(a - c)v + (b - d)w = 0$ and $(a - c)v = (d - b)w$, etc.; (vi) if $av + bw + cx = dv + ew + fx$, then (?); (vii) if $av + bw + cx = 0$, and $a \neq 0$, then $v = (-a^{-1}b)w + (-a^{-1}c)x$; (viii) if $av + bw + cx = 0$, and $b \neq 0$, then (?); etc.

The statements that we have made about real numbers by no means exhaust their properties. In what follows we shall undoubtedly need to make use of some that we have not listed above. When we do, we shall justify what we do by simply saying "property of real numbers."

1d. THE REAL NUMBERS: INEQUALITIES, ABSOLUTE VALUE, AND DISTANCE

At this point we remind the reader of the so-called "inequality relations" among real numbers. They are $>$ ("greater than"), $<$ ("less than"), $\geq$

("greater than or equal to"), and $\leq$ ("less than or equal to"). Concerning these relations, we shall assume the following familiar facts, for arbitrary real numbers a, b, c, d.

(*Note:* From now on, we shall find it convenient to use the abbreviation *iff* for the well-known phase "if and only if." Thus, if P, Q are statements, "P iff Q" means "If P then Q *and* if Q then P.")

1d1. (i) $a > 0$ iff a is positive; (ii) $a < 0$ iff a is negative; (iii) $a > 0$ iff $-a < 0$ (and similarly for $<$, $\geq$, $\leq$); (iv) $a \geq 0$ iff a is nonnegative; (v) $a \leq 0$ iff a is nonpositive.

1d2. (i) $a > b$ iff $b < a$ iff $a - b > 0$ iff $b - a < 0$; (ii) $a \geq b$ iff $b \leq a$ iff $a - b \geq 0$ iff $b - a \leq 0$.

1d3. $a > b$ iff $a + c > b + c$ (and similarly for $<$, $\geq$, $\leq$).

1d4. (i) If $a > b$ and $c > d$, then $a + c > b + d$ (and similarly for $<$, $\geq$, $\leq$); (ii) if $a > 0$ and $b > 0$, then $ab > 0$ (and similarly for $\geq$); (iii) if $a < 0$ and $b < 0$, then $ab > 0$; etc.

1d5. If $c > 0$, then $ac > bc$ iff $a > b$, and if $c < 0$, then $ac > bc$ iff $a < b$ (and similarly for $<$, $\geq$, $\leq$).

1d6 ("Transitivity" Property). If $a > b$ and $b > c$, then $a > c$ (and similarly for $<$, $\geq$, $\leq$).

1d7 ("Trichotomy" Property).   One and only one of the following three statements must be true: $a < b$, $a = b$, $a > b$.

1d8. One and only one element in the set $\{a, -a\}$ must be nonnegative. (Proof?)

(Note the special use of braces in the preceding statement. In fact, from now on we shall often follow the standard practice in which braces are used to enclose the symbols that represent the elements of a set, and commas are used to separate these symbols.)

Statement 1d8 enables us to make the following definition.

1d9. $|a|$ (read "the absolute value of a") is the unique nonnegative element of the set $\{a, -a\}$.

Among the many facts that are true about the absolute value of real numbers, at this point we state and prove only the following.

1d10. $|ab| = |a| \cdot |b|$.

Proof: First of all, $|ab|$ is the unique nonnegative element of the set $\{ab, -ab\}$, and $|a| = \pm a$ is nonnegative, and $|b| = \pm b$ is nonnegative (?1). Hence $|a| \cdot |b|$ is nonnegative (?2), and is equal to $(\pm a)(\pm b) = \pm ab$ (?3). That is to say, $|a| \cdot |b|$ is the unique nonnegative element of the set $\{ab, -ab\}$ (?4). Hence $|ab| = |a| \cdot |b|$ (?5). ‖

With respect to the concept of distance, we make the following fundamental assumption. (*Note:* By a *Euclidean space* we shall mean a line, or a plane, or three-dimensional space.)

1d11. If A, B are points in any Euclidean space, we assume that there exists a unique nonnegative real number, called "the distance from A to B" [abbreviation: dis(A, B)].

In effect, then, we are assuming that we have chosen a unit of distance which we keep fixed throughout. More facts about the concept of distance will be developed in the problems that follow.

Problems

1. Find each of the following.
    (a) $|7|$.   (b) $|-7|$.   (c) $|0|$.   (d) $|9 - 7|$.   (e) $|7 - 9|$.
2. Solve each of the following for x, and illustrate by locating your solutions on a scaled line.
    (a) $|x| = 7$.   (b) $|x| = 0$.   (c) $|x| = -7$.   (d) $|x - 3| = 5$.
    (e) $|3 - x| = 5$.   (f) $|x - 3| = 3$.   (g) $|x - a| = a$.
    (h) $|x - a| = b$.
3. Suppose A, B are points on a scaled line, and x_A, x_B are the real numbers that label A, B respectively.
    (a) Express dis(A, B) in terms of x_A, x_B.
    (b) Illustrate on a scaled line, and find dis(A, B) and dis(B, A), if x_A, x_B are respectively:
    (i) 7, 11.   (ii) 0, 7.   (iii) $-7, 0$:   (iv) 7, 7.   (v) 7, -7.
4. Suppose A, B, C are points.
    (a) dis$(A, B) = 0$ iff?
    (b) What is the relationship between dis(A, B) and dis(B, A)?
    (c) What is the relationship between dis(A, B), dis(B, C), and dis(A, C)?
    (d) In terms of the concept of distance, $B \in$ line segment AC iff?
    (e) Suppose A, B are distinct (i.e., $A \neq B$). Using the concept of distance, define line AB and ray AB. (We may think of ray AB as consisting of line segment AB together with the extension of line segment AB through B.)

5. Suppose a, b are real numbers. Prove each of the following.
    (a) $|a| = 0$ iff $a = 0$.   (b) $|a| = a$ iff $a \geq 0$.
    (c) $|a| = -a$ iff?   (d) $|a|^2 = a^2$.
    (e) $|a| = |-a|$.   (f) $|a - b| = |b - a|$.
    (g) $a^2 \geq 0$.   (h) $a \leq |a|$.
    (i) $\sqrt{a^2} = |a|$. (Recall that $\sqrt{k}$, where k is a nonnegative real number,
        means "the *nonnegative* real number whose square is k.")
    (j) If a and b are positive, then $a^2 > b^2$ iff $a > b$, and $a^2 < b^2$ iff $a < b$.
    (k) If b is positive, then $a^2 > b^2$ iff $a > b$ or $a < -b$. (Illustrate.)
    (l) If b is positive, then $a^2 < b^2$ iff $-b < a < b$. (Illustrate.)
    (m) If $b \neq 0$, then $|a/b| = |a|/|b|$.

1e.   DIRECTION

We shall suppose that the reader finds the statements of the following
paragraph plausible.

In Fig. 1e1 the direction from A to B is the same as the direction from

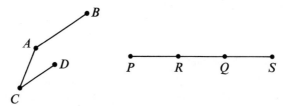

Fig. 1e1

C to D [we write: $\operatorname{dir}(A, B) = \operatorname{dir}(C, D)$]; the direction from A to B is
opposite to the direction from D to C [we write $\operatorname{dir}(A, B) = -\operatorname{dir}(D, C)$];
$\operatorname{dir}(A, B) \neq \operatorname{dir}(A, C)$; $\operatorname{dir}(A, B) \neq -\operatorname{dir}(A, C)$; $\operatorname{dir}(P, Q) = \operatorname{dir}(R, S)$;
$\operatorname{dir}(P, Q) = -\operatorname{dir}(S, R)$.

For our purposes, an intuitive grasp of the concept of direction will
suffice. We shall therefore make a number of statements about this concept,
without proof. All are intuitively, or, in the light of past geometric study,
quite plausible, except possibly the first.

The first has to do with the direction from any point to itself. We shall
find it convenient to assume that the direction from any point to itself is the
same as the direction from any other point to itself [i.e., $\operatorname{dir}(A, A) =
\operatorname{dir}(B, B)$], but that $\operatorname{dir}(A, A) \neq \operatorname{dir}(B, C)$ if $B \neq C$. This is accomplished
by statement 1e1.

PROBLEM. Draw a diagram to illustrate each of the following statements. (*Note:* In the following statements s is assumed to be a real number,
and A, B, C, A', B', C' are assumed to be points in some Euclidean space.

1e1. $\operatorname{dir}(A, A) = \operatorname{dir}(B, C)$ iff $B = C$.

1e2. $\operatorname{dir}(A, B) = -\operatorname{dir}(B, A)$.

1e3. $-[-\operatorname{dir}(A, B)] = \operatorname{dir}(A, B)$.

1e4. $\operatorname{dir}(A, B) = \operatorname{dir}(A', B')$ iff $\operatorname{dir}(B, A) = \operatorname{dir}(B', A')$.

1e5. Suppose $A \neq B$ and $A' \neq B'$. Then line AB is parallel to line $A'B'$ iff $\operatorname{dir}(A, B) = \operatorname{dir}(A', B')$ or $\operatorname{dir}(A, B) = -\operatorname{dir}(A', B')$.

(*Note:* We are assuming the following definition of parallel lines. Lines l, m are parallel iff they lie in a plane and have either none of their points or all of their points in common. In the last case, the lines are, of course, identical. Indeed, if we did not permit a line to be parallel to itself, statement 1e5 would not be true.)

1e6. If $\operatorname{dir}(A, B) = \operatorname{dir}(A, C)$, then A, B, C are "collinear" (i.e., A, B, C lie in one straight line).

1e7. If $\operatorname{dir}(A, B) = \operatorname{dir}(B, C)$, then $\operatorname{dir}(A, C) = \operatorname{dir}(A, B)$ and $\operatorname{dis}(A, C) = \operatorname{dis}(A, B) + \operatorname{dis}(B, C)$.

1e8. If $\operatorname{dir}(A, B) = \operatorname{dir}(A, C)$ and $\operatorname{dis}(A, B) = \operatorname{dis}(A, C)$, then $B = C$.

1e9. Suppose A, B, C are distinct. Then $C \in$ line segment AB iff $\operatorname{dir}(A, C) = \operatorname{dir}(A, B)$ and $\operatorname{dis}(A, C) = s \cdot \operatorname{dis}(A, B)$, where $0 < s < 1$; $B \in$ line segment AC iff $\operatorname{dir}(A, C) = \operatorname{dir}(A, B)$ and $\operatorname{dis}(A, C) = s \cdot \operatorname{dis}(A, B)$, where $s > 1$; and $A \in$ line segment BC iff $\operatorname{dir}(A, B) = -\operatorname{dir}(A, C)$.

1e10. Suppose AC is a line segment and B is a point. Then B is the midpoint of line segment AC iff $\operatorname{dir}(A, B) = \operatorname{dir}(B, C)$ and $\operatorname{dis}(A, B) = \operatorname{dis}(B, C)$.

1e11. Suppose $ABB'A'$ is a quadrilateral. Then $ABB'A'$ is a parallelogram iff $\operatorname{dir}(A, B) = \operatorname{dir}(A', B')$ and $\operatorname{dis}(A, B) = \operatorname{dis}(A', B')$.

1e12. If $\operatorname{dir}(A, B) = \operatorname{dir}(A', B')$ and $\operatorname{dis}(A, B) = \operatorname{dis}(A', B')$, then $\operatorname{dir}(A, A') = \operatorname{dir}(B, B')$ and $\operatorname{dis}(A, A') = \operatorname{dis}(B, B')$.

1e13. Suppose that $\operatorname{dir}(A', B') = \operatorname{dir}(A, B)$, $\operatorname{dis}(A', B') = s \cdot \operatorname{dis}(A, B)$, $\operatorname{dir}(B', C') = \operatorname{dir}(B, C)$, and $\operatorname{dis}(B', C') = s \cdot \operatorname{dis}(B, C)$, where $s > 0$. Then $\operatorname{dir}(A', C') = \operatorname{dir}(A, C)$ and $\operatorname{dis}(A', C') = s \cdot \operatorname{dis}(A, C)$.

1e14. Suppose that $\text{dir}(A', B') = -\text{dir}(A, B)$, $\text{dis}(A', B') = s \cdot \text{dis}(A, B)$, $\text{dir}(B', C') = -\text{dir}(B, C)$, and $\text{dis}(B', C') = s \cdot \text{dis}(B, C)$, where $s > 0$. Then $\text{dir}(A', C') = -\text{dir}(A, C)$ and $\text{dis}(A', C') = s \cdot \text{dis}(A, C)$.

1e15. Suppose we are given a positive real number s and points P, P', Q in a Euclidean space E. Then there exists a unique point Q' in E such that $\text{dir}(Q, Q') = \text{dir}(P, P')$ and $\text{dis}(Q, Q') = s \cdot \text{dis}(P, P')$.

1f. FUNCTIONS

By the process of squaring or by the process of doubling, we assign to each real number a real number. For example, to the number 3 the first process assigns the number 9 and the second process the number 6. In fact, a recurrent phenomenon in mathematics is a correspondence that assigns a unique object to each element of a given set D. Such a correspondence is called a *function*. The given set D is called the *domain* of the function.

We often use a letter of the alphabet to denote a function. For example, we might call the first of the functions described in the preceding paragraph f and the second g. The domain of both f and g, then, is the set of all real numbers. Furthermore, if x is an element in the domain of *any* function f, we let $f(x)$ (read "f of x") represent the object that the function f assigns to x. For example, if f, g are the particular functions just defined, then $f(3) = 9$, $g(3) = 6$, and more generally, if x is any real number, then $f(x) = x^2$, and $g(x) = 2x$.

We make the following important assumption about the equality of functions.

1f1. Suppose f, g are functions. Then $f = g$ iff f and g have the same domain, and for each x in that domain, $f(x) = g(x)$. (We say: Two functions are equal iff they have the same domain and the same "action" on each element of that domain.)

For example, let j be the function with domain $\{0, 2\}$, defined by the formula $j(x) = x^2$, and let k be the function whose domain consists of all nonnegative even integers that are less than 3, such that $k(y) = 2y$ for each nonnegative even integer y. Then $j = k$ (?).

.

Chapter **2**

Translations and
Cartesian Coordinates

2a. *TRANSLATIONS*

All of us have a fairly clear physical idea of what it means to move a point a given distance in a given direction—say 1 inch to the right or 3 feet up. A motion that moves each of a set of points the same distance in the same direction is called a *translation* of the set of points. Note, then, that we may think of a translation as a function. For example, suppose H is the plane of this page. The translation that moves each point of H 1 inch to the right may be thought of as a function t, with domain H, such that, for each point $x \in H$, $t(x)$ is a point of H 1 inch to the right of x. (See Fig. 2a1.)

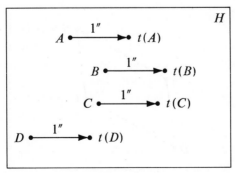

Fig. 2a1

Translations whose domains are Euclidean spaces are of exceptional importance in both pure and applied mathematics. We therefore define the concept precisely:

2a1 (Definitions).   A *translation* of a Euclidean space E is a function t, with domain E, such that, for each A, $B \in E$, $\text{dir}(A, t(a)) = \text{dir}(B, t(B))$ and $\text{dis}(A, t(A)) = \text{dis}(B, t(B))$.

Furthermore, we define dir t (the *direction of t*) to be the constant $\text{dir}(A, t(A))$, and $|t|$ (the *absolute value* or *magnitude of t*) to be the constant $\text{dis}(A, t(A))$, where, in both cases, A is any point of E.

For example, if we define the direction to our right to be "east," and we understand the unit of distance to be the inch, then for the translation t defined in the first paragraph of this section, dir t = east, and $|t| = 1$.

The following useful criterion for equality of translations is now easily proved.

2a2.   Translations t, u of a Euclidean space E are equal if they have the same direction and the same absolute value.

Proof: First of all, t and u have the same domain, namely $E(?1)$. Furthermore, for each $x \in E$, $\text{dir}(x, t(x)) \stackrel{?2}{=} \text{dir } t \stackrel{?3}{=} \text{dir } u \stackrel{?4}{=} \text{dir}(x, u(x))$, and $\text{dis}(x, t(x)) \stackrel{?5}{=} |t| \stackrel{?6}{=} |u| \stackrel{?7}{=} \text{dis}(x, u(x))$. Therefore, for each $x \in E$, $t(x) = u(x)$ (?8). Hence $t = u$ (?9).   ‖

ILLUSTRATIVE EXAMPLE.   Suppose $ABCD$ is a parallelogram in a plane H (see Fig. 2a2), t is a translation of H that carries A into B [i.e., such that $t(A) = B$], and u is a translation of H that carried D into C. Then t and u are exactly the same translation, i.e., $t = u$ (?).

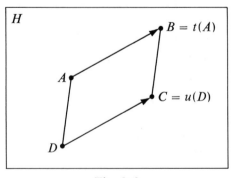

Fig. 2a2

Intuitively, given points P, Q in a Euclidean space E, there is a unique motion of E in a fixed direction that will carry P into Q. [The fixed direction is, of course, dir(P, Q).] More precisely:

2a3.   Let P, P' be points in a Euclidean space E. Then there exists a unique translation t of E such that $t(P) = P'$.

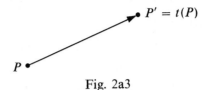

$$P' = t(P)$$

Fig. 2a3

(*Note:*   Proofs of statements that are fairly evident intuitively will often be omitted in the text, but will be found in the Appendix, as will occasional supplementary comments on the textual material. For example, a proof of statement 2a3 will be found in the Appendix.)

A useful symbol for the translation t of the preceding statement is $\overrightarrow{PP'}$ (read "the translation that carries P into P'" or, more briefly, "translation PP'"). That is to say:

2a4 (Definition).   Let A, B be points in a Euclidean space E. Then the unique translation t of E, such that $t(A) = B$, will be denoted $\overrightarrow{AB}$ (read "translation AB"). Hence $\overrightarrow{AB}(A) = B$.

Another popular symbol for $\overrightarrow{AB}$ is, in a diagram, an arrow drawn from point A to point B. In Fig. 2a4, for example, we see represented the translation $\overrightarrow{AB} = \overrightarrow{CD} = \overrightarrow{EF}$ of a plane H. Note that this sequence of equations

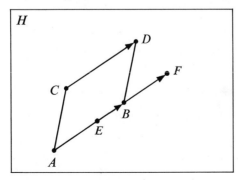

Fig. 2a4

tells us that the translation that carries A into B also carries C into D, and E into F; and that $\overrightarrow{AB}(A) = B$, $\overrightarrow{CD}(E) = F$, etc.

2a5.   Suppose t is a translation of a Euclidean space E, A is any point in E, and $t(A) = B$. The $t = \overrightarrow{AB}$..

  Proof: t and $\overrightarrow{AB}$ are translations of E such that $t(A) = B$ (?1) and $\overrightarrow{AB}(A) = B$ (?2). Therefore $t = AB$ (?3).   ‖

As a consequence of statement 2a5, if t is a translation of a Euclidean space E, and A is either a given or an arbitrary point of E, we may always assume that t may be written in the form $\overrightarrow{AB}$, where $B = t(A)$. Often therefore, without further ado, given a translation t of a Euclidean space E, we shall write "Let $t = \overrightarrow{AB}$" or "Let $t = \overrightarrow{PQ}$," etc.

It may be confessed at this point that when a physical or social scientist speaks of a *vector*, what he has in mind may usually be regarded as a translation; and, in representing his vectors, the scientist usually employs the arrow symbolism illustrated in Fig. 2a4. Although the mathematician uses the term *vector* in a more general sense, in this text (unless otherwise noted) we shall consider the terms *vector* and *translation* to be synonymous.

Problems

1. $|\overrightarrow{AB}| = ?$

2.   dir $\overrightarrow{AB} = ?$

3.   Suppose $\overrightarrow{AA'}$ and $\overrightarrow{BB'}$ are translations of a Euclidean space E. Illustrate by means of a diagram and prove each of the following.

   (a) $\overrightarrow{AA'} = \overrightarrow{BB'}$ iff $\mathrm{dir}(A, A') = \mathrm{dir}(B, B')$ and $\mathrm{dis}(A, A') = \mathrm{dis}(B, B')$.

   (b) If $\overrightarrow{AA'} = \overrightarrow{BB'}$, then $\overrightarrow{AB} = \overrightarrow{A'B'}$.

   (c) If $A \neq A'$ and $B \neq B'$ and $\overrightarrow{AA'} = \overrightarrow{BB'}$, then line AA' is parallel to line BB'.

   (d) If $\overrightarrow{AB} = \overrightarrow{AB'}$, then $B = B'$. (*Hint:* See 1e8.)

   (e) If $\overrightarrow{AA'} = \overrightarrow{BB'}$, then $\overrightarrow{A'A} = \overrightarrow{B'B}$.

   (f) If $\overrightarrow{AB} = \overrightarrow{BB'}$, then A, B, B' are collinear.

4.   Illustrate by means of a diagram and prove that if $ABB'A'$ is a quadrilateral in a Euclidean space, then $\overrightarrow{AB} = \overrightarrow{A'B'}$ iff $ABB'A'$ is a parallelogram.

5. Illustrate by means of a diagram and prove that in a Euclidean space, if AC is a line segment and B is a point, then B is the midpoint of line segment AC iff $\overrightarrow{AB} = \overrightarrow{BC}$.

2b. VECTOR ADDITION

2b1 (Definition). Let $\overrightarrow{AB}$, $\overrightarrow{BC}$ be vectors of a Euclidean space E. Then we define $\overrightarrow{AB} + \overrightarrow{BC}$ to be the vector $\overrightarrow{AC}$ of E.

ILLUSTRATIVE EXAMPLE. Given vectors $\overrightarrow{AB}$, $\overrightarrow{AC}$, $\overrightarrow{DE}$, $\overrightarrow{FG}$ as in Fig. 2b1, find $\overrightarrow{AB} + \overrightarrow{AC}$ and $\overrightarrow{DE} + \overrightarrow{FG}$.

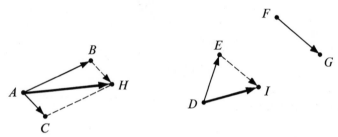

Fig. 2b1

Solution: Find a point H such that $\overrightarrow{BH} = \overrightarrow{AC}$. (This may be done by the well-known "completing the parallelogram" device, i.e., by constructing a parallelogram $BACH$.) Then $\overrightarrow{AB} + \overrightarrow{AC} = \overrightarrow{AB} + \overrightarrow{BH} = \overrightarrow{AH}$. For the other part of the example, find a point I such that $\overrightarrow{EI} = \overrightarrow{FG}$. Then $\overrightarrow{DE} + \overrightarrow{FG} = \overrightarrow{DE} + \overrightarrow{EI} = \overrightarrow{DI}$. ‖

Throughout the rest of this text, E will represent a Euclidean space, and V will represent the set of all vectors of E. We observe then (see statement 1b1):

2b2. $+$ is closed in V.

Indeed, addition of vectors behaves like addition of real numbers in many other significant respects:

2b3. $+$ is associative in V.

Proof: Let t, u, $v \in V$. We wish to prove that $(t + u) + v = t + (u + v)$. Let $t = \overrightarrow{AB}$, $u = \overrightarrow{BC}$, $v = \overrightarrow{CD}$. Then (see Fig. 2b2)

$$(t + u) + v \overset{?1}{=} (\overrightarrow{AB} + \overrightarrow{BC}) + \overrightarrow{CD} \overset{?2}{=} \overrightarrow{AC} + \overrightarrow{CD} \overset{?3}{=} \overrightarrow{AD} \overset{?4}{=} \overrightarrow{AB} + \overrightarrow{BD}$$

$$\overset{?5}{=} \overrightarrow{AB} + (\overrightarrow{BC} + \overrightarrow{CD}) \overset{?6}{=} t + (u + v). \quad \|$$

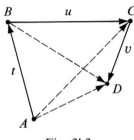

Fig. 2b2

2b4. $+$ is commutative in V.

Proof: Let t, u, $\in V$. We wish to prove that $t + u = u + t$. Let $t = \overrightarrow{AB}$ and let $u = \overrightarrow{AA'} = \overrightarrow{BB'}$. Then (see Fig. 2b3) $\overrightarrow{AB} = \overrightarrow{A'B'}$ (?1).

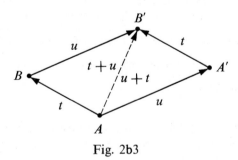

Fig. 2b3

Therefore $t + u \overset{2}{=} \overrightarrow{AB} + \overrightarrow{BB'} \overset{?3}{=} \overrightarrow{AB'} \overset{?4}{=} \overrightarrow{AA'} + \overrightarrow{A'B'} \overset{?5}{=} \overrightarrow{AA'} + \overrightarrow{AB} \overset{?6}{=} u + t. \quad \|$

2b5. $+$ is identive in V; in fact, for each point A in E, $\overrightarrow{AA}$ is an additive identity in V.

Proof: We wish to prove that, for each $t \in V$, $t + \overrightarrow{AA} = t$ and $\overrightarrow{AA} + t = t$. Let $t = \overrightarrow{AB}$. Then $\overrightarrow{AA} + t \overset{?1}{=} \overrightarrow{AA} + \overrightarrow{AB} \overset{?2}{=} \overrightarrow{AB} \overset{?3}{=} t$. Therefore $t + \overrightarrow{AA} = t$ (?4). ‖

2b6. $+$ is inversive in V.

Proof: We wish to prove that, for each $t \in V$ and $A \in E$, there is an element $-t \in V$ such that $t + (-t) = \overrightarrow{AA}$ and $(-t) + t = \overrightarrow{AA}$. Let $t = \overrightarrow{AB}$. Then it is easy to see that $-t = \overrightarrow{BA}$ does the trick (?). ‖

In summary:

2b7. V^+ is an abelian group.

Now we have earned a sizable bonus: Since we have just shown that statements 1b1–1b4 and 1b15 are as true for addition of vectors as they are for addition of real numbers (i.e., these five statements remain true when "S" is replaced by "V"), it follows that all logical consequences of these statements, and hence all of statements 1b1–1b17, are also true for addition of vectors. That is to say, *every one of statements 1b1–1b17* remains true when "S" is replaced by "V."

This is comforting knowledge, for it means that a good many of the techniques familiar to us from our study of elementary algebra may be applied, with no change whatever, to vectors (see, for example, statement 1b17).

There is, however, one slight possibility of confusion which needs to be eliminated before we proceed any further. It has to do with the additive identity, which we now know—by statement 1b5—to be as unique in V as it is in the set of all real numbers. To avoid confusing the additive identity of V with the real number 0, we make the following definition.

2b8 (Definition). We shall use the symbol 0_V to denote the unique additive identity of V. (Hence $0_V = \overrightarrow{AA}$, where A is any point of E.)

By statement 1b6, the additive inverse of any vector is also unique. Hence, from the proof of statement 2b6:

2b9. Let $\overrightarrow{AB}$ be a vector in V. Then $-\overrightarrow{AB} = \overrightarrow{BA}$.

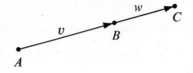

Fig. 2b4

The following statement is easy to see intuitively (see Fig. 2b4).

2b10.   Let $v, w \in V$, and suppose dir $v =$ dir w. Then dir$(v + w) =$ dir v, and $|v + w| = |v| + |w|$.

Problems

Assuming $A, B, C, D \in E$, and $v, w \in V$, illustrate and prove each of the following statements.

1. $|0_V| = 0$.

2. If $|\overrightarrow{AB}| = 0$, then $A = B$.

3. If $\overrightarrow{AB} = 0_V$, then $A = B$.

4. If $|\overrightarrow{AB}| = 0$, then $\overrightarrow{AB} = 0_V$.

5. (a) $\overrightarrow{AB} - \overrightarrow{AC} = \overrightarrow{CB}$.

    (b) If $\overrightarrow{AB} + \overrightarrow{AC} = \overrightarrow{AD}$, then $\overrightarrow{AB} = \overrightarrow{CD}$.

6. If $\overrightarrow{AB} = \overrightarrow{AC}$, then $B = C$.

7. (a) $|-v| = |v|$.

    (b) dir$(-v) = -$dir v.

8. If dir $w = -$dir v and $|w| = |v|$, then $w = -v$.

9. If A, B, C are collinear and $\overrightarrow{AB} = \overrightarrow{CD}$, then A, B, C, D are collinear.

10. If A, B, C are collinear and $\overrightarrow{AB} + \overrightarrow{AC} = \overrightarrow{AD}$, then A, B, C, D are collinear.

11. If $\overrightarrow{AB} + \overrightarrow{AC} = \overrightarrow{AD}$, then A, B, C, D are "coplanar" (i.e., lie in a plane).

2c.   THE PRODUCT OF A SCALAR AND A VECTOR

Given a vector v, what should we understand by $2v$? A reasonable interpretation for $2v$ would be a vector whose direction is the same as that of v and whose magnitude is twice the magnitude of v (see Fig. 2c1). Then what about $-2v$? A natural definition for $-2v$ would be a vector whose direction is opposite to that of v and whose magnitude is, again, twice that of v (see Fig. 2c1).

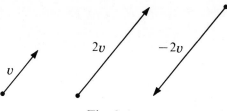

Fig. 2c1

The following definition suggests itself.

2c1 (Definition). Let $\overrightarrow{AB} \in V$ and let s be a real number. If $s > 0$, then there exists a unique point $C \in E$ such that $\text{dir}(A, C) = \text{dir}(A, B)$ and $\text{dis}(A, C) = s \cdot \text{dis}(A, B)$ (?1). In this case we define $s \cdot \overrightarrow{AB} = \overrightarrow{AC}$ (see Fig. 2c2). If $s = 0$, we define $s \cdot \overrightarrow{AB} = 0_V$. If $s < 0$, then there exists a unique point $D \in E$ such that $\text{dir}(A, D) = \text{dir}(B, A)$ and $\text{dis}(A, D) = |s| \cdot \text{dis}(B, A)$ (?2). In this case we define $s \cdot \overrightarrow{AB} = \overrightarrow{AD}$ (see Fig. 2c2).

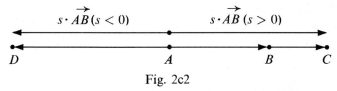

Fig. 2c2

In the context of this course, real numbers traditionally go under the alternate name of *scalars*. Hence what we have just defined is the product of a scalar and a vector.

Problems

1. Supposing that s is a scalar and $v \in V$, illustrate and prove each of the following.

(a) $|sv| = |s||v|$. (*Hint:* Let $v = \overrightarrow{AB}$ and consider three cases, $s > 0$, $s = 0$, $s < 0$.)

(b) If $s > 0$, then dir $sv = $ dir v.

(c) If $s < 0$, then dir $sv = -$dir v.

(d) $sv = 0_V$ iff $s = 0$ or $v = 0_V$.

(e) $1v = v$.

(f) $\text{dir}(-s)v = -\text{dir } sv$.

(g) $|(-s)v| = |sv|$.

(h) $(-s)v = -(sv)$.

(i) $sv + (-s)v = 0_V$.

2. Supposing that A, B, C, A', $B' \in E$, illustrate and prove each of the following.

(a) If $\mathrm{dir}(A', B') = \mathrm{dir}(A, B)$, then $\overrightarrow{A'B'}$ is a positive scalar multiple of AB.

(b) If $\mathrm{dir}(A', B') = -\mathrm{dir}(A, B)$, then $\overrightarrow{A'B'}$ is a negative scalar multiple of $\overrightarrow{AB}$.

(c) If $A \neq B$ and $A' \neq B'$, then line $A'B'$ is parallel to line AB iff $\overrightarrow{A'B'}$ is a scalar multiple of $\overrightarrow{AB}$.

(d) If $A \neq B$ and A', B are points on a line parallel to line AB, then $\overrightarrow{A'B'}$ is a scalar multiple of $\overrightarrow{AB}$.

(e) A, B, C are collinear iff $\overrightarrow{AB}$ is a scalar multiple of $\overrightarrow{AC}$ or $\overrightarrow{AC}$ is a scalar multiple of $\overrightarrow{AB}$.

(f) If $A \neq B$, then $C \in$ line AB iff $\overrightarrow{AC}$ is a scalar multiple of $\overrightarrow{AB}$.

(g) If A, B, C are distinct and $\overrightarrow{AC} = s \cdot \overrightarrow{AB}$, then $C \in$ line segment AB iff $0 < s < 1$; $B \in$ line segment AC iff $s > 1$; $A \in$ line segment BC iff $s < 0$.

3. Draw representations of vectors v, w, and then of each of the following.

(a) $3v$, $2(3v)$, and $6v$.

(b) $-3v$, $2(-3v)$, and $-6v$.

(c) $2v$, $3v$, $5v$, and $2v + 3v$.

(d) $2v$, $-3v$, $-v$, and $2v - 3v$.

(e) $2v$, $2w$, $2v + 2w$, $v + w$, and $2(v + w)$.

(f) $-2v$, $-2w$, $(-2)v + (-2)w$, $v + w$, and $-2(v + w)$.

2d.   THE STRUCTURE "VECTOR SPACE OVER THE REAL NUMBERS"

In the light of the preceding Problem 3, the following three statements become exceedingly plausible. (For proofs, see Appendix.)

2d1. Suppose r, s are scalars and $v \in V$. Then $r(sv) = (rs)v$.

2d2. Suppose r, s are scalars and $v \in V$. Then $(r + s)v = rv + sv$.

2d3. Suppose s is a scalar and v, $w \in V$. Then $s(v + w) = sv + sw$.

Just as we collected together several important properties to define the structure called a *group*, we now similarly define another important structure.

2d4 (Definition).   A set W is said to be a *vector space over the real numbers* iff:

(i) W^+ is an abelian group.

(ii) For each real number s and for each $v \in W$, the product sv is defined and is an element of W.

(iii) If r, s are real numbers and v, $w \in W$, then

(a) $r(v + w) = rv + rw$,   (b) $(r + s)v = rv + sv$,

(c) $r(sv) = (rs)v$,   (d) $1v = v$.

It is now an easy matter to verify that we have proved that V satisfies all of the conditions we have just placed on W. Hence:

2d5. V (the set of all vectors of a Euclidean space E) is a vector space over the real numbers.

Again, knowing that V is a special mathematical structure (this time a vector space), we find ourselves earning a bonus. For the properties we have set down in defining a vector space are closely related to the properties of a "field" used in proving statement 1c7. In fact, essentially the same proofs which establish that statement 1c7 is true for any field serve to prove that the following analog of statement 1c7 is true for any vector space over the real numbers. (We make the statement, however, for the particular vector space V.)

2d6.   Suppose a, b, c, d, e, f are real numbers and $v, w, x \in V$. Then (i) $a(-v) = (-a)v = -(av)$; (ii) $(-a)(-v) = av$; (iii) $a(v - w) = av - aw$, and $(a - b)v = av - bv$; (iv) if $av = bv$, then $(a - b)v = 0_V$; (v) if $av + bw = cv + dw$, then $(a - c)v + (b - d)w = 0_V$, and $(a - c)v = (d - b)w$, etc.; (vi) if $av + bw + cx = dv + ew + fx$, then (?); (vii) if $av + bw + cx = 0_V$ and $a \neq 0$, then $v = (-a^{-1}b)w + (-a^{-1}c)x$; (viii) if $av + bw + cx = 0_V$ and $b \neq 0$, then (?); etc.

The discovery of additional properties that the algebra of vectors has in common with the algebra of real numbers is welcome, for it means (cf. the remarks following statement 2b7) that even more of the techniques which we used in working with real numbers may be carried over to vectors.

Problems

1.   Supposing that s is a scalar and $v \in V$, illustrate and prove each of the following.

(a) $sv + s(-v) = 0_V$.   (b) $3v - 2v = v$.

(c) $2v + 3v = 5v$.   (d) $v + v = 2v$.

2. Supposing that $A, B, C \in E$, illustrate and prove each of the following.

   (a) B is the midpoint of line segment AC iff $\overrightarrow{AC} = 2 \cdot \overrightarrow{AB}$ iff $\overrightarrow{AB} = \frac{1}{2} \cdot \overrightarrow{AC}$.

   (b) If B is the midpoint of line segment AC, then $3 \cdot \overrightarrow{AB} + (-1)\overrightarrow{AC} = 5 \cdot \overrightarrow{AB} + (-2)\overrightarrow{AC}$.

2e. LINEAR INDEPENDENCE OF VECTORS

2e1 (Definition).   Suppose $r, s, t, \ldots$ are scalars and $v, w, x, \ldots \in V$. Then $rv + sw$ is called a *linear combination of v and w*, with *coefficients* r, s; $rv + sw + tx$ is called a *linear combination of v, w, and x*, with *coefficients* r, s, t; etc.

   The following statement is intuitively plausible.

2e2.   Suppose $A, B, C, D \in E$ and $\overrightarrow{AD}$ is a linear combination of $\overrightarrow{AB}$ and $\overrightarrow{AC}$. Then A, B, C, D are coplanar (see Fig. 2e1).

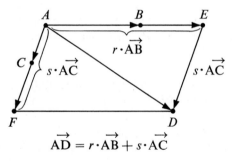

$$\overrightarrow{AD} = r \cdot \overrightarrow{AB} + s \cdot \overrightarrow{AC}$$

Fig. 2e1

   Suppose B is the midpoint of line segment AC. Then [see 2d Problem 2b—i.e., at the end of Section 2d, Problem 2(b)], the vector $v = 3 \cdot \overrightarrow{AB} + (-1)\overrightarrow{AC}$ is also expressible as $v = 5 \cdot \overrightarrow{AB} + (-2)\overrightarrow{AC}$. Thus it is sometimes possible for different linear combinations of given vectors to equal the same vector. However, we shall show that this is not always the case. First we frame a precise definition of the unique expressibility concept here indicated, and then we state important conditions under which it holds.

2e3.   In V vectors v, w (or v, w, x) are said to be *linearly independent* iff any vector that is expressible as a linear combination of v, w (or v, w, x) is (except for order of terms) uniquely so expressible.

(Hence the vectors $\overrightarrow{AB}$, $\overrightarrow{AC}$ discussed above are *not* linearly independent. They are said to be *linearly dependent*.)

2e4. If A, B, C are noncollinear points in E, then $\overrightarrow{AB}$, $\overrightarrow{AC}$ are linearly independent.

Proof: Suppose $r \cdot \overrightarrow{AB} + s \cdot \overrightarrow{AC} = t \cdot \overrightarrow{AB} + u \cdot \overrightarrow{AC}$. Then $(r - t)\overrightarrow{AB} = (u - s)\overrightarrow{AC}$ (?1). If $r - t \neq 0$ or $u - s \neq 0$, then $\overrightarrow{AB}$ is a scalar multiple of $\overrightarrow{AC}$, or $\overrightarrow{AC}$ is a scalar multiple of $\overrightarrow{AB}$ (?2), so that A, B, C are collinear (?3), contradicting our hypothesis. Hence $r - t = 0$ and $u - s = 0$, so that $r = t$ and $s = u$ (?4). Therefore $\overrightarrow{AB}$, $\overrightarrow{AC}$ are linearly independent (?5). ‖

2e5. If A, B, C, D are noncoplanar points in E, then $\overrightarrow{AB}$, $\overrightarrow{AC}$, $\overrightarrow{AD}$ are linearly independent.

Proof: Suppose $r_1 \cdot \overrightarrow{AB} + r_2 \cdot \overrightarrow{AC} + r_3 \cdot \overrightarrow{AD} = s_1 \cdot \overrightarrow{AB} + s_2 \cdot \overrightarrow{AC} + s_3 \cdot \overrightarrow{AD}$. Then $(r_1 - s_1)\overrightarrow{AB} + (r_2 - s_2)\overrightarrow{AC} + (r_3 - s_3)\overrightarrow{AD} = 0_V$ (?1). If $r_1 - s_1 \neq 0$, then $\overrightarrow{AB}$ is a linear combination of $\overrightarrow{AC}$ and $\overrightarrow{AD}$ (?2), so that A, B, C, D are coplanar (?3), contradicting our hypothesis. Hence $r_1 - s_1 = 0$, so that $r_1 = s_1$(?4). Similarly, $r_2 = s_2$ and $r_3 = s_3$. Therefore $\overrightarrow{AB}$, $\overrightarrow{AC}$, $\overrightarrow{AD}$ are linearly independent (?5).   ‖

Problems (Optional)

1. (Alternate characterization of linear independence.) Prove that vectors v, w in V are linearly independent iff: if $rv + sw = 0_V$, then $r = 0$ and $s = 0$. Prove that vectors v, w, x in V are linearly independent iff: if $rv + sw + tx = 0_V$, then $r = 0$, $s = 0$, and $t = 0$.
2. Prove each of the following.
   (a) Any two vectors of a line are linearly dependent.
   (b) Any three vectors of a plane are linearly dependent.
   (c) Any four vectors of three-dimensional space are linearly dependent.

2f. VECTORS IN GEOMETRIC PROOFS (Optional)

Many theorems of Euclidean geometry may be proved by utilizing the information about vectors that we now have at hand.

ILLUSTRATIVE EXAMPLE 1.   Prove that the diagonals of a parallelogram bisect each other.

Proof: Suppose $ABCD$ is the given parallelogram and E is the intersection of its diagonals (see Fig. 2f1). We wish to prove that E is the midpoint of line segment AC and also of line segment DB.

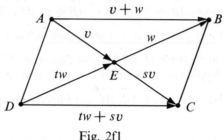

Fig. 2f1

Let $\overrightarrow{AE} = v$ and $\overrightarrow{EB} = w$. Then $\overrightarrow{EC} = sv$ and $\overrightarrow{DE} = tw$ (?1). Hence $tw + sv \overset{?2}{=} \overrightarrow{DC} \overset{?3}{=} \overrightarrow{AB} \overset{?4}{=} v + w \overset{?5}{=} 1v + 1w$. But v, w are linearly independent (?6). Therefore $s = 1$ and $t = 1$ (?7). Therefore $\overrightarrow{AE} = \overrightarrow{EC}$ and $\overrightarrow{DE} = \overrightarrow{EB}$ (?8). Therefore (?9). ‖

ILLUSTRATIVE EXAMPLE 2.   Prove that the line segment joining the midpoints of the nonparallel sides of a trapezoid is parallel to the parallel sides of the trapezoid and equal to half their sum in length.

Proof: Suppose $ABCD$ is the given trapezoid and E, F are the midpoints of the nonparallel sides AD, BC respectively (see Fig. 2f2). We wish to

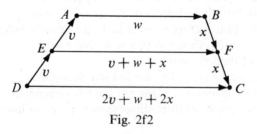

Fig. 2f2

prove that $\overrightarrow{EF}$ is a scalar multiple of $\overrightarrow{AB}$ (?1) and that $|\overrightarrow{EF}| = \frac{1}{2}(|\overrightarrow{AB}| + |\overrightarrow{DC}|)$ (?2).

Let $\overrightarrow{EA} = v$, $\overrightarrow{AB} = w$, and $\overrightarrow{BF} = x$. Then $\overrightarrow{DE} = v$ and $\overrightarrow{FC} = x$ (?3); $\overrightarrow{EF} = v + w + x$ and $\overrightarrow{DC} = 2v + w + 2x$ (?4).

Now, $2v + w + 2x = sw$ (?5). Hence $v + w + x = \frac{1}{2}(s + 1)w$ (?6); i.e., $\overrightarrow{EF}$ is a scalar multiple of $\overrightarrow{AB}$ (?7).

Finally,

$$\tfrac{1}{2}(|\overrightarrow{AB}| + |\overrightarrow{DC}|) \overset{?8}{=} \tfrac{1}{2}(|\overrightarrow{AB} + \overrightarrow{DC}|) \overset{?9}{=} \tfrac{1}{2}|2v + 2w + 2x|$$

$$\overset{?10}{=} |v + w + x| \overset{?11}{=} |\overrightarrow{EF}|. \quad \|$$

Problems (Optional)

Using vector methods, prove each of the following.

1. The line segment joining the midpoints of two sides of a triangle is parallel to the third side and one-half its length.
2. Let A, B, C, D be the midpoints of successive sides of any quadrilateral $PQRS$ in E. Then $ABCD$ is a parallelogram.
3. If the diagonals of a quadrilateral bisect each other, then the quadrilateral is a parallelogram.
4. The medians of a triangle meet in a point M (called the *centroid of the triangle*) that trisects each median.
5. The line segments joining each vertex of a tetrahedron to the centroid of the opposite face intersect in a point that divides each of these segments in the same ratio. (What is that ratio?)

2g. CARTESIAN COORDINATES

The reader is undoubtedly familiar with Cartesian (also called *rectangular*) coordinate systems in a plane, and has used them to identify points in a plane by means of ordered pairs of real numbers; in such a system he can find, for example, the point $(0, 0)$, the point $(7, -11)$, etc. [The word *ordered* in the term *ordered pair* refers to the fact that we consider the *ordered* pair (a, b) to be equal to the *ordered* pair (c, d) iff $a = c$ and $b = d$.] The reader may also be familiar with Cartesian coordinate systems in three dimensions, and how they are used to identify points in three-dimensional space by means of ordered triples of real numbers, such as $(0, 0, 0)$, $(\sqrt{2}, -\frac{2}{3}, \pi)$, etc.

[Ordered pairs and ordered triples are special cases of the general concept of an *ordered set* (also called a *sequence*). Note that in the above paragraph we have used parentheses to enclose the symbols representing the successive elements of sequences. We shall continue to follow this standard practice.]

In this section we shall use vectors to establish Cartesian coordinate systems, since this procedure greatly facilitates the development of analytic geometry.

(*Note:* Until now we have used "*E*" to represent any Euclidean space. From now on we shall use "*E2*" to represent a plane and "*E3*" to represent three-dimensional space.)

We begin by defining several terms.

2g1 (Definitions).   A *unit* vector is one whose absolute value is 1. Two vectors are said to be *orthogonal* if their directions are at right angles to each other.   From now on, in *E2*, *i*, *j* will represent unit orthogonal vectors (see Fig. 2g1), and in *E3*, *i*, *j*, *k* will represent unit mutually orthogonal vectors, i.e., vectors any pair of which is orthogonal (see Fig. 2g2).

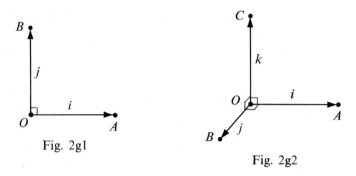

Fig. 2g1

Fig. 2g2

(Note in Fig. 2g2 that although the vectors *i*, *j*, *k* are all of the same length, namely 1, the arrow that we have drawn to represent the vector *j* is shorter in length than the arrows that we have drawn to represent *i* and *k*. This has been done to conform with the foreshortening that seems to take place when we look at a line segment that does not lie in a plane perpendicular to our line of sight.)

We shall make the following very plausible assumptions.

2g2.   In *E2* unit orthogonal vectors *i*, *j* exist, with *i* in any given direction. (In fact, if *v* is any nonzero vector of *E2*, we may always choose a unit of distance so that $v = i$.)   In *E2* a counterclockwise rotation of 90° carries *i* into *j*.   In *E3* unit mutually orthogonal vectors exist, with *i* in any given direction. (In fact, as in the case of *E2*, if *v* is any nonzero vector of *E3*, we may always choose a unit of distance so that $v = i$.)   In *E3* (*i*, *j*, *k*) are always in the configuration of Fig. 2g2.   Such a configuration is called a *left-handed system*. [A left-handed system in *E3* may be identified as follows: Suppose $\overrightarrow{OA}$, $\overrightarrow{OB}$ are nonzero vectors.   Imagine that you are lying in the plane *OAB*, between $\overrightarrow{OA}$ and $\overrightarrow{OB}$, with either the back of your head or your nose on *O* and your left arm along $\overrightarrow{OA}$.   In this position, if the nonzero vector $\overrightarrow{OC}$ is in the direction you are facing, then the sequence $(\overrightarrow{OA}, \overrightarrow{OB}, \overrightarrow{OC})$ is said to be a *left-handed system* of vectors. Note, therefore, that if (v_1, v_2, v_3) is a left-handed system of vectors, then so are $(v_2, v_1, -v_3)$, $(-v_1, v_2, -v_3)$, and $(v_1, -v_2, -v_3)$. (Diagrams?)]

In $E2$, if $\overrightarrow{OA}$ and $\overrightarrow{OB}$ are orthogonal vectors, then O, A, B are not collinear. In $E3$, if $\overrightarrow{OA}$, $\overrightarrow{OB}$, and $\overrightarrow{OC}$ are mutually orthogonal vectors, then O, A, B, C are not coplanar.

Now we shall show how vectors may be used to assign coordinates to points.

2g3. In $E2$ vectors i, j are linearly independent (Proof?), and in $E3$ vectors i, j, k are linearly independent (Proof?).

The preceding statement enables us to set up a Cartesian coordinate system in $E2$ and also in $E3$. Here is how it is done for $E3$: Choose any point O in $E3$ (henceforth called the *origin* of our coordinate system). Let $i = \overrightarrow{OA}$, $j = \overrightarrow{OB}$, $k = \overrightarrow{OC}$ (see Fig. 2g3). We call lines OA, OB, OC the

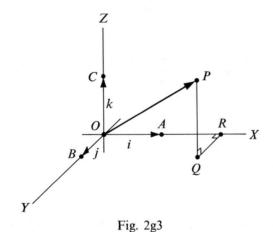

Fig. 2g3

X, Y, Z axes respectively, and the planes determined by the X and Y axes the XY plane, etc. [From now on we shall deal mainly with Euclidean spaces in which coordinate systems have been chosen. We shall denote a space $E2$ in which a Cartesian coordinate system (i.e., O, i, j) has been chosen by $E2'$, and similarly for $E3'$. E' will represent either $E2'$ or $E3'$.]

Suppose P is any point in $E3'$. Let Q be the point of intersection with

the XY plane of a line through P, parallel to line OC, and let R be the point of intersection with the X axis of a line through Q, parallel to the Y axis. Then, first of all, $\overrightarrow{OP} = \overrightarrow{OR} + \overrightarrow{RQ} + \overrightarrow{QP}$ (?1). But $\overrightarrow{OR} = a \cdot \overrightarrow{OA}$, $\overrightarrow{RQ} = b \cdot \overrightarrow{OB}$, and $\overrightarrow{QP} = c \cdot \overrightarrow{OC}$, where a, b, c are scalars (?2). Hence $\overrightarrow{OP} = ai + bj + ck$ (?3). The ordered triple of real numbers, (a, b, c), that may thus be associated with P is unique (?4). For this reason we may use (a, b, c) as a symbol for P. That is to say:

2g4.   In $E3'$ point $P = (a, b, c)$ iff $\overrightarrow{OP} = ai + bj + ck$.

PROBLEM.   Carry out a development for $E2$ analogous to the preceding development for $E3$, arriving finally at the following statement.

2g5.   In $E2'$ point $P = (a, b)$ iff $\overrightarrow{OP} = ai + bj$.

In $E2'$, if point $P = (a, b)$, we call the ordered pair (a, b) the *coordinates* of P. More particularly, a is called the x *value*, or *abscissa*, of P, and b is called the y *value*, or *ordinate*, of P. It should be understood that the coordinates of P depend upon the choice of O, i, j; that is to say, the same point may have different coordinates for different choices of O, i, j.

Except for the terms *abscissa* and *ordinate*, a similar discussion holds for $E3'$.

We shall also find it convenient to use x_P to represent the x value of a point P, etc. Thus it will always be true that in $E2'$, $P = (x_P, y_P)$, and in $E3'$, $P = (x_P, y_P, z_P)$. Hence, directly from statements 2g4 and 2g5, we have the following statement.

2g6.   If P is a point in $E3'$, then $\overrightarrow{OP} = x_P i + y_P j + z_P k$, and if P is a point in $E2'$, then $\overrightarrow{OP} = x_P i + y_P j$.

Problems

1.   (a) Illustrate and prove that if $\overrightarrow{PQ}$ is a vector of $E2'$, then

$$\overrightarrow{PQ} = (x_Q - x_P)i + (y_Q - y_P)j.$$

   (*Hint:*   By 2b, Problem 5a, $\overrightarrow{OQ} - \overrightarrow{OP} = $?)
   (b) What about $E3'$?

2.   Let v be any vector in $E2'(E3')$. Prove that v is uniquely expressible as a linear combination of i, j (i, j, k).

3. Prove that if u is a unit vector, then $|su| = |s|$.

4. In $E2'$ illustrate and express as a linear combination of i, j: $\overrightarrow{OP} + \overrightarrow{OQ}$, $\overrightarrow{PQ}$, and $\overrightarrow{QP}$, given that:

   (a) $\overrightarrow{OP} = 2i + 3j$, $\overrightarrow{OQ} = i + j$.

   (b) $\overrightarrow{OP} = 2i - 3j$, $\overrightarrow{OQ} = -i + j$.

5. In $E3'$ illustrate and express as a linear combination of i, j, k: $\overrightarrow{OP} + \overrightarrow{OQ}$, $\overrightarrow{PQ}$, and $\overrightarrow{QP}$, given that:

   (a) $P = (1, 2, 3)$, $Q = (0, 2, 0)$.

   (b) $P = (-3, 2, -1)$, $Q = (2, -3, 4)$.

6. Illustrate and prove that if $A \neq B$ and $C \neq D$ are points in $E2'$ such that $\operatorname{dir}(D, C) = \operatorname{dir}(A, B)$ and $x_B > x_A$, then $x_C > x_D$.

2h. DISTANCE IN E'

First we shall consider the problem of finding a convenient formula for the distance from the tail to the tip of a vector in $E2'$; i.e., we seek a formula for $|ai + bj|$.

If $a \neq 0$ and $b \neq 0$, the desired result is easily attained. For if we let $ai = \overrightarrow{PQ}$, and $bj = \overrightarrow{QR}$ (see Fig. 2h1), then PQR is a right triangle (?1), and

$$|ai + bj| \overset{?2}{=} |\overrightarrow{PR}| \overset{?3}{=} \sqrt{|ai|^2 + |bj|^2} \overset{?4}{=} \sqrt{|a|^2 + |b|^2} \overset{?5}{=} \sqrt{a^2 + b^2}.$$

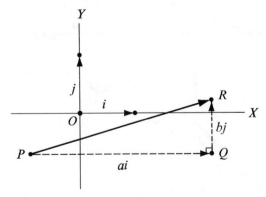

Fig. 2h1

If $a = 0$, it turns out that the same formula holds. For then

$$|ai + bj| = |bj| \overset{?6}{=} |b| \overset{?7}{=} \sqrt{b^2} \overset{?8}{=} \sqrt{a^2 + b^2}.$$

Similarly, for $b = 0$. We have proved the following statement.

2h1. In $E2'$, $|ai + bj| = \sqrt{a^2 + b^2}$.

Actually, essentially the same proof would serve to establish the following assertion.

2h2. In $E3'$, $|ai + bj| = |ai + bk| = |aj + bk| = \sqrt{a^2 + b^2}$.

The following generalization of the preceding statement can now easily be proved.

2h3. In $E3'$, $|ai + bj + ck| = \sqrt{a^2 + b^2 + c^2}$.

Proof: If $c = 0$ or $b = 0$ or $a = 0$, the result easily follows from (?1).
Otherwise let $ai = \overrightarrow{AB}$, $bj = \overrightarrow{BC}$, $ck = \overrightarrow{CD}$ (see Fig. 2h2). Then ACD is a right triangle and

$$|ai + bj + ck| \overset{?2}{=} |\overrightarrow{AD}| = \sqrt{|ai + bj|^2 + |ck|^2} \overset{?3}{=} \sqrt{a^2 + b^2 + c^2}. \quad \|$$

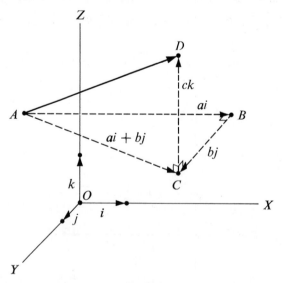

Fig. 2h2

Formulas for the distance between any two points in $E2'$ or $E3'$ easily follow:

2h4. Let A, B be points in $E2'$. Then

$$\text{dis}(A, B) = \sqrt{(x_A - x_B)^2 + (y_A - y_B)^2}.$$

Proof:

$$\text{dis}(A, B) \overset{?1}{=} |\overrightarrow{AB}| \overset{?2}{=} |(x_B - x_A)i + (y_B - y_A)j|$$
$$\overset{?3}{=} \sqrt{(x_B - x_A)^2 + (y_B - y_A)^2}$$
$$\overset{4?}{=} \sqrt{(x_A - x_B)^2 + (y_A - y_B)^2}. \ \|$$

2h5. Let A, B be points in $E3'$. Then

$$\text{dis}(A, B) = \sqrt{(x_A - x_B)^2 + (y_A - y_B)^2 + (z_A - z_B)^2}.$$

(Proof?)

Problems

1. Illustrate and find the distance between each of the following pairs of points in $E2'$.

    (a) $(1, 2)$, $(4, 6)$. (b) $(-2, 3)$, $(4, -5)$.
    (c) $(0, 0)$, $(5, 12)$. (d) $(4, -3)$, $(-1, -2)$.
    (e) $(1, 1)$, $(1, -2)$. (f) $(4, -3)$, $(-2, -3)$.

2. Illustrate and prove that if A, B are points in $E2'$ such that $x_A = x_B$, then $\text{dis}(A, B) = |y_A - y_B|$; and if $y_A = y_B$, then (?).

3. Illustrate and find the distance between each of the following pairs of points in $E3'$.

    (a) $(1, 2, 3)$, $(4, -4, 5)$. (b) $(0, 3, 0)$, $(0, -5, 0)$.

4. State, illustrate, and prove facts analogous to those of Problem 2 that hold in $E3'$.

5. Suppose $A = (-2, 3)$ and $B = (3, 7)$ are points in $E2'$. Find the intersection of the perpendicular bisector of line segment AB and the X axis.

6. (Optional). Using vector methods, prove that the sum of the squares of the sides of a parallelogram is equal to the sum of the squares of the diagonals.

2i. THE ANGLE BETWEEN TWO NONZERO VECTORS IN E', AND THE SCALAR PRODUCT OF TWO VECTORS IN E'

First we shall seek a simple formula for the angle formed by two nonzero vectors in $E2'$ (i.e., the angle between the directions of the vectors). Suppose

$v = ai + bj$ and $w = ci + dj$ are nonzero vectors in $E2'$ and suppose θ is the angle between their directions. Let $P = (a, b)$ and let $Q = (c, d)$ (see Fig. 2i1). Then $\overrightarrow{OP} = v$, and $\overrightarrow{OQ} = w$ (?1), and $|\overrightarrow{PQ}|^2 = |\overrightarrow{OP}|^2 + |\overrightarrow{OQ}|^2 - 2|\overrightarrow{OP}||\overrightarrow{OQ}|\cos\theta$ (?2). Therefore $(a - c)^2 + (b - d)^2 = a^2 + b^2 + c^2 + d^2 - 2|v||w|\cos\theta$ (?3). There easily follows (?4):

2i1. Let $v = ai + bj$, $w = ci + dj$ be nonzero vectors in $E2'$ and let θ be the angle between v and w. Then $\cos\theta = (ac + bd)/|v||w|$.

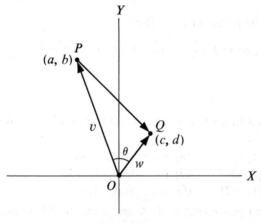

Fig. 2i1

The following definition makes it possible to phrase this result (and results to come) more neatly.

2i2 (Definition). Let $v = ai + bj$, $w = a'i + b'j$ be vectors in $E2'$. Then we define $v \cdot w = aa' + bb'$. Similarly, if $v = ai + bj + ck$, $w = a'i + b'j + c'k$ are vectors in $E3'$, then we define $v \cdot w = aa' + bb' + cc'$. (Since the product $v \cdot w$ of two vectors is always a scalar, this product is called the *scalar product* of the vectors v, w; it is also often called the *dot product* of the vectors v, w.)

Now we can rephrase statement 2i1:

2i3. Let v, w be nonzero vectors in $E2'$ and let θ be the angle between v and w. Then $\cos\theta = v \cdot w/|v||w|$.

An analogous statement is true in $E3'$.

2i4. Let v, w be nonzero vectors in $E3'$ and let θ be the angle between v and w. Then $\cos \theta = v \cdot w / |v| \, |w|$. (Proof?)

Hence we may combine statements 2i3 and 2i4:

2i5. Let v, w be nonzero vectors in E' and let θ be the angle between v and w. Then $\cos \theta = v \cdot w / |v| \, |w|$.

ILLUSTRATIVE EXAMPLE. Given the points $A = (4, -5)$, $B = (1, -1)$, $C = (5, 2)$ in $E2'$, find $\angle ABC$.

Solution: Let $v = \overrightarrow{BA}$ and let $w = \overrightarrow{BC}$. Then $v = 3i - 4j$ and $w = 4i + 3j$ (?). Hence $\cos \angle ABC = v \cdot w / |v| \, |w| = (3i - 4j) \cdot (4i + 3j)/5 \cdot 5 = 0$. Therefore $\angle ABC = 90°$. (Illustration?) ‖

The following important properties of the scalar product of two vectors may now be easily proved.

2i6. The scalar product is commutative. (Proof?)

2i7. The scalar product is distributive over addition; i.e., if v, w, x are vectors in E', then $v \cdot (w + x) = v \cdot w + v \cdot x$. (Proof?)

2i8. If v, w are vectors in E', then $v \perp w$ iff $v \cdot w = 0$. (Proof?)

Problems

1. Find $v \cdot w$, given:
   (a) $v = 3i - 4j$, $w = 3i + 4j$.
   (b) $v = 3i - 4j + 12k$, $w = 3i + 4j - 12k$.
   (c) $v = 3i - 4j$, $w = 4i + 3j$.
   (d) $v = 3i - 4j + 12k$, $w = 4i + 3j$.

2. In each of (a)–(d) of Problem 1 find the angle between v and w, and illustrate.

3. Find and draw a unit vector in $E2'$ whose direction is $\mathrm{dir}(3i - 4j)$. [*Hint:* For any positive s, $\mathrm{dir}\, s(3i - 4j) = \mathrm{dir}(3i - 4j)$.]

4. Find and draw a unit vector in $E2'$ whose direction is perpendicular to $\mathrm{dir}(i + j)$.

5. Find $\measuredangle ABC$ and illustrate, given:

(a) $A = (1, 2)$, $B = (3, 4)$, $C = (5, 6)$.

(b) $A = (0, 0)$, $B = (1, 7)$, $C = (5, 5)$.

(c) $A = (1, 2)$, $B = (3, 4)$, $C = (2, 3)$.

(d) $A = (1, 2, -1)$, $B = (3, -1, 2)$, $C = (-1, 2, 5)$.

6. Given $A = (0, 6)$, $B = (0, -4)$, $C = (5\sqrt{3}, 1)$, prove that $\triangle ABC$ is equilateral.

7. Suppose d is a diagonal of a cube, e is an edge of the same cube, f is a diagonal of a face of the cube, and d, e, f meet at a vertex of the cube. Find the angles made by e and f, d and e, and d and f, and illustrate.

8. Is the scalar product of two vectors in a Euclidean space independent of or dependent upon the coordinate system chosen? Justify your answer.

9. Prove: If v, w, x are vectors in E', and s is a scalar, then

(a) $v \cdot O_v = O_v$.

(b) $v \cdot (-w) = -(v \cdot w) = (-v) \cdot w$.

(c) $v \cdot (w - x) = v \cdot w - v \cdot x$.

(d) $v \cdot (sw) = s(v \cdot w) = (sv) \cdot w$.

10 (Optional).   Using vector methods, prove each of the following.

(a) The three altitudes of a triangle meet in a point.

(b) The three perpendicular bisectors of the sides of a triangle meet in a point.

Chapter 3

Lines and Planes in E'

3a. DIRECTION OF A LINE IN E': DIRECTION NUMBERS

Suppose $A \neq B$ and $C \neq D$ are points in $E2'$. We seek a simple criterion for determining whether or not line AB is parallel to line CD. Suppose $\overrightarrow{AB} = ai + bj$ and $\overrightarrow{CD} = ci + dj$. Then we know that line AB is parallel to line CD iff $ai + bj = s(ci + dj)$ for some scalar s (?1), hence iff $a = sc$ and $b = sd$ for some scalar s (?2), hence iff $(a, b) = (sc, sd)$ for some scalar s (?3).

The following definition enables us to phrase the preceding result (and results to come) more neatly.

3a1 (Definition). Let s, a, b, c, d, etc. be real numbers. Then we define the products $s(a, b) = (sa, sb)$, $s(a, b, c) = (sa, sb, sc)$, $s(a, b, c, d) = (sa, sb, sc, sd)$, etc.

We may now make the following statement.

3a2. Suppose $A \neq B$ and $C \neq D$ are points in $E2'$, $\overrightarrow{AB} = ai + bj$, and $\overrightarrow{CD} = ci + dj$. Then line AB is parallel to line CD iff $(a, b) = s(c, d)$ for some scalar s.

Because of its usefulness in determining parallelism of lines, the ordered pair (a, b) just encountered is given a special name:

3a3 (Definition). Suppose $A \neq B$ are points in $E2'$ and $\overrightarrow{AB} = ai + bj$. Then we refer to the ordered pair (a, b) as (a sequence of) *direction numbers* for line AB; and similarly for $E3'$ (?).

35

We now have:

3a4. In $E2'$ suppose lines l, m have direction numbers (a, b), (c, d) respectively. Then $l \parallel m$ iff $(a, b) = s(c, d)$ for some scalar s; furthermore, if $c \neq 0$ and $d \neq 0$, then $l \parallel m$ iff $a/c = b/d$. (Proof?)

[*Note:* If $a/c = b/d$ or if $(a, b) = s(c, d)$, then we say that (a, b) and (c, d) are *proportional*; and similarly for ordered triples. Thus two lines in $E2'$ are parallel iff their direction numbers are proportional.]

Direction numbers for a line are easily derived:

3a5. Suppose $A \neq B$ are points in $E2'$. Then $(x_B - x_A, y_B - y_A)$ are direction numbers for line AB. (Proof?)

PROBLEM. Carry out a development for $E3'$ analogous to the preceding development for $E2'$ in order to arrive at the following two statements.

3a6. In $E3'$ suppose lines l, m have direction numbers (a, b, c), (d, e, f) respectively. Then $l \parallel m$ iff $(a, b, c) = s(d, e, f)$ for some scalar s; furthermore, if $d \neq 0$, and $e \neq 0$, and $f \neq 0$, then $l \parallel m$ iff $a/d = b/e = c/f$.

3a7. Suppose $A \neq B$ are points in $E3'$. Then $(x_B - x_A, y_B - y_A, z_B - z_A)$ are direction numbers for line AB.

Again, the introduction of a rather natural definition enables us to phrase our results even more neatly.

3a8 (Definition). Let a, b, c, d, e, f be real numbers. Then we define

$$(a, b) + (c, d) = (a + c, b + d),$$

and

$$(a, b, c) + (d, e, f) = (a + d, b + e, c + f).$$

There easily follows:

3a9. Let S be the set of all ordered pairs of real numbers and T the set of all ordered triples of real numbers. Then S^+ and T^+ are groups, with additive identities $(0, 0)$ and $(0, 0, 0)$ respectively. If $(a, b) \in S$ and $(a, b, c) \in T$, then $-(a, b) = (-a, -b)$ and $-(a, b, c) = (-a, -b, -c)$. If (a, b), $(c, d) \in S$ and (a, b, c), $(d, e, f) \in T$, then $(a, b) - (c, d) = (a - c, b - d)$ and $(a, b, c) - (d, e, f) = (a - d, b - e, c - f)$. (Proof?)

Statements 3a4–3a7 may now be summarized:

3a10. In E' direction numbers for line AB are given by $B - A$, and two lines are parallel iff their direction numbers are proportional.

ILLUSTRATIVE EXAMPLE 1.   Suppose $A = (-3, 4)$, $B = (4, -2)$, $C = (1, 2)$, and $D = (15, -10)$ are points in $E2'$. Then $B - A = (7, -6)$ and $D - C = (14, -12)$ are direction numbers for lines AB, CD respectively; since $(14, -12) = 2(7, -6)$, lines AB and CD are parallel (?) (see Fig. 3a1).

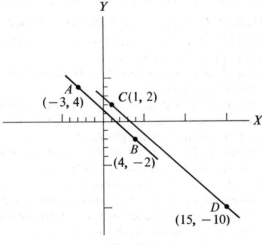

Fig. 3a1

ILLUSTRATIVE EXAMPLE 2.   Find a line through $(1, 2, 3)$ with direction numbers $(7, 0, -2)$.

Solution: $(1, 2, 3) + (7, 0, -2) = (8, 2, 1)$. Hence the line through $(1, 2, 3)$ and $(8, 2, 1)$ has direction numbers $(7, 0, -2)$, and is the line we seek. (This line is unique, since lines through the same point, with the same direction numbers, must be parallel and hence identical.) It is now easy, of course, to draw the required line in $E3'$. ‖

Problems

1. Prove that $(0, 0)$ are not direction numbers of any line in $E2'$ but that any other ordered pair of real numbers are direction numbers of some line in $E2'$. Prove a similar statement for $E3'$.

2. (a) Show that direction numbers for a line are by no means unique. Prove, in fact, that if $D = (a, b)$ are direction numbers of a line in $E2'$, then so are $sD = (sa, sb)$, for any nonzero scalar s. Prove a similar statement for $E3'$.

   (b) Suppose k, l are parallel lines in E' and k has direction numbers D. Then l has direction numbers D also.

3. State and prove a criterion in terms of direction numbers for the perpendicularity of lines.

4. For each of the following determine whether or not lines AB and CD are parallel or perpendicular and illustrate.

   (a) $A = (0, 0)$, $B = (7, 11)$, $C = (-3, -4)$, $D = (4, 7)$.

   (b) $A = (1, 2, 3)$, $B = (3, 2, 1)$, $C = (0, 0, 0)$, $D = (2, 0, 2)$.

5. Draw the quadrilateral with vertices $(-1, 3)$, $(4, 5)$, $(8, 2)$, $(3, 0)$, and prove that it is a parallelogram.

6. Draw the quadrilateral with vertices $(6, -2)$, $(4, 4)$, $(-5, 1)$, $(-3, -5)$, and prove that it is a rectangle.

7. Given the points $(0, 0)$ and $(a, 0)$, find two other points such that the four form the vertices of a square. (What about the existence and uniqueness of the solution to this problem?)

8. Given the points $(0, 0)$, $(a, 0)$, $(0, b)$, find another point such that the four form the vertices of a rectangle. (What about the existence and uniqueness of the solution to this problem?)

9. Given the points $(0, 0)$, $(a, 0)$, (b, c), find another point such that the four form the vertices of a parallelogram. (What about the existence and uniqueness of the solution to this problem?)

10. Draw a line through $(1, 2, -1)$ with direction numbers:

    (a) $(0, 0, 1)$.   (b) $(-1, -2, 1)$.   (c) $(1, 2, -1)$.

11. (a) Find *one* sequence of direction numbers for each of the coordinate axes in $E2'$ and $E3'$.

    (b) Find *all* direction numbers for each of the coordinate axes in $E2'$ and $E3'$.

12. Illustrate and prove that in $E2'$ a line AB is parallel to the X axis iff $y_A = y_B$, to the Y axis iff $x_A = x_B$. Furthermore, if $y_A = y_B$, then $dis(A, B) = |x_B - x_A|$, and if $x_A = x_B$, then $dis(A, B) = |y_B - y_A|$. (What about $E3'$?)

13. Illustrate and prove that if $ABCD$ is a trapezoid in $E2'$, such that $dir(A, B) = dir(D, C)$, $A = (0, 0)$, B is on the positive X axis, $dis(A, B) = p$, $D = (q, r)$, and $dis(D, C) = s$, then $B = (p, 0)$, and $C = (q + s, r)$. Prove, furthermore, that if $ABCD$ is a parallelogram, then $C = (q + p, r)$; and if, even more particularly, $ABCD$ is a rectangle, then $D = (0, r)$ and $C = (p, r)$. (*Hint:* See Problem 12 above and 2g Problem 6.)

14 (Optional).   Suppose S is the set of all ordered pairs of real numbers. Is S a vector space over the real numbers? How about the set T of all ordered triples of real numbers? Justify your answers.

15 (Optional).   In $E3'$ find the foot of the perpendicular from the point $A = (0, 0, 20)$ to the line through the points $B = (1, 2, 3)$ and $C = (2, 4, 7)$, and find the area of triangle ABC.

3b.   DIRECTION OF A VECTOR IN E′: DIRECTION ANGLES AND DIRECTION COSINES

3b1 (Definition).   Let v be a nonzero vector in $E2'$. Then the ordered pair of angles (α, β) between v and i, j respectively $(0° \leq \alpha, \beta \leq 180°)$ are called the *direction angles* of v (see Fig. 3b1); and if w is a nonzero vector in $E3'$, then the ordered triple of angles (α, β, γ) between v and i, j, k respectively $(0° \leq \alpha, \beta, \gamma \leq 180°)$ are called the *direction angles* of w (see Fig. 3b2). In E' the cosines of the direction angles of a vector are called the *direction cosines* of the vector.

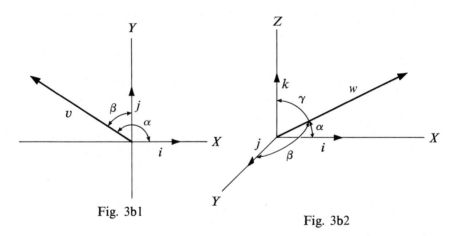

Fig. 3b1

Fig. 3b2

3b2.   In $E2'$ let (α, β) be the direction angles of a nonzero vector $v = ai + bj$. Then $\cos \alpha = a/|v|$ and $\cos \beta = b/|v|$.

Proof: $\cos \alpha \overset{?1}{=} v \cdot i/|v| \, |i| \overset{?2}{=} a/|v|$. Similarly, $\cos \beta = b/|v|$ (?3).   ‖

3b3.   In $E3'$ let (α, β, γ) be the direction angles of a nonzero vector $v = ai + bj + ck$. Then $\cos \alpha = a/|v|$, $\cos \beta = b/|v|$, and $\cos \gamma = c/|v|$. (Proof?)

3b4.   In E' the direction cosines of a nonzero vector $\overrightarrow{AB}$ are direction numbers for line AB.

Proof: We consider two cases.

CASE 1.   In $E2'$ let $\overrightarrow{AB} = ai + bj$, and let (α, β) be direction angles for $\overrightarrow{AB}$. Then $(\cos \alpha, \cos \beta) \overset{?1}{=} (a/|v|, b/|v|) \overset{?2}{=} (1/|v|)(a, b)$. But (a, b) are direction numbers for line AB (?3). Therefore $(\cos \alpha, \cos \beta)$ are direction numbers for line AB (?4). ‖

CASE 2.   In $E3'$ (Proof?).

3b5.   In $E2'$ let (α, β) be direction angles of a nonzero vector. Then $\cos^2 \alpha + \cos^2 \beta = 1$.

Proof: Let $v = ai + bj$ be the given vector (?1). Then

$$\cos^2 \alpha + \cos^2 \beta \overset{?2}{=} (a/|v|)^2 + (b/|v|)^2 \overset{?3}{=} 1. \quad ‖$$

3b6.   In $E3'$ let (α, β, γ) be direction angles of a nonzero vector. Then $\cos^2 \alpha + \cos^2 \beta + \cos^2 \gamma = 1$. (Proof?)

3b7.   In $E2'$ let (a, b) be direction numbers for line AB. Then the direction cosines of $\overrightarrow{AB}$ are $s(a, b)$, where $s = \pm 1/\sqrt{a^2 + b^2}$.

Proof: Let $(\cos \alpha, \cos \beta)$ be the direction cosines of $\overrightarrow{AB}$. Then $(\cos \alpha, \cos \beta)$ are direction numbers for line AB (?1). Therefore

$$(\cos \alpha, \cos \beta) = s(a, b),$$

where s is a scalar (?2). Therefore $\cos \alpha = sa$ and $\cos \beta = sb$ (?3). Therefore $s^2 a^2 + s^2 b^2 = 1$ (?4). Therefore $s = \pm 1/\sqrt{a^2 + b^2}$ (by properties of real numbers). Therefore $(\cos \alpha, \cos \beta) = (\pm 1/\sqrt{a^2 + b^2})(a, b)$ (?5). ‖

3b8.   In $E3'$ let (a, b, c) be direction numbers for line AB. Then the direction cosines of $\overrightarrow{AB}$ are $s(a, b, c)$, where $s = \pm 1/\sqrt{a^2 + b^2 + c^2}$. (Proof?)

3b9.   In $E2'$ let (α, β), (α', β') be direction angles of nonzero vectors v, v' respectively, and let θ be the angle formed by v, v'. Then

$$\cos \theta = \cos \alpha \cos \alpha' + \cos \beta \cos \beta'.$$

Proof: Let $v = ai + bj$, $v' = a'i + b'j$. Then

$$\cos \theta \overset{?1}{=} v \cdot v'/|v| \, |v'| \overset{?2}{=} (aa' + bb')/|v| \, |v'|$$

$$\overset{?3}{=} \frac{a}{|v|} \cdot \frac{a'}{|v'|} + \frac{b}{|v|} \cdot \frac{b'}{|v'|}$$

$$\overset{?4}{=} \cos \alpha \cos \alpha' + \cos \beta \cos \beta'. \quad ‖$$

3b10.   In $E3'$ let (α, β, γ), $(\alpha', \beta', \gamma')$ be direction angles of nonzero vectors v, v' respectively, and let θ be the angle formed by v, v'. Then

$$\cos \theta = \cos \alpha \cos \alpha' + \cos \beta \cos \beta' + \cos \gamma \cos \gamma'.$$

(Proof?)

ILLUSTRATIVE EXAMPLE.   Two lines in $E3'$ have direction numbers $(1, 1, 0)$ and $(0, 1, 1)$ respectively. Find the acute angle formed by the two lines.

Solution: By statement 3b7, direction cosines of vectors parallel to the given lines are $(1/\sqrt{2}, 1/\sqrt{2}, 0)$ and $(0, 1/\sqrt{2}, 1/\sqrt{2})$. If θ is the angle formed by these vectors, then, by statement 3b10,

$$\cos \theta = \frac{1}{\sqrt{2}} \cdot 0 + \frac{1}{\sqrt{2}} \cdot \frac{1}{\sqrt{2}} + 0 \cdot \frac{1}{\sqrt{2}} = \frac{1}{2}.$$

Therefore $\theta = 60°$, which, being an acute angle, is the solution of the problem. ‖

Problems

1.   For each of the following find the direction cosines and the direction angles of $\overrightarrow{AB}$, and illustrate.

(a) $A = (0, 0)$, $B = (1, 1)$.

(b) $A = (1, 2)$, $B = (3, 4)$.

(c) $A = (0, 0, 0)$, $B = (1, 1, 1)$.

(d) $A = (3, 4, 5)$, $B = (3, -4, 12)$.

2.   Find the direction cosines and the direction angles of each of the following vectors of $E3'$, and illustrate:

(a) i.   (b) j.   (c) k.

(d) $i + j$.   (e) $i + (\sqrt{3})j$.   (f) $-i$.

(g) $-j$.   (h) $-k$.   (i) $-i - j$.

3.   Find all possible vectors in $E3'$ for which $\alpha = \beta = 45°$, and illustrate.

4.   In $E3'$ suppose direction numbers for line AB are $(3, 4, 12)$ and line AB passes through the point $(1, 2, 3)$. Draw line AB and find all possible direction cosines of $\overrightarrow{AB}$.

5.   Suppose two lines through $(1, 0, 2)$ have direction numbers $(-1, 2, 2)$ and $(4, 3, 0)$. Draw the lines, find the direction cosines of two vectors parallel to the lines, and find the acute angle formed by the lines.

3c. DIRECTION OF A LINE IN E2': INCLINATION AND SLOPE

In the special case of $E2'$ there are two well-known indicators of the direction of a line. The first is an angle.

3c1 (Definition). In $E2'$ suppose the counterclockwise angle from dir i to line l is θ, where $0 \leq \theta < 180°$ (see Fig. 3c1). Then θ is called the *inclination* of l.

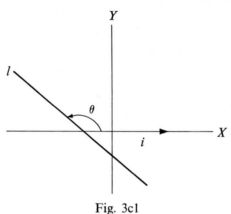

Fig. 3c1

3c2. In $E2'$ two lines are parallel iff their inclinations are equal. (Illustration and proof?)

The existence of another direction indicator, with a nice uniqueness property, follows from the next statement.

3c3. In $E2'$ suppose (p, q) are direction numbers of a line l and $p \neq 0$. Then the ratio q/p is constant for l. [I.e., if (p', q') are direction numbers of l, then $p' \neq 0$ and $q/p = q'/p'$.]

Proof: For some scalar s, $(p, q) \overset{?1}{=} s(p', q') \overset{?2}{=} (sp', sq')$. Therefore $p = sp'$ and $q = sq'$ (?3). Therefore $s \neq 0$ and $p' \neq 0$ (?4), and $q/p \overset{?5}{=} sq'/sp' \overset{?6}{=} q'/p'$. ‖

3c4 (Definition). In $E2'$ suppose (p, q) are direction numbers of a line l and $p \neq 0$. Then the real number q/p (which we have proved to be unique for l) is called the *slope* of l.

It is now easy to see that:

3c5. Lines in $E2'$ with slopes m_1, m_2 are parallel iff $m_1 = m_2$. (Proof?)

3c6. Lines in $E2'$ with slopes m_1, m_2 are perpendicular iff $m_1 m_2 = -1$. (Proof?)

There is a close connection between the slope and the inclination of a line in $E2'$:

3c7. In $E2'$ let l be a line with slope m and inclination θ. Then $m = \tan \theta$.

Proof: $m = q/p$, where (p, q) are direction numbers of l, and $p \neq 0$. Let k be the line through $(0, 0)$ and (p, q) (see Fig. 3c2). Then (p, q) are direction numbers for k (?1). Therefore $k \parallel l$ (?2). Therefore θ is the inclination of k (?3). Hence (by the definition of the tangent function) $\tan \theta = q/p$. Hence $m = \tan \theta$ (?4). ‖

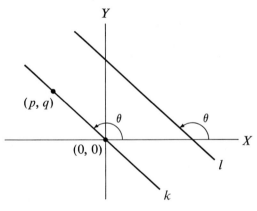

Fig. 3c2

ILLUSTRATIVE EXAMPLE. Through the point $P = (-7, 3)$ draw lines with slopes $1/12$, $-5/12$, and 0.

Solution: Draw the vectors $\overrightarrow{PA} = 12i + 1j$, $\overrightarrow{PB} = 12i - 5j$, and $\overrightarrow{PC} = 12i + 0j$. Then direction numbers for lines PA, PB, and PC are $(12, 1)$, $(12, -5)$, and $(12, 0)$ respectively (?1); hence lines PA, PB, and PC are the required lines, with slopes $1/12$, $-5/12$, and 0 respectively (?2) (see Fig. 3c3). ‖

Note that lines with positive slope slant upward to the right; that lines with zero slope are "horizontal" (i.e., parallel to the X axis); that lines with negative slope slant downward to the right; and that for vertical lines (i.e., lines parallel to the Y axis) there is no slope. Finally, the larger the absolute value of the slope of a line, the steeper the line.

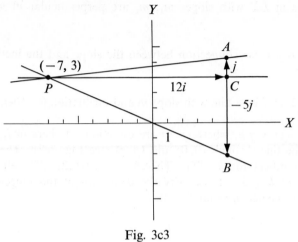

Fig. 3c3

There is a useful formula for the angle between two nonvertical lines in $E2'$, in terms of the slopes of the lines:

3c8. In $E2'$ let θ be the counterclockwise angle from line l_1 to line l_2, let m_1, m_2 be the slopes of l_1, l_2 respectively, and suppose $m_1 m_2 \neq -1$ (see Fig. 3c4). Then $\tan \theta = (m_2 - m_1)/(1 + m_1 m_2)$.

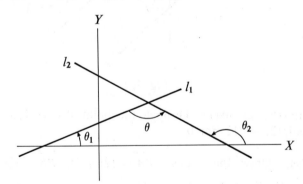

Fig. 3c4

Proof: Let the inclinations of l_1, l_2 be θ_1, θ_2 respectively. We consider three cases.

CASE 1. $\theta_2 > \theta_1$. Then (see Fig. 3c4) $\theta_2 = \theta_1 + \theta$ (?1). Therefore $\tan \theta = \tan(\theta_2 - \theta_1) = (\tan \theta_2 - \tan \theta_1)/(1 + \tan \theta_1 \tan \theta_2) = $ (?2).

CASE 2. $\theta_2 < \theta_1$. [Proof (optional)? *Hint:* Draw a new figure.]

CASE 3. $\theta_2 = \theta_1$. (Proof?) ‖

Problems

1. (a) Draw a line through the origin with slope 1; with slope -1; with slope 0; with slope $-1/2$; with slope $\sqrt{3}/2$. Find the inclination of each of these lines.

    (b) Do the same for a line through the point $(-7, -11)$ rather than through the origin.

2. Derive the formula $m = (y_B - y_A)/(x_B - x_A)$ for the slope of a non-vertical line AB.

3. For each of the following find the slope of line AB, express $\overrightarrow{AB}$ as a linear combination of i and j, and illustrate.

    (a) $A = (1, 2)$, $B = (3, 6)$.

    (b) $A = (-1, 2)$, $B = (2, -1)$.

    (c) $A = (1, 2)$, $B = (6, 2)$.

    (d) $A = (2, -5)$, $B = (-2, 5)$.

4. For each of the following find the counterclockwise angle from line AB to line AC, and illustrate.

    (a) $A = (3, 6)$, $B = (0, 3)$, $C = (2, 4)$.

    (b) $A = (-3, -3)$, $B = (1, 5)$, $C = (2, 2)$.

    (c) $A = (5, 0)$, $B = (1, 4)$, $C = (2, -3)$.

    (d) $A = (2, 3)$, $B = (4, 1)$, $C = (7, -2)$.

    (e) $A = (5, 13)$, $B = (1, 5)$, $C = (5, 0)$.

5 (Optional). Prove that there exists no equilateral triangle in $E2'$ such that all of the coordinates of its vertices are rational numbers. (Recall that a rational number is a number that can be written in the form a/b, where a, b are integers and $b \neq 0$.)

3d. *EQUATIONS OF A LINE IN E'*

Intuitively, a line should be determined by its direction and one of its points. That is to say, given the direction of a line and one point on the line, we should be able to find all points on the line. We now show that in $E2'$ this is indeed the case.

3d1. In $E2'$ let A be a point on line l and let (p, q) be direction numbers of l. Then point $(x, y) \in l$ iff, for some scalar s, $x = x_A + sp$ and $y = y_A + sq$.

Proof: Suppose that, for some scalar s, $x = x_A + sp$ and $y = y_A + sq$. If $(x, y) = A$, then certainly $(x, y) \in l$ (?1). Otherwise, there is a line k

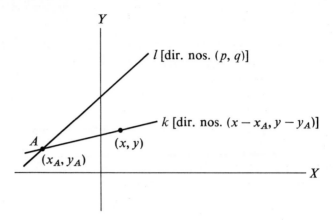

Fig. 3d1

through (x, y) and A (Fig. 3d1) with direction numbers $(x - x_A, y - y_A)$ (?2), and hence with direction numbers $s(p, q)$ (?3). Therefore $k \parallel l$ (?4). Therefore $k = l$ (?5). Therefore $(x, y) \in l$ (?6).

Conversely, suppose $(x, y) \in l$ (Fig. 3d2). If $(x, y) = A$, then $x = x_A + sp$ and $y = y_A + sq$, for the scalar $s = $ (?7). Otherwise, $(x - x_A, y - y_A)$ are direction numbers for l (?8). Therefore $(x - x_A, y - y_A) = s(p, q)$, for some scalar s (?9). Therefore (?10). $\parallel$

Whenever we have one or more equations involving x, y, which hold true iff (x, y) is in a given set of points in $E2'$, we say that the set of points is the *graph* of the equations, and the equations are the equations of the given set of points. (Similarly, of course, for $E3'$.) Hence we may rephrase statement 3d1 as follows.

3d2. In $E2'$ equations of a line l that has direction numbers (p, q) and that passes through point A are

$$x = x_A + sp,$$
$$y = y_A + sq,$$

where each (real) value of s determines a point of l. (These equations are called *parametric* equations for the line l, with *parameter s*.)

ILLUSTRATIVE EXAMPLE 1.   Draw the line l in $E2'$ whose parametric equations are $x = 1 + s$, $y = 1 - s$.

Solution: The real number $s = 0$ determines the point $(1, 1)$ on the line, and the real number $s = 1$ determines the point $(2, 0)$ on the line. Now we may draw the required line l (see Fig. 3d3). $\parallel$

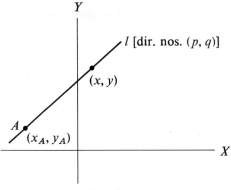

Fig. 3d2

ILLUSTRATIVE EXAMPLE 2.   Find parametric equations for a line through $A = (3, 4)$ with direction numbers $(-1, 2)$ (Fig. 3d4).

Solution: By statement 3d2, parametric equations for the given line are $x = 3 - s$, $y = 4 + 2s$. The real number $s = 1$ determines the point $(2, 6)$ on the line, etc.   ‖

Again intuitively, a line in $E2'$ should also be determined by two points. Indeed, it is:

3d3.   In $E2'$ parametric equations, with parameter s, for line AB are

$$x = x_A + s(x_B - x_A),$$
$$y = y_A + s(y_B - y_A).$$

(Proof?)

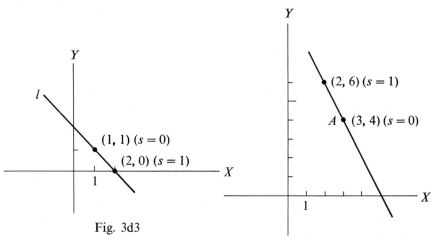

Fig. 3d3

Fig. 3d4

The parameters that we have just encountered may be eliminated. For example:

3d4. In $E2'$ if $p \neq 0$ and $q \neq 0$, then an equation for a line l that has direction numbers (p, q) and that passes through point A is

$$\frac{x - x_A}{p} = \frac{y - y_A}{q}.$$

Proof: It is sufficient to prove that the equation of this statement is *equivalent* to the equations of statement 3d2 (i.e., that if either is true, then the other is true).

Suppose $(x - x_A)/p = (y - y_A)/q$. Let $s = (x - x_A)/p = (y - y_A)/q$. Then $x = x_A + sp$ and $y = y_A + sq$ (?1).
Conversely, suppose $x = x_A + sp$ and $y = y_A + sq$. Then (?2). ‖

PROBLEM.   Carry out a development analogous to that which we carried out in statements 3d2–3d4 and their proofs to arrive at the following statements.

3d5. In $E3'$ parametric equations, with parameter s, for a line l that has direction numbers (p, q, r) and that passes through point A are

$$x = x_A + sp,$$
$$y = y_A + sq,$$
$$z = z_A + sr.$$

3d6. In $E3'$ parametric equations, with parameter s, for line AB are

$$x = x_A + s(x_B - x_A),$$
$$y = y_A + s(y_B - y_A),$$
$$z = z_A + s(z_B - z_A).$$

3d7. In $E3'$ if $p \neq 0, q \neq 0$, and $r \neq 0$, then equations for a line l that has direction numbers (p, q, r) and that passes through point A are

$$\frac{x - x_A}{p} = \frac{y - y_A}{q} = \frac{z - z_A}{r}.$$

Problems

1. For each of the following write parametric and nonparametric equations for a line that passes through A and that has direction numbers D, and illustrate.

(a) $A = (2, 4)$, $D = (-1, 3)$.

(b) $A = (1, 2, 3)$, $D = (1, 2, 3)$.

(c) $A = (0, 0)$, $D = (2, -5)$.

(d) $A = (0, 0, 0)$, $D = (-2, 3, 4)$.

(e) $A = (3, 4)$, $D = (1, 0)$.

(f) $A = (1, 2, 3)$, $D = (1, 0, 0)$.

2. Draw the graph in $E3'$ of each of the following.

(a) $x = 1 + s$, $y = 1 - s$, $z = s$.

(b) $\dfrac{x - 1}{1} = \dfrac{y - 2}{2} = \dfrac{z - 3}{3}$.

(c) $x = 1$, $y = 1$, $z = s$.   (d) $\dfrac{x}{-1} = \dfrac{y}{2} = \dfrac{z - 4}{3}$.

(e) $x = y$, $z = 0$.   (f) $x = y = z$.

3. For each of the following write parametric and nonparametric equations for line AB and illustrate.

(a) $A = (-2, 3)$, $B = (3, 4)$.

(b) $A = (1, 2, 3)$, $B = (-1, 0, 1)$.

(c) $A = (1, 2, 3)$, $B = (-1, 2, 4)$.

(d) $A = (0, 0, 0)$, $B = (1, 1, 1)$.

4. It is rather obvious that in $E3'$ a point (x, y, z) is on the X axis iff $y = 0$ and $z = 0$. That is to say, in $E3'$ equations of the X axis are $y = 0$, $z = 0$. Similarly, for each of the following, write one or two equations of which the given set of points is the graph and illustrate.

(a) The Y axis in $E3'$.   (b) The Z axis in $E3'$.

(c) The X axis in $E2'$.   (d) The Y axis in $E2'$.

(e) A vertical line in $E2'$ through the point (a, b).

(f) A horizontal line in $E2'$ through the point (a, b).

(g) In $E2'$ a line through $(0, 0)$ and $(1, 1)$.

(h) In $E3'$ a line through $(0, 0, 0)$ and $(1, 1, 1)$.

(i) In $E3'$ the XY plane.

(j) In $E3'$ the XZ plane.

(k) In $E3'$ the YZ plane.

(l) In $E3'$ a line through $(1, 2, 3)$ parallel to the X axis.

(m) In $E3'$ a line through $(1, 2, 3)$ parallel to the Y axis.

(n) In $E3'$ a line through $(1, 2, 3)$ parallel to the Z axis.

(o) In $E3'$ a plane through the Z axis and the point $(1, 1, 0)$.

(p) In $E3'$ a plane through $(1, 2, 3)$ parallel to the X axis.

(q) In $E3'$ a plane through $(1, 2, 3)$ parallel to the Y axis.

(r) In $E3'$ a plane through $(1, 2, 3)$ parallel to the Z axis.

5 (Optional). In $E3'$ find equations of a line through $(0, 0, 20)$ perpendicular to and intersecting the line whose parametric equations are $x = 1 + t, y = 2 + 2t, z = 3 + 4t$.

6 (Optional). Prove that statements 3d2 and 3d5 may be neatly combined into the following single statement.

In E' a parametric equation with parameter s for a line l that has direction numbers D and that passes through point A, is $P = A + sD$ (where P is any point of l).

(What about statements 3d3 and 3d6?)

3e. LINEAR INTERPOLATION IN E'

In $E2'$ suppose (x, y) is a point on line AB. Then (by statement 3d3), for some scalar s, $x = x_A + s(x_B - x_A)$ and $y = y_A + s(y_B - y_A)$. We know that each point (x, y) on line AB is determined by some real value of s. We seek now to gain further insight into the role of the parameter s in these equations. More particularly, we seek to discover the relation between the value of s and the position of the point (x, y) on the line AB (see Figs. 3e1–3e3).

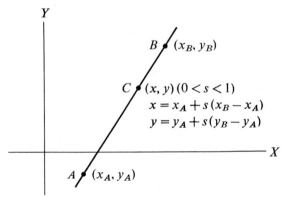

Fig. 3e1

For convenience, let $C = (x, y)$. Then $C = A + s(B - A)$ (?1). Furthermore, $\overrightarrow{AC} \overset{?2}{=} (x - x_A)i + (y - y_A)j \overset{?3}{=} s(x_B - x_A)i + s(y_B - y_A)j \overset{?4}{=}$ $s[(x_B - x_A)i + (y_B - y_A)j] \overset{?5}{=} s \cdot \overrightarrow{AB}$. Hence if $s = 0$, then $C = (x, y) = A$; if $s = 1$, then $C = (x, y) = B$ (?6). Otherwise (see 2c Problem 2g), we know that the point $C = (x, y) \in$ line segment AB iff $0 < s < 1$ (this is the case illustrated in Fig. 3e1). In this case the process of finding C is called *interpolation*. We know that $B \in$ line segment AC iff $s > 1$ (see Fig. 3e2), and

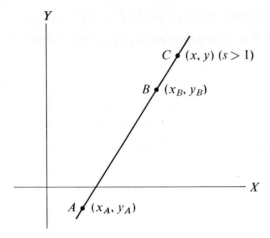

Fig. 3e2

$A \in$ line segment BC iff $s < 0$ (see Fig. 3e3). In the latter two cases the process of finding C is called *extrapolation*.

But we know even more. Using 2c Problem 1a we have $\text{dis}(A, C) = |\overrightarrow{AC}| = |s \cdot \overrightarrow{AB}| = |s| \, |\overrightarrow{AB}| = |s| \, \text{dis}(A, B)$.

Note that the point C is such that $\overrightarrow{AC} = s \cdot \overrightarrow{AB}$ is unique; for if $\overrightarrow{AC'} = s \cdot \overrightarrow{AB}$, then $\overrightarrow{AC} = \overrightarrow{AC'}$, and hence (by 2b Problem 6), $C = C'$.

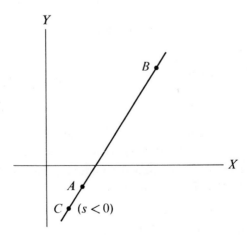

Fig. 3e3

Exactly analogous results apply in $E3'$. In summary:

3e1. In E' let $A \neq B$ be points and let s be a real number. Then the unique point C on line AB such that $\overrightarrow{AC} = s \cdot \overrightarrow{AB}$ [and hence also dis$(A, C) =$ $|s|$ dis(A, B)] is $C = A + s(B - A)$.

ILLUSTRATIVE EXAMPLE. Suppose $A = (-1, 2, 3)$ and $B = (8, -4, 6)$. Find a point C on line segment AB one-third of the way from A to B, a point D such that $\overrightarrow{AD} = 2 \cdot \overrightarrow{AB}$, and a point E such that $\overrightarrow{AE} = -2 \cdot \overrightarrow{AB}$ (see Fig. 3e4).

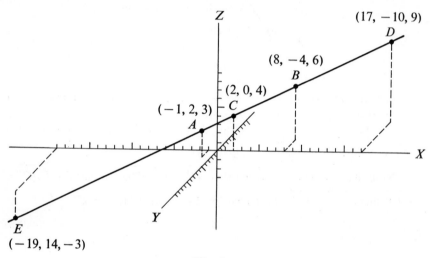

Fig. 3e4

Solution: $C = A + \frac{1}{3}(B - A) = (-1, 2, 3) + \frac{1}{3}(9, -6, 3) = (2, 0, 4)$; $D = A + 2(B - A) = (17, -10, 9)$; $E = A - 2(B - A) = (-19, 14, -3)$. ‖

Problems

1. Prove that the midpoint of a line segment in E' is the average of its endpoints, i.e., that the midpoint of line segment AB is $\frac{1}{2}(A + B)$.

2. For each of the following find the midpoint and the trisection points of line segment AB, and illustrate.

   (a) $A = (-2, 3)$, $B = (4, -3)$.

   (b) $A = (3, -6)$, $B = (-3, 6)$.

   (c) $A = (0, 0, 0)$, $B = (6, -6, 12)$.

   (d) $A = (6, 0, 4)$, $B = (0, 6, 10)$.

3. In each of Problems 2a and 5b above find the points in which line AB intersects the X axis and the Y axis.

4. In each of the following find the points in which line AB intersects the coordinate planes, and illustrate.

   (a) $A = (-1, 2, 3)$, $B = (5, -2, -3)$.

   (b) $A = (4, 4, -6)$, $B = (2, -4, 6)$.

5. Given points $A = (-5, 5)$, $B = (3, 8)$, and $C = (1, -2)$ in $E2'$, find each of the following, and illustrate.

   (a) The lengths of the sides of triangle ABC.

   (b) The midpoints of the sides of triangle ABC.

   (c) The lengths of the medians of triangle ABC.

6. In $E2'$ suppose point $A = (3, -4)$. Find point B, and illustrate, given that line segment AB has:

   (a) Midpoint $(0, 0)$.   (b) Midpoint $(2, -1)$.

   (c) Midpoint $(1, -2)$.   (d) Midpoint $(3, 0)$.

   (e) Point of trisection nearest A, $(0, 0)$.

   (f) Point of trisection nearest B, $(0, 0)$.

   (g) Point of trisection nearest A, $(2, -1)$.

   (h) Point of trisection nearest B, $(2, -1)$.

7. Given points $A = (-2, 3)$ and $B = (1, -3)$ in $E2'$, find and illustrate each of the following.

   (a) A point C on ray AB such that $\text{dis}(A, C) = 2\,\text{dis}(A, B)$.

   (b) A point C on ray BA such that $\text{dis}(B, C) = 2\,\text{dis}(B, A)$.

   (c) A point C on line segment AB dividing it in the ratio $1:2$.

   (d) Two points C on line AB such that $\text{dis}(A, C) = 3\,\text{dis}(A, B)$.

8. Given points $P = (-2, 4)$ and $Q = (3, -1)$ in $E2'$, find two points R on ray PQ "dividing" line segment PQ in the ratio $3:2$, and illustrate.

9. Find formulas for the points of trisection of a line segment AB in E'.

10. In $E2'$, given points $A = (-2, 1)$ and $B = (4, 5)$, find a point C such that $\overrightarrow{AC} = s \cdot \overrightarrow{AB}$, where s has the following value, and illustrate.

    (a) 1.   (b) 2.   (c) $-\frac{1}{2}$.   (d) -2.

11. As an immediate corollary of 3e1, we have: In E', $\overrightarrow{AC} = s \cdot \overrightarrow{AB}$ iff $C - A = s(B - A)$. Prove this statement more directly.

3f. EQUATIONS OF A LINE IN E2'

Recalling the definition of slope (3c4) and using statement 3d2, we easily arrive at another useful form for the equation of a line. (The proof is almost the same as that of statement 3d4.)

3f1 (Point Slope Form). In $E2'$ an equation for a line that has slope m and that passes through point A is

$$y - y_A = m(x - x_A).$$

There immediately follows (see 3c Problem 2):

3f2 (Two Point Form). In $E2'$ an equation for a nonvertical line AB is

$$y - y_A = \frac{y_B - y_A}{x_B - x_A} (x - x_A).$$

ILLUSTRATIVE EXAMPLE 1. In $E2'$ find equations for a line l_1 through $(-7, 11)$ with slope -2, and a line l_2 through $(7, -11)$ and $(-2, -8)$.

Solution: By statement 3f1, an equation for l_1 is $y - 11 = -2(x + 7)$, which is equivalent to $y = -2x - 3$. [To draw line l_1, note that its slope is -2; hence $(1, -2)$ are direction numbers for l_1, and hence $(-7, 11) + (1, -2) = (-6, 9)$ is a point on l_1. Now we know two points on l_1 and can therefore draw this line; alternatively, we can easily find another point on l_1 by letting $x = 0$ in the equation $y = -2x - 3$, by which means we easily see that $(0, -3)$ is a point on l_1. Of course, by assigning other values to x, we may find as many more points as we please on l_1. It is now left to the reader to draw the graphs of both l_1 and l_2.]

As for l_2, by statement 3f2, letting $A = (7, -11)$ and $B = (-2, -8)$, an equation of l_2 is

$$y + 11 = \left(\frac{-8 + 11}{-2 - 7} \right)(x - 7),$$

which is equivalent to $x + 3y + 26 = 0$. ‖

Special cases of points on a line in $E2'$ are points in which the line intersects the X and Y axes:

3f3. Suppose a line l in $E2'$ meets the X and Y axes in the points $(a, 0)$ and $(0, b)$ respectively. Then the real number a is called the *X-intercept* of l and the real number b is called the *Y-intercept* of l.

3f4 (Slope–Intercept Form).   In $E2'$ an equation for a line l with slope m and Y-intercept b is

$$y = mx + b.$$

Proof: $A = (0, b)$ is a point on l (?1). Therefore an equation for l is $y - b = m(x - 0)$ (?2), which is equivalent to (?3). ‖

ILLUSTRATIVE EXAMPLE 2.   Find an equation for a line l in $E2'$ with slope $-3/4$ and Y-intercept -2 (Fig. 3f1).

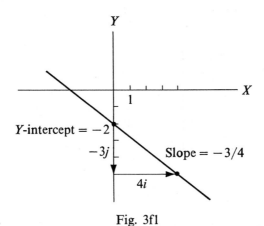

Fig. 3f1

Solution: By statement 3f4, an equation for l is $y = (-3/4)x - 2$, which is equivalent to $3x + 4y + 8 = 0$. (Actually, *either* of these equivalent equations is acceptable as a solution to the problem. The second looks prettier perhaps, but in some situations the first may be more useful and hence preferable.) ‖

ILLUSTRATIVE EXAMPLE 3.   In $E2'$ draw the graph of the equation $3x - y = 6$.

Solution: The given equation is equivalent to $y = 3x - 6$. Hence, by statement 3f4, its graph is a line with slope 3 and Y-intercept -6. Now we may draw the line, either by the method illustrated in Fig. 3f1 or by the use of direction numbers as in Illustrative Example 1. Alternatively, as soon as we recognize that the graph is a line, we may let $x = 0$ in the given equation to find that $(0, -6)$ is a point on the line, and we may let $y = 0$ in the given equation to find that $(2, 0)$ is a point on the line, and then we may draw the line. ‖

The following two special cases of the preceding form are worth noting.

3f5. In $E2'$, $y = mx$ is the equation of a line through the origin with slope m, and $y = b$ is the equation of a horizontal line with Y-intercept b. (Proof and illustration?)

But what about *vertical* lines? Since a point (x, y) lies on a vertical line with X-intercept a iff $x = a$ (see Fig. 3f2):

3f6. In $E2'$, $x = a$ is the equation of a vertical line with X-intercept a.

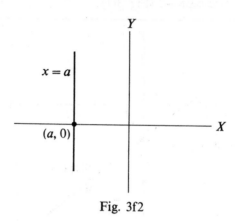

Fig. 3f2

We now introduce a commonly used synonym for perpendicularity.

3f7. Line l_1 is said to be *normal* to line l_2 iff $l_1 \perp l_2$; the same is true for two vectors, or a line and a vector, or a line and a plane, etc.

This concept is used in the following neat form of the equation of a line.

3f8 (Point–Normal Form). In $E2'$ let l be a line through the point (a, b) and let (A, B) be direction numbers of a line n normal to l (Fig. 3f3). Then an equation of l is

$$Ax + By = Aa + Bb.$$

Proof: Let (x, y) be a point such that $Ax + By = Aa + Bb$. If $(x, y) = (a, b)$, then certainly $(x, y) \in l$ (?1). Otherwise (Fig. 3f4), there is a line k through (x, y) and (a, b) with direction numbers $(x - a, y - b)$ (?2). But (A, B) are direction numbers for n (?3), and $A(x - a) + B(y - b) = Ax + By - Aa - Bb = 0$ (?4). Therefore $k \perp n$ (?5). Therefore $k = l$ (?6). Therefore $(x, y) \in l$ (?7).

Conversely, suppose $(x, y) \in l$ (Fig. 3f3). If $(x, y) = (a, b)$, then certainly $Ax + By = Aa + Bb$ (?8). Otherwise, $(x - a, y - b)$ are direction

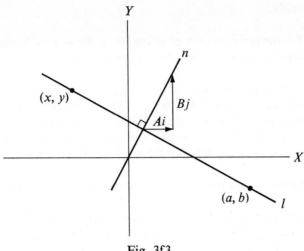

Fig. 3f3

numbers for l (?9), and (A, B) are direction numbers for n (?10), and $l \perp n$ (?11). Therefore $A(x - a) + B(y - b) = 0$ (?12). Therefore (?13). ‖

The following is an immediate consequence of statement 3f8.

3f9. In $E2'$ each line has an equation of the form $Ax + By + C = 0$, where A, B, C are real numbers and A, B are not both zero.

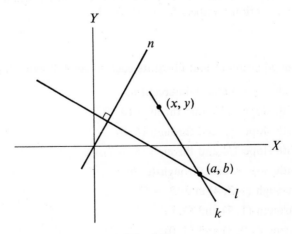

Fig. 3f4

Conversely:

3f10. In $E2'$ the graph of each equation $Ax + By + C = 0$, where A, B, C are real numbers and A, B are not both zero, is a line.

Proof: If $A \neq 0$, we may let $y = 0$ and solve for x in the given equation, and correspondingly if $B \neq 0$ (?1). Hence, in any case, we may find at least one point (a, b) on the graph of the given equation, and hence such that $Aa + Bb + C = 0$. Therefore the given equation is equivalent to $Ax + By = -C = Aa + Bb$. But the graph of this equation is a line (?2). ‖

The motivation for the following nomenclature is now clear.

3f11 (Definition). If A, B, C are real numbers and A, B are not both zero, then the equation $Ax + By + C = 0$ is called a *linear equation in E2'*.

Thus we may summarize statements 3f9 and 3f10 in the following pleasant way.

3f12. In $E2'$ every line has a linear equation, and the graph of every linear equation is a line.

In fact, we might have gone just a bit further in the proof of statement 3f10 to justify the following statement.

3f13. In $E2'$ if $Ax + By + C = 0$ is a linear equation whose graph is the line l, then (A, B) are direction numbers for any line normal to l; hence $(-B, A)$ are direction numbers for l. (Proof?)

Problems

1. Find an equation of and illustrate each of the following lines.

(a) With slope 3 and Y-intercept 6.

(b) With slope $-1/2$ and through $(0, 3)$.

(c) With slope $2/3$ and through $(6, 0)$.

(d) With slope $1/4$ and through $(5, -7)$.

(e) With slope k and through (a, b).

(f) Through $(-7, 4)$ and $(2, -6)$.

(g) Through $(1, 7)$ and $(5, 6)$.

(h) Through $(0, 3)$ and $(4, 0)$.

(i) With slope 0 and Y-intercept 7.

(j) With X-intercept 7 and Y-intercept 11.

(k) Through $(1, 2)$ and with direction numbers of normal line $(3, 4)$.

(l) Through $(1, 1)$ and normal to the line whose equation is $3x + 4y = 5$.

2. (a) Prove that a line with X-intercept $a \neq 0$ and Y-intercept $b \neq 0$ has the equation $(x/a) + (y/b) = 1$. (This is called the *intercept form* of the equation of a line.)

(b) Use the intercept form to solve Problems 1h and 1j above.

3. (a) Prove that the lines with the equations

$$Ax + By + C = 0,$$
$$Bx - Ay + D = 0$$

are perpendicular.

(b) Prove that the lines

$$Ax + By + C = 0,$$
$$Dx + Ey + F = 0$$

are parallel iff (A, B) and (D, E) are proportional, and that they are identical iff (A, B, C) and (D, E, F) are proportional.

4. Find an equation of a line through each of the following pairs of points. In each case:

(i) Verify that the given points satisfy the equation of the line.

(ii) Sketch the given points and the line.

(iii) On the line locate a point P different from the given points, and verify that P satisfies the equation of the line.

(iv) If possible, find (algebraically) a point Q satisfying the equation of the line such that $y_Q = 1$, and verify that Q lies on the line.

(a) $(2, 3)$, $(7, 11)$.   (b) $(0, 0)$, $(5, 5)$.

(c) $(0, 0)$, $(-5, -5)$.   (d) $(-1, 2)$, $(5, -3)$.

(e) $(2, 4)$, $(-3, -7)$.   (f) $(2, -4)$, $(-2, -4)$.

(g) $(1, -3)$, $(-7, 2)$.   (h) $(0, 4)$, $(4, 0)$.

(i) $(3, 4)$, $(2, 5)$.   (j) $(7, 1)$, $(3, -3)$.

(k) $(2, 2)$, $(2, 2)$.   (l) $(-4, 2)$, $(-4, 2)$.

5. Draw the graphs in $E2'$ of each of the following equations, using whatever method seems best.

(a) $3x + 5y = 30$.   (b) $2x - y = 7$.

(c) $y = -x$.   (d) $4x - 2y - 12 = 0$.

(e) $y = x\sqrt{3} - 3$.   (f) $x\sqrt{5} + y\sqrt{4} = 1$.

(g) $2x + y = 7$.   (h) $14x + 7y = 49$.

(i) $2x + y = 11$.   (j) $y - 7 = 0$.

(k) $x + y = 5$.   (l) $x - 5 = 0$.

6 (a)–(l).   Find the slope and Y-intercept of each of the lines in Problem 5.

7.   In each of the following cases prove that the given lines are parallel and draw the lines.

(a) $y = 2x + 1$; $y = 2x - 5$.   (b) $y = x - 1$; $x - y = 1$.

(c) $2x + 3y = 6$; $2x + 3y = 12$.   (d) $y = 0$; $y = 5$.

(e) $x + 2y = 3$; $2x + 4y = 7$.   (f) $x = 2$; $x = -3$.

(g) $x - 2y = 7$; $2y - x = 7$.   (h) $y = x$; $x = y + 1$.

8.   In each of the following cases prove that lines u and v are parallel, and draw the lines u and v.

(a) $u: y = 3x - 2$; v passes through $(2, 4)$, $(4, 10)$.

(b) u passes through $(-1, 4)$, $(3, -2)$; v passes through $(3, 2)$, $(1, 5)$.

(c) u is perpendicular to $x + 7 = 0$; v passes through $(1, 2)$, $(5, 2)$.

9.   In each of the following cases prove that lines u and v are perpendicular, and draw the lines u and v.

(a) $u: y = 2x + 3$; $v: x + 2y = 6$.

(b) $u: y = 3x + 3$; v passes through $(3, 4)$, $(6, 3)$.

(c) u passes through $(2, -3)$, $(3, -2)$; v passes through $(7, 11)$, $(12, 6)$.

(d) $u: 2x + 3y = 6$; $v: 3x - 2y = 6$.

(e) $u: x = 3$; $v: y = -2$.

(f) $u: x = 0$; $v: y = 0$.

10.   Find an equation of and illustrate each of the following lines.

(a) Through $(3, 7)$ parallel to $2x - 3y = 13$.

(b) Through $(3, 7)$ perpendicular to $2x - 3y = 13$.

(c) Through $(1, 2)$ parallel to $x - 7 = 0$.

(d) Through $(1, 2)$ perpendicular to $x - 7 = 0$.

(e) Through $(1, 2)$ parallel to $y - 7 = 0$.

(f) Through $(1, 2)$ perpendicular to $y - 7 = 0$.

(g) Through $(1, 2)$ parallel to $x + y = 7$.

(h) Through $(1, 2)$ perpendicular to $x + y = 7$.

11 (Optional).   Let l be a line in $E2'$ and suppose a line OR normal to l intersects line l in P. If $O \neq P$, let α be the angle from i to $\overrightarrow{OP}$; if

$O = P$, let α be the angle from i to $\overrightarrow{OR}$. Prove that in either case:

(a) $(\cos \alpha, \sin \alpha)$ are direction numbers for line OR.

(b) If $d = |\overrightarrow{OP}|$, then an equation for line l is $x \cos \alpha + y \sin \alpha = d$. (This is called the equation of l in *normal form;* $\overrightarrow{OP}$ is called *the normal to l.*)

(c) If $Ax + By = C$ is an equation of l, then $\cos \alpha = sA$, $\sin \alpha = sB$, and $d = sC$, where $s = 1/\sqrt{A^2 + B^2}$ if $C > 0$, and $s = -1/\sqrt{A^2 + B^2}$ if $C < 0$.

3g. DISTANCE FROM A POINT TO A LINE IN E2′ AND GRAPHS OF LINEAR INEQUALITIES IN E2′

3g1. Let $Ax + By + C = 0$ be the equation of line l in $E2'$ and let (p, q) be a point in $E2'$. Then the (perpendicular) distance from (p, q) to l is

$$\frac{|Ap + Bq + C|}{\sqrt{A^2 + B^2}}.$$

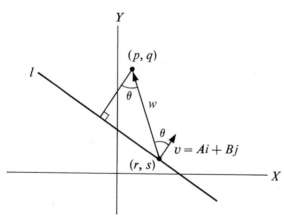

Fig. 3g1

Proof: Let (r, s) be any point on l, let $v = Ai + Bj$, let $w = (p - r)i + (q - s)j$, and let θ be the angle between v and w (Fig. 3g1). Then $Ar + Bs + C = 0$ (?1), and $v \perp l$ (?2), and the distance we seek is $|d|$, where $d = |w| \cos \theta$.

But $v \cdot w \overset{?3}{=} |v| \, |w| \cos \theta = |v| \, d$. Therefore

$$d = (v \cdot w)/|v| \overset{?4}{=} [A(p - r) + B(q - s)]/|v| \overset{?5}{=} (Ap + Bq + C)/\sqrt{A^2 + B^2}.$$

Therefore (?6). ‖

[*Note:* If B is positive, then v is directed "upwards" (as in Fig. 3g1); for all points "above" l, θ is acute, hence $\cos \theta$ is positive, hence d is positive; for all points "below" l, θ is obtuse, hence $\cos \theta$ is negative, hence d is negative. (What if B is negative?)]

The following definition therefore suggests itself.

3g2 (Definition).   Suppose $Ax + By + C = 0$, with $B > 0$, is the equation of a line l in $E2'$, and (p, q) is a point in $E2'$. Then the *signed distance d* from (p, q) to l is defined to be $d = (Ap + Bq + C)/\sqrt{A^2 + B^2}$.

ILLUSTRATIVE EXAMPLE 1.   Find the position of each of the points $(7, 11)$, $(10, 2)$ with respect to the line $3x - 4y = 12$, and find the distance from each of these points to the given line.

Solution: For convenience, we transform the given equation into an equivalent equation in the form $Ax + By + C = 0$, with B positive: $-3x + 4y + 12 = 0$. Then $d = (-21 + 44 + 12)/5 = 7$, for the point $(7, 11)$, and $d = (-30 + 8 + 12)/5 = -2$, for the point $(10, 2)$. Therefore $(7, 11)$ is above the given line and $(10, 2)$ is below the given line; the distances from $(7, 11)$ and $(11, 2)$ to the given line are, respectively, $|7| = 7$ and $|-2| = 2$. (It is left to the reader to illustrate this example graphically.) ‖

Suppose A, B, C are real numbers such that A, B are not both zero. We define the graph in $E2'$ of the inequality $Ax + By + C > 0$ to be the set of all points in $E2'$ that satisfy this inequality, i.e., the set of all points (p, q) in $E2'$ such that $Ap + Bq + C > 0$. (Similarly, of course, for $Ax + By + C < 0$, $Ax + By + C \geq 0$, etc.)

There easily follows:

3g3.   Suppose $Ax + By + C = 0$, with $B > 0$, is the equation of a line l in $E2'$. Then the graph in $E2'$ of $Ax + By + C > 0$ is the set of all points in $E2'$ that are above l, and the graph in $E2'$ of $Ax + By + C < 0$ is the set of all points in $E2'$ that are below l.

Proof: (p, q) is above l iff $(Ap + Bq + C)/\sqrt{A^2 + B^2} > 0$ (?1), which is true iff $Ap + Bq + C > 0$ (?2). Therefore the graph in $E2'$ of $Ax + By + C > 0$ is the set of all points in $E2'$ above l (?3). Similarly (?4).   ‖

ILLUSTRATIVE EXAMPLE 2.   In $E2'$ draw (a representative portion of) the graphs of $x + 4y = 10$, of $x + 4y > 10$, and of $x + 4y \geq 10$.

Solution: (See Fig. 3g2.) The graph of $x + 4y = 10$ is a straight line through the points $(10, 0)$ and $(2, 2)$. The graph of $x + 4y > 10$ (since this inequality is equivalent to $x + 4y - 10 > 0$, and since $4 > 0$) is the set of points in $E2'$ above the graph of $x + 4y = 10$ (see the shaded area in Fig. 3g2). Finally, the graph of $x + 4y \geq 10$ consists of all the points that are either in the first graph or in the second graph—the so-called *union* of these two sets—and hence of all the points in $E2'$ that are in the line whose equation is $x + 4y = 10$ *and* all the points in $E2'$ that are above that line. ‖

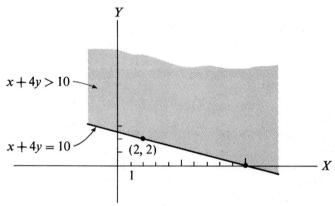

Fig. 3g2

Problems

1. In each of the following cases find the distance from the given point to the given line and illustrate each with a diagram.

    (a) $(2, 3)$, $3x + 4y = 5$. (b) $(7, 11)$, $y = x + 5$.
    (c) $(-1, 2)$, $x = y + 5$. (d) $(2, 2)$, $x + y = 4$.
    (e) $(-2, -3)$, $5x + 12y + 60 = 0$.
    (f) $(2, 2)$, $x + y = 0$. (g) $(7, 11)$, $y = 5$.
    (h) $(7, 11)$, $x = 5$. (i) (u, v), $y = -p$.
    (j) $(0, 0)$, $Ax + By + C = 0$. (k) (a, a), $y = 0$.

2. (a) Find the length of the altitude AA' of triangle ABC, given that $A = (-5, 5)$, $B = (3, 8)$, and $C = (1, -2)$.

    (b) Find the area of the triangle ABC above by using the usual altitude–base formula.

    (c) Find the area of triangle ABC above by inscribing it in a rectangle with sides parallel to the X and Y axes and computing the areas of the rectangle and several right triangles.

3. Draw representative portions of the graph of each of the following inequalities.

(a) $y - x > 0$.   (b) $y - x \leq 0$.

(c) $2x - y + 1 > 0$.   (d) $y > 0$.

(e) $x \geq 7$.   (f) $7 < x + y < 11$.

4. Find the (perpendicular) distance between each of the following pairs of parallel lines, and illustrate.

(a) $3x + 4y = 12$, $3x + 4y = 24$.

(b) $3x + 4y = 12$, $3x + 4y + 24 = 0$.

3h. *INTERSECTION OF LINES IN E2'*

As far as the intersection of two lines in a plane is concerned, we may distinguish these cases:

(i) The lines intersect in no points, in which case the lines are parallel and different.

(ii) The lines intersect in exactly one point.

(iii) The lines intersect in more than one point, in which case the lines are identical and hence parallel.

Now in drawing the graphs of a pair of linear equations, any one of (i), (ii), (iii) above may occur.

But to find the points of intersection of lines in $E2'$ and, in fact, of any pair of graphs, we shall generally prefer an algebraic approach. A point will lie on several graphs iff the point (i.e., its coordinates) satisfies the equation of each of these graphs. To find points of intersection of graphs, therefore, we solve the equations of the graphs "simultaneously;" i.e., we find ordered pairs of real numbers which satisfy these equations.

The three cases we have listed above as well as methods of solving pairs of simultaneous linear equations are illustrated in the examples below.

ILLUSTRATIVE EXAMPLE 1. Solve the equations $2x + 3y = 6$ and $y = -(2x/3) + 2$ simultaneously.

Solution: Substituting $-(2x/3) + 2$ for y in the first equation, we obtain

$$2x + 3\left(-\frac{2x}{3} + 2\right) = 6$$

$$2x - 2x + 6 = 6$$

$$6 = 6.$$

Apparently we have gotten nowhere! The result $6 = 6$ is true but indicates no solution. Actually, our work shows that no matter what real number x is, if y is determined by the second equation, then the first equation will be satisfied.

The reason for this peculiarity may be seen if we take a closer look at the equation $y = -(2x/3) + 2$. It is equivalent to $3y = -2x + 6$, or $2x + 3y = 6$. In other words, the two given equations are equivalent. Any pair of values of x and y which satisfies one satisfies the other.

It is hardly necessary to verify that in this case the graphs of the given equations are identical lines, and that there are an infinite number of simultaneous solutions of these equations. ‖

ILLUSTRATIVE EXAMPLE 2. Solve the equations $2x + 3y = 6$ and $4x + 6y = 7$ simultaneously.

Solution: Doubling the first: $4x + 6y = 12$,

writing the second: $4x + 6y = 7$,

and subtracting: $0 = 5$,

we have an even *more* peculiar result!

Actually, what we have shown in this case is that if there were a simultaneous solution to the given equations, then 0 would equal 5. But the conclusion is impossible; therefore there can be no simultaneous solution to these two equations and hence no point satisfying both.

The straight lines which are the graphs of these equations must therefore be parallel but not identical, which facts the reader may verify by drawing the graphs of these equations. ‖

ILLUSTRATIVE EXAMPLE 3. Solve the equations $3x + 2y = 1$ and $5x - 3y = 8$ simultaneously.

Solution: Multiplying the first by 3: $9x + 6y = 3$,

and the second by 2: $10x - 6y = 16$,

and adding: $19x = 19$,

we obtain $x = 1$.

Substituting $x = 1$ in the first, we obtain

$$3 + 2y = 1$$
$$2y = -2$$
$$y = -1.$$

(Alternatively, y might have been found by multiplying the first equation by 5, the second by -3, and adding.)

In this case, then, there is a unique solution: $x = 1$, $y = -1$. In other words, the lines whose equations are $3x + 2y = 1$ and $5x - 3y = 8$

meet in one and only one point: $(1, -1)$. This, again, may be checked graphically by the reader. ‖

Actually, simple criteria exist for determining which of the above three cases hold, directly from the equations of the given lines (see 3f Problem 3b).

Problems

1. Find the intersection of each of the following pairs of lines, and then draw the lines in *E2'*.

   (a) $3x + 4y = 6$; $x - y = 9$.

   (b) $2x + y = 13$; $3x - 2y = 6$.

   (c) $2x + y = 8$; $6x + 3y = 20$.

   (d) $3x - y = 7$; $39x - 13y = 91$.

   (e) $2x + 3y = 6$; $3x - 5y + 10 = 0$.

2. (a) Prove that for each real number k, $k(3x + 4y - 6) + (x - y - 9) = 0$ is an equation of a line that passes through the point of intersection of the lines in Problem 1(a).

   (b) Using (a) above, find an equation of a line that passes through the point of intersection of the lines in Problem 1(a) and that is parallel to the line whose equation is $x + y = 5$.

3i. FAMILIES OF LINES

We know that the graph in *E2'* of $y = mx + b$, where m and b are arbitrary real numbers, may be any nonvertical line in *E2'*. But suppose we take a special case of this equation, say $y = 2x + b$. What can we say about the graph of this equation in *E2'*? We can say that the graph may be any line with slope 2. The set of all lines in *E2'* that are graphs of $y = 2x + b$, where b is any real number, is called a *one-parameter family* of lines, with parameter b. The value of b that we use to determine a particular member of this family is, of course, the *Y*-intercept of that member. (See Fig. 3i1.)

Indeed, the set of all graphs in *E2'* of $y = mx + b$ itself is also a family of lines—a *two-parameter family*, with parameters m, b. This family is simply the set of all nonvertical lines in *E2'*.

Now consider the linear equations

(1) $x + 2y - 8 = 0$,

(2) $x - 3y - 3 = 0$.

Suppose we form from these the linear combination

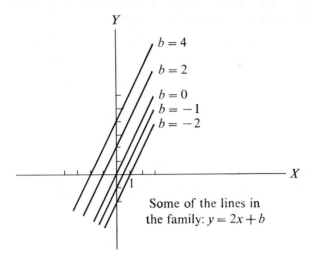

Some of the lines in
the family: $y = 2x + b$

Fig. 3i1

(3) $$p(x + 2y - 8) + q(x - 3y - 3) = 0.$$

Then clearly any point (a, b) that satisfies both Eq. (1) and Eq. (2) satisfies
Eq. (3) also. Hence Eq. (3) represents a two-parameter family (with parameters p and q), each member of which passes through the point of intersection
of Eq. (1) and Eq. (2). [We know that Eqs. (1) and (2) do intersect.
Why (?1).]

In fact, more generally, we can prove the following statement.

3i1. Let the graphs in $E2'$ of the linear equations $A_1x + B_1y + C_1 = 0$
and $A_2x + B_2y + C_2 = 0$ be l_1, l_2 respectively. Then

$$p(A_1x + B_1y + C_1) + q(A_2x + B_2y + C_2) = 0$$

is the equation of a two-parameter family of lines, with parameters p and
q, which consists of all lines in $E2'$ through the point of intersection of l_1
and l_2, if l_1 and l_2 intersect, and which consists of all lines in $E2'$ parallel to l_1
and l_2, if l_1 and l_2 are parallel.

[*Note:* We shall understand, in statement 3i1, that certain values of
p and q are to be excluded. For example, in Eq. (3) we exclude $(p, q) =$
$(0, 0)$. Why (?2). If the given equations were $x + 2y - 8 = 0$ and
$2x + 4y - 7 = 0$, we would exclude $(p, q) = (0, 0)$ and $(p, q) = (2, -1)$
and what other values (?3).]

ILLUSTRATIVE EXAMPLE. Suppose l_1 and l_2 are the graphs of Eqs. (1)
and (2) above. Find an equation of a line that passes through the intersection of l_1 and l_2 and also the point $(7, 11)$.

Solution: The required equation must be a special case of Eq. (3) above and must be satisfied by $(7, 11)$. Hence

$$p(7 + 22 - 8) + q(7 - 33 - 3) = 0$$
$$21p - 29q = 0.$$

This equation is clearly satisfied by $p = 29$, $q = 21$. Hence the required equation is

$$29(x + 2y - 8) + 21(x - 3y - 3) = 0,$$

which is equivalent to

(4) $10x - y - 59 = 0.$

It is left to the reader to verify that Eq. (4) satisfies the conditions of the problem, and to illustrate graphically. ‖

Problems

1. Describe each of the following families of lines in $E2'$, and illustrate graphically.

    (a) $y = mx.$ (b) $y = mx + 2.$
    (c) $x = k.$ (d) $y = k.$
    (e) $y - 7 = m(x - 11).$ (f) $Ax + By = 0.$

2. Write equations for the following families in $E2'$.

    (a) All lines through $(7, 11)$.
    (b) All lines parallel to $x + y = 5$.
    (c) All lines normal to $x + y = 5$.
    (d) All lines tangent to the circle with radius 1 and whose center is at the origin.

3. (a) Write an equation for the family of all lines in $E2'$ passing through the intersection of $x + y = 18$ and $2x - y = 3$.
    (b) Find an equation of the member of the family that passes through the origin.
    (c) Find values of the parameters that produce the horizontal member of the family.
    (d) Find values of the parameters that produce the vertical member of the family.
    (e) Illustrate graphically all of the above.

4. Carry out a treatment analogous to that of Problem 3 (but with what difference?) for the equations $y = 2x - 3$ and $4x - 2y = 7$.

5. (Optional). Suppose l_1 and l_2 are the graphs in $E2'$ of the linear equations

$A_1x + B_1y + C_1 = 0$ and $A_2x + B_2y + C_2 = 0$, p and q are real numbers, and line l is the graph of

$$p(A_1x + B_1y + C_1) + q(A_2x + B_2y + C_2) = 0.$$

Prove that if $l_1 \parallel l_2$, then l is parallel to both l_1 and l_2.

3j. LINEAR PROGRAMMING (Optional)

It is a popular and securely entrenched belief that mathematics is a body of knowledge, indeed probably the only body of knowledge, that has entirely completed its growth. A great many people think it inconceivable that the mathematics of today should differ from that of yesterday, or that new mathematics might be created tomorrow. Even those who admit the possibility of something novel under the mathematical sun generally believe that it must be in the stratospheric realm of mathematics, far beyond the level of accessibility of ordinary people.

A case in point which refutes these misapprehensions is the branch of mathematics called *linear programming*. Fewer than 25 years have elapsed since mathematicians first began working in this field. Today it is a flourishing area of research which has to do with problems like the following.

PROBLEM. Suppose we have available two types of breakfast cereal, one called "Eggzees," whose price is 1¢ per ounce, and one called "Yums," whose price is 2¢ per ounce. Each proudly proclaims on its package its enrichment with vitamins P and Q. Eggzees claims that in every ounce it contains 1 unit of vitamin P and 2 units of vitamin Q; Yums claims 4 units of vitamin P and 3 units of vitamin Q per ounce. Both packages agree that a person's minimum daily requirement of vitamin P is 10 units, and of vitamin Q, 15 units.

How can a person supply his daily needs for vitamin P and Q, *at least cost*, with the cereals Eggzees and Yums?

Discussion and Solution: First we tabulate our information:

Brand	Price (¢ per Oz.)	Vitamin P (Units per Oz.)	Vitamin Q (Units per Oz.)	No. of Oz.
Eggzees	1	1	2	x
Yums	2	4	3	y

It is clear that we could satisfy our needs entirely with Eggzees, by using 10 ounces of that cereal, at a minimum cost of 10¢ (this would—unavoidably

—give us 5 more units of vitamin Q than we really need); or entirely with Yums, by using 5 ounces of that cereal, again at a minimum cost of 10¢ (but with what unwanted but unavoidable bonus?). However, there is a possibility that some mixture of the two cereals might give us our needed vitamins P and Q at less cost. We investigate this possibility, calling the number of ounces of Eggzees and Yums consumed in a day x and y respectively.

Then our daily consumption of Eggzees and Yums would supply $x + 4y$ units of vitamin P and $2x + 3y$ units of vitamin Q. Our desire is to be supplied with *not less than* 10 units of vitamin P and 15 units of vitamin Q per day, i.e., to satisfy the following conditions:

(1) $x + 4y \geq 10,$

(2) $2x + 3y \geq 15.$

Since (however attractive the prospect), we cannot eat a negative number of ounces of crisp, crunchy, flavorful, vitamin-packed breakfast cereal, we add the conditions:

(3) $x \geq 0,$

(4) $y \geq 0.$

Now, considering the situation graphically, what we are seeking is the set of all points in $E2'$ that satisfy all of the relations (1)–(4); that is to say, the set of all points in $E2'$ that lie simultaneously in the graphs of each of the relations (1)–(4); i.e., the *intersection* of these graphs.

The graph of (1), $x + 4y \geq 10$ (see Fig. 3g2), is the set of all points in $E2'$ that are on or above the graph of $x + 4y = 10$ (the vertically striped region in Fig. 3j1, together with its border).

Similarly, the graph of (2), $2x + 3y \geq 15$, is the horizontally striped region in Fig. 3j1, together with its border. To satisfy conditions (3) and (4), we reject all points with negative x or y values; i.e., we restrict ourselves to quadrant I and its border. The intersection of the graphs of relations (1)–(4) is the shaded region in Fig. 3j2, together with its border. [The coordinates of the vertex $(6, 1)$ were found by solving the equations $x + 4y = 10$ and $2x + 3y = 15$ simultaneously.]

Now we know that the solution (x, y) that we seek to our problem must represent a point in the shaded region in Fig. 3j2 or on its border. (Let us call this region, together with its border, S.) Indeed, we seek a point (x, y) in S such that the cost C in cents of x ounces of Eggzees and y ounces of Yums is a minimum. But referring to the table above, we see that

(5) $C = x + 2y.$

Let us see whether we could possibly satisfy our demands with the expenditure of only a penny, i.e., in such a way that $C = x + 2y = 1$. We

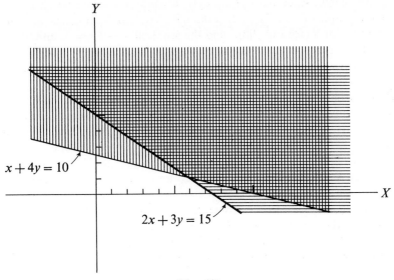

Fig. 3j1

examine the set of all points (x, y) such that $x + 2y = 1$, i.e., the graph of $x + 2y = 1$, but we discover (see Fig. 3j2) that no point of this line lies in the required set S. We shall have to spend more than a penny.

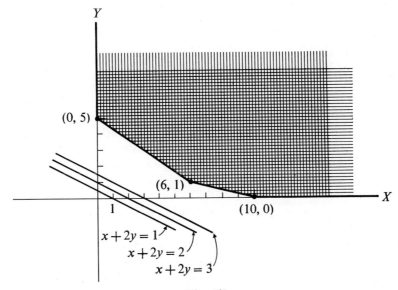

Fig. 3j2

We therefore, perhaps grudgingly, attempt a solution in which $C = 2$. But the graph of $x + 2y = 2$, although closer to S, still has no point in common with S (see Fig. 3j2); and the graph of $x + 2y = 3$, although even closer to S, succeeds no better in reaching it.

Now we see what needs to be done. We must find the smallest value of C for which the line $x + 2y = C$ intersects S, knowing that, as C becomes larger, the line $x + 2y = C$ moves to the right and approaches S. (Note that the moving line does not change its *direction* as it moves. Why not?)

Intuitively, it is clear that as we approach a region, we reach its border before we reach its interior. As a matter of fact, our moving line $x + 2y = C$ must reach a *vertex* of S no later than it reaches any other point of the border of S. For if it is not parallel to an edge of S, it will touch all the points of an edge, including a vertex, at the same time.

In our case we can see from Fig. 3j2 that the vertex $(6, 1)$ is the first point that the moving line $x + 2y = C$ will reach. Indeed, the following fundamental theorem can be proved, which will, in subsequent problems, save us a good deal of the preceding analysis.

Theorem. In $E2'$ let S be a region that is the intersection of sides of lines (including their borders) and let A, B be real numbers. Then of all points in S, if one point makes $Ax + By$ assume a minimum value, it is a vertex point on the border of S.

(Incidentally, if one point makes $Ax + By$ assume a *maximum* value, it is a vertex point on the border of S also.)

Returning to our problem, since the line $x + 2y = C$ that passes through $(6, 1)$ must be satisfied by $(6, 1)$, we have $6 + 2 \cdot 1 = C$, i.e., $C = 8$. That is the smallest value of C for which our conditions can be met; and $(6, 1)$ is the only point that satisfies $x + 2y = C = 8$ and also lies in S. Therefore $x = 6$, $y = 1$ is the unique solution to our problem: 6 ounces of Eggzees and 1 ounce of Yums per day will supply us with at least our minimum daily requirement of vitamins P and Q, at a minimum cost of 8¢ per day.

The theorem above would have enabled us to reach this conclusion more quickly. For according to our theorem, the solution must be one of the vertex points $(0, 5)$, $(6, 1)$, or $(10, 0)$. For these three points, $C = x + 2y = 10$, 8, 10 respectively. The minimum value of C is 8, attained by letting $x = 6$ and $y = 1$.

What we have just accomplished in the way of distributing our breakfast between two competing cereals may not seem to be of overwhelming importance. But serious "distribution" problems very much like this actually occur with great frequency in commercial, industrial, and military situations, and, as a consequence, the science of linear programming has found wide practical application.

We conclude this section with an algebraic solution of our cereal problem. From (5), $x = C - 2y$. Substituting into (1), we have $C - 2y + 4y \geq 10$, i.e.,

$$(6) \qquad\qquad C + 2y \geq 10.$$

Similarly, substituting into (2), we have

$$(7) \qquad\qquad 2C - y \geq 15.$$

Multiplying (7) by the positive number 2, we obtain

$$(8) \qquad\qquad 4C - 2y \geq 30,$$

and adding (6) and (8), we have

$$5C \geq 40,$$

from which

$$(9) \qquad\qquad C \geq 8.$$

Thus, if (1), (2), and (5) are to be satisfied, C can have no value less than 8. The question is: Can C have the value 8? If so, it must be the minimum we seek. But if $C = 8$, then, from (6), $y \geq 1$ and, from (7), $1 \geq y$. Thus if $C = 8$, then $y = 1$ and, from (5), $x = 6$. It is easy to verify that $(6, 1)$ satisfies conditions (1)–(4), so that $(6, 1)$ is our solution, and 8 is indeed the minimum possible value of C.

Problems (Optional)

1. Solve the Eggzees and Yums problem under the following conditions and illustrate graphically.

   (a) The same as the text, except that Eggzees cost 1.5¢ per ounce.

   (b) The same as the text, except that Yums cost 2.5¢ per ounce.

   (c) The same as the text, except that Eggzees cost 2¢ and Yums 3¢ per ounce.

   (d) The same as the text, except that we now take into account vitamin R also. Eggzees contains 4 units of vitamin R per ounce, Yums 9 units, and the minimum daily requirement of vitamin R is 36 units.

2. A customer who needs 20 large white buttons and 30 small white buttons finds that a store sells white buttons only on cards containing 2 large and 5 small buttons and in boxes containing 10 large and 5 small buttons. Determine how he should make his purchase in order to get the buttons he needs at least cost, if:

   (a) The cards cost 10¢, the boxes 25¢ each.

   (b) The cards cost 5¢, the boxes 30¢ each.

   (c) The cards cost 5¢, the boxes 25¢ each.

3. A man has two machines with which he can manufacture either skate keys or can openers. To manufacture a skate key requires using machine I for 1 minute and machine II for 2 minutes; to manufacture a can opener requires using machine I for 1 minute and machine II for 1 minute. During each hour machine I cannot be used for more than 50 minutes, machine II for more than 55 minutes. There is a market for as many skate keys and can openers as he can produce. For maximum profit, how many of each should he manufacture per hour if the profit on a skate key is 10¢ and the profit on a can opener is:

(a) 4¢.   (b) 5¢.   (c) 6¢.   (d) 10¢.   (e) 11¢.

4. Suppose the items in Problem 3 are being manufactured not for profit but for private use. Determine how many of each item should be produced per hour if the following are to be maximized.
(a) Total number of pieces produced.
(b) Total time during which equipment is in use.

5. Each capsule of Dose is required by law to contain at least 8 grains of doo, 20 grains of soo, and 24 grains of foo. A company has on hand supplies of Dis and Dat from which to manufacture Dose. A gram of Dis contains 1 grain each of doo, soo, and foo. A gram of Dat contains 1 grain of doo, 3 grains of soo, and 4 grains of foo. To minimize cost, determine how many grams of Dis and how many grams of Dat each capsule should contain, if Dis costs 10¢ per gram and the cost per gram of Dat is:

(a) 5¢.   (b) 10¢.   (c) 20¢.   (d) 30¢.
(e) 35¢.   (f) 40¢.   (g) 45¢.

3k. ANALYTIC PROOFS OF GEOMETRIC THEOREMS (Optional)

Analytic geometry affords a method of proving geometric theorems which is notable in that it demands a minimum of ingenuity. For example, let us see how two theorems that are first encountered in high school geometry and that we proved by vector methods in Section 2f may be proved by means of analytic geometry.

ILLUSTRATIVE EXAMPLE 1.   Prove that the diagonals of a parallelogram bisect each other.

Proof: Given a parallelogram (Fig. 3k1), introduce a Cartesian coordinate system in such a way that one vertex A is the origin and another vertex B lies on the positive X axis, and let dis$(A, B) = p$. Then (see 3a Problem 13), the points A, B, C, D may be labeled as in Fig. 3k1.

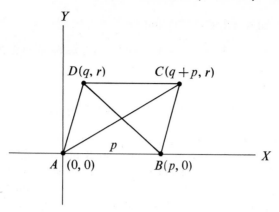

Fig. 3k1

The midpoint of diagonal AC is (?1) and the midpoint of diagonal BD is (?2). Hence (?3). ‖

ILLUSTRATIVE EXAMPLE 2. Prove that the line segment joining the midpoints of the nonparallel sides of a trapezoid is parallel to the parallel sides of the trapezoid and equal to half their sum in length.

Proof: Given a trapezoid (Fig. 3k2), introduce a coordinate system in such a way that one vertex A is the origin and another vertex B lies on the positive X axis, and let dis$(A, B) = p$ and dis$(D, C) = s$. Then (see 3a Problem 13), the points A, B, C, D may be labeled as in Fig. 3k2.

Now let M, N be the midpoints of sides AD, BC respectively. Then $M = (q/2, r/2)$ and $N = ((p + q + s)/2, r/2)$. Therefore line segment MN

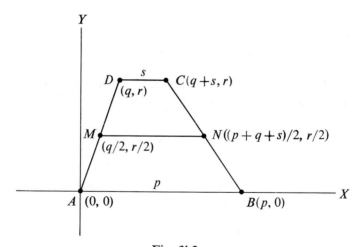

Fig. 3k2

is parallel to sides AB, CD (?1) and

$$\text{dis}(M, N) \overset{?2}{=} (p + q + s)/2 - q/2 = (p + s)/2. \;\|$$

Problems (Optional)

Using analytic geometry, prove each of the following.
   1–5.   (2f Problems 1–5).
   6.   The diagonals of a rectangle are equal in length.
   7.   The diagonals of a rhombus are perpendicular to each other.
   8.   If the diagonals of a quadrilateral are perpendicular to each other and bisect each other, then the quadrilateral is a rhombus.
   9.   The midpoint of the hypotenuse of a right triangle is equidistant from each of the vertices of the triangle.
   10.   A converse of Problem 9.
   11.   The sum of the squares of the lengths of the sides of a parallelogram is equal to the sum of the squares of the lengths of its diagonals.
   12.   The point of intersection of lines joining the midpoints of opposite sides of a quadrilateral bisects the line segment joining the midpoints of the diagonals of the quadrilateral.
   13.   The diagonals of an isosceles trapezoid are equal in length.
   14.   A converse of Problem 13.
   15.   The altitudes of a triangle intersect in a point H.
   16.   The perpendicular bisectors of the sides of a triangle intersect in a point O that is the center of the circumscribed circle of the triangle.
   17.   If M, O, H are as in Problems 4, 15, and 16, then M trisects line segment OH.

3l.   PLANES IN E3'

We shall need the following geometric fact.

311.   In $E3$ let H be a plane, let Q be a point in H, let n be a line normal to H, and let P be a point $\neq Q$. Then $P \in H$ iff line $PQ \perp n$ (Fig. 311).

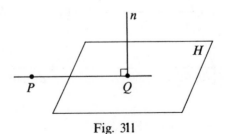

Fig. 311

Now we need to modify the proof of statement 3f8 only slightly in order to arrive at a proof of the following generalization of that statement.

312. In $E3'$ let H be a plane through the point (a, b, c) and let (A, B, C) be direction numbers of a line n normal to H (Fig. 312). Then an equation of H is

$$A(x - a) + B(y - b) + C(z - c) = 0,$$

or equivalently

$$Ax + By + Cz = Aa + Bb + Cc.$$

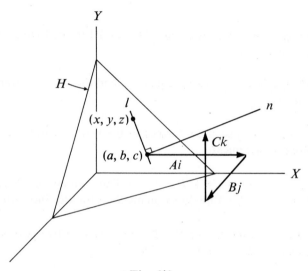

Fig. 312

Proof: Let (x, y, z) be a point such that $A(x - a) + B(y - b) + C(z - c) = 0$. If $(x, y, z) = (a, b, c)$, then certainly $(x, y, z) \in H$ (?1). Otherwise (Fig. 312), there is a line l through (x, y, z) and (a, b, c) with direction numbers $(x - a, y - b, z - c)$ (?2). But (A, B, C) are direction numbers for n (?3). Therefore $l \perp n$ (?4). Therefore $(x, y, z) \in H$ (?5).

Conversely, suppose $(x, y, z) \in H$. If $(x, y, z) = (a, b, c)$, then certainly $A(x - a) + B(y - b) + C(z - c) = 0$. Otherwise, the line l through (x, y, z) and (a, b, c) is such that $l \perp n$ (?6). Therefore $A(x - a) + B(y - b) + C(z - c) = 0$ (?7). ∥

The following is an immediate consequence of statement 312.

313. In $E3'$ each plane has an equation of the form $Ax + By + Cz + D = 0$, where A, B, C, D are real numbers and A, B, C are not all zero.

Conversely:

314. In $E3'$ the graph of each equation $Ax + By + Cz + D = 0$, where A, B, C, D are real numbers and A, B, C are not all zero, is a plane. (Proof? *Hint:* See the proof of statement 3f10.)

It is customary to generalize Definition 3f11 as follows.

315 (Definition). If A, B, C, D are real numbers and A, B, C are not all zero, then the equation $Ax + By + Cz + D = 0$ is called a *linear equation in E3'*.

Thus we may summarize statements 313 and 314 in the following neat if not altogether happy way.

316. In $E3'$ every plane has a linear equation, and the graph of every linear equation is a plane.

In fact, we may go just a bit further in the proof of statement 314 to justify the following statement.

317. In $E3'$ if $Ax + By + Cz + D = 0$ is a linear equation whose graph is the plane H, then (A, B, C) are direction numbers for any line normal to H.

ILLUSTRATIVE EXAMPLE 1.   In $E3'$ draw a representative portion of the graph of the equation $2x - 3y + 4z = 24$.

Solution: Since the given equation is obviously equivalent to a linear equation in $E3'$, its graph, by statement 316, is a plane. Letting $y = z = 0$, we see that the X-intercept of the graph is 12; similarly, its Y-intercept is -8 and its Z-intercept is 6. Since three points determine a plane, we now have at hand enough information to determine a triangle which forms a representative portion of the required plane (see Fig. 313). Extending the sides of this triangle, as in Fig. 313, enables us to picture more of the required graph. ‖

ILLUSTRATIVE EXAMPLE 2.   In $E3'$ draw a representative portion of the graph of the equation $2y + z = 10$.

Solution: Again by statement 316, the required graph is a plane. But in this case only two intercepts exist: the Y-intercept, 5, and the Z-intercept, 10. No X-intercept exists, since the given equation cannot be satisfied if

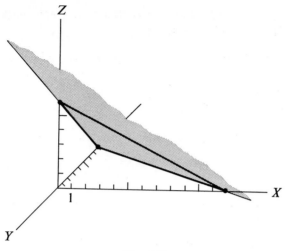

Fig. 313

$y = z = 0$. Hence the graph is a plane parallel to the X axis, with the above mentioned intercepts (see Fig. 314). ‖

The intersections of a graph in $E3'$, with the coordinate planes (called the *traces* of the graph), are often useful in drawing the graph. Thus the trace in the XY plane of the graph in $E3'$ of $2y + z = 10$ is the graph in the XY plane of the equation $y = 5$ (derived from $2y + z = 10$ by setting $z = 0$, since a point of $E3'$ is in the XY plane iff $z = 0$). This trace is, of course, the line labeled "$y = 5$" in Fig. 314. Similarly, the traces in the XZ and YZ

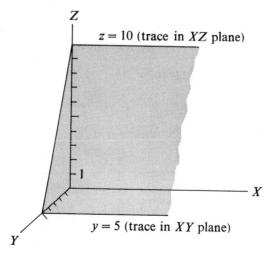

Fig. 314

planes of the graph in $E3'$ of $2y + z = 10$ are the graphs in these planes of $z = 10$ and $2y + z = 10$ respectively.

ILLUSTRATIVE EXAMPLE 3.   In $E3'$ suppose l is the line through $(4, 2, 3)$ and $(6, 5, 2)$. (a) Find an equation for the family of all planes containing l. (b) Find an equation of the plane through l perpendicular to the plane whose equation is $x + y + z = 10$.

Solution: (a) By 312, any plane H through $(4, 2, 3)$ can be written in the form

(1) $$Ax + By + Cz = 4A + 2B + 3C.$$

If H is to contain l, then $(6, 5, 2)$ must lie in H also; hence $(6, 5, 2)$ must satisfy Eq. (1); i.e.,

(2) $$6A + 5B + 2C = 4A + 2B + 3C.$$

Solving for C in (2) and substituting in Eq. (1), we have

(3) $$Ax + By + (2A + 3B)z = 10A + 11B.$$

Thus any plane through l can be written in the form of Eq. (3). Conversely, it is easy to verify that $(4, 2, 3)$ and $(6, 5, 2)$ satisfy Eq. (3), and hence that any plane whose equation is in the form of Eq. (3) contains l. (If two distinct points of a line l lie in a plane, then the plane contains all of l.)

Therefore Eq. (3) is an equation for the family of all planes containing l (regarding A, B as parameters not both of which can be equal to zero).

(b) We seek a member of the family of Eq. (3) that is perpendicular to the plane whose equation is $x + y + z = 10$. Since planes are perpendicular iff their normals are perpendicular, we now need to satisfy only the added condition

(4) $$(1)(A) + (1)(B) + (1)(2A + 3B) = 0, \quad \text{or} \quad B = -3A/4.$$

Hence if we let $A = 4$, then $B = -3$, and all our requirements are satisfied.

Substituting in Eq. (3), we now arrive at the solution

(5) $$4x - 3y - z = 7.$$

It is easy to verify that $(4, 2, 3)$ and $(6, 5, 2)$ satisfy Eq. (5) and that this plane is perpendicular to the plane whose equation is $x + y + z = 10$ [see Fig. 315; note that in drawing the graph of Eq. (5) we have made use of the convenient intercept $(0, 0, -7)$.] ‖

ILLUSTRATIVE EXAMPLE 4.   In $E3'$ let l be the line whose equations are $(x - 1)/2 = (y - 2)/3 = (z - 5)/-2$. Find the three planes that pass through l perpendicular to the coordinate planes.

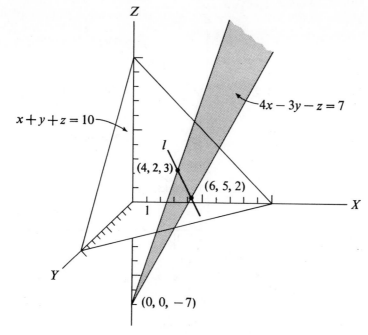

Fig. 315

Solution: The points on l satisfy $(x-1)/2 = (y-2)/3$, $(x-1)/2 = (z-5)/-2$, and $(y-2)/3 = (z-5)/-2$, which are equivalent to $3x-2y = -1$, $x+z = 6$, and $2y+3z = 19$. These (by the perpendicularity of normals criterion, for example) are easily seen to be equations of planes perpendicular to the XY, XZ, and YZ planes respectively (see Fig. 316). (Note that any two of these planes intersect in l, and hence that any two of these equations may be regarded as equations of l.) ‖

ILLUSTRATIVE EXAMPLE 5.   Find two points on the line of intersection of the planes

$$x + y + z = 10,$$
$$4x - 3y - z = 7.$$

Solution: Eliminating z in the given equations and solving for x, we obtain

(1) $$x = \frac{2y + 17}{5}.$$

Eliminating y in the given equations and again solving for x, we have

(2) $$x = \frac{-2z + 37}{7}.$$

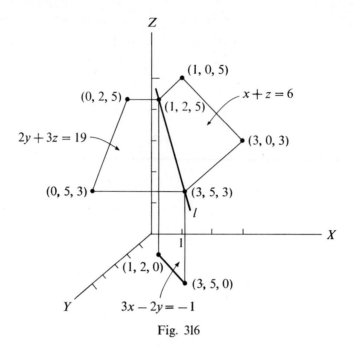

Fig. 316

Hence the given equations are equivalent to

$$x = \frac{y + \frac{17}{2}}{\frac{5}{2}} = \frac{z - \frac{37}{2}}{-\frac{7}{2}},$$

or

$$\frac{x}{2} = \frac{y + \frac{17}{2}}{5} = \frac{z - \frac{37}{2}}{-7}.$$

It follows (see statement 3d7) that $(0, -\frac{17}{2}, \frac{37}{2})$ is a point on the line of intersection of the given planes, and that direction numbers of that line of intersection are $(2, 5, -7)$. Hence another point on the line of intersection of the given planes is $(0, -17/2, 39/2) + (2, 5, -7) = (2, -3.5, 11.5)$. Now it is easy to draw the line of intersection of the given planes. ‖

Problems

1. Draw a representative portion of the graph in $E3'$ of each of the following equations.

    (a) $x + y + z = 10.$ (b) $x + y = z.$
    (c) $2x + 3y + 4z = 24.$ (d) $x + y + z = 0.$
    (e) $2x - 3y - 4z = 24.$ (f) $y = z.$
    (g) $x = 10.$ (h) $x + y = 10.$

2. (a) Find an equation for the family of all planes in $E3'$ that pass through the points $(1, 4, 9)$ and $(9, 4, 1)$.
    (b) Find the member of the family of part (a) that passes through the point $(2, 2, 2)$, and illustrate.
    (c) Using the methods of parts (a) and (b), find an equation of the plane in $E3'$ that passes through the points $(1, 4, 5)$, $(9, -2, 3)$, and $(-3, 6, 7)$, and illustrate.
    (d) Solve part (c) by substituting the given points $(1, 4, 5)$, $(9, -2, 3)$, $(-3, 6, 7)$ for (x, y, z) in the general equation of a plane $Ax + By + Cz + D = 0$ and by finding a solution of the resulting three equations in the unknowns A, B, C, D.
    (e) Find an equation of the plane in $E3'$ that passes through the points $(-1, 6, 7)$, $(2, -2, -4)$, and $(3, 7, 4)$; also find the intercepts and traces of this plane; illustrate.

3. Find an equation of a plane that passes through the points $(1, 0, 2)$ and $(-2, 3, 4)$ and is perpendicular to the plane $x = y$, and illustrate.

4. Let l be the line in $E3'$ that passes through the point $(3, -2, 4)$ and that has direction numbers $(4, 5, 2)$. Find the three planes that pass through l perpendicular to the coordinate planes, and illustrate.

5. In each of the following find two points on the line of intersection of the given planes, and illustrate.

    (a) $x + y + z = 10$, $2x - 2y - z = 10$.
    (b) $x + y + z = 10$, $x + y - z = 10$.
    (c) $x + y + z = 10$, $x = y$.

6. (a) Find an equation of a plane in $E3'$ that passes through the point $(3, 4, 7)$ and that is perpendicular to the line $(x - 1)/3 = (y + 4)/-2 = (z - 5)/4$. Find the intercepts and traces of this plane, and illustrate.
    (b) Find an equation of a plane in $E3'$ that passes through the point $(-2, 3, 5)$ and that is perpendicular to the line through $(3, 5, 7)$ and $(5, -4, 0)$. Find the intercepts and traces of this plane, and illustrate.

7. Prove that planes $Ax + By + Cz + D = 0$ and $A'x + B'y + C'z + D' = 0$ are:

    (a) Perpendicular iff $AA' + BB' + CC' = 0$.
    (b) Parallel iff (A, B, C) and (A', B', C') are proportional.
    (c) Identical iff (A, B, C, D) and (A', B', C', D') are proportional.

8. Find equations of a line in $E3'$ that passes through $(1, 2, 3)$ and that is perpendicular to the plane $x + y + z = 10$, and illustrate.

9. Find an equation of a plane in $E3'$ that passes through $(12, 8, 6)$ and that is parallel to the plane $2x + 3y + 4z = 24$, and illustrate.

10. Find a criterion for parallelism of a line through (a, b, c) whose direction numbers are (p, q, r) and a plane whose equation is $Ax + By + Cz + D = 0$. How about perpendicularity? When will the plane actually contain the line?

11. Find the acute angle formed by the planes $x + 2y + z = 6$ and $2x + y - z = 8$, and illustrate. (*Hint:* The acute angle formed by two planes is the same as the acute angle formed by lines normal to the planes.)

12. (a) Show (generalizing statement 3g1) that if $Ax + By + Cz + D = 0$ is the equation of a plane H in $E3'$ and if (p, q, r) is a point in $E3'$, then the (perpendicular) distance from (p, q, r) to H is

$$|Ap + Bq + Cr + D|/\sqrt{A^2 + B^2 + C^2};$$

and that if $C > 0$, then the "signed distance"

$$d = (Ap + Bq + Cr + D)/\sqrt{A^2 + B^2 + C^2}$$

is positive iff (p, q, r) is "above" H, negative iff (p, q, r) is below H.
(b) (Optional)   What if $C = 0$?
(c) Find the distance from each of the points $(3, 4, 12)$ and $(1, 1, 0)$ to the plane $3x + 4y + 12z = 12$; determine from the signed distance whether each of these points is above or below the given plane, and illustrate.

13. Find the feet of the perpendiculars from the given points to the given plane in Problem 12c. (*Hint:* Find equations of lines through each of the given points normal to the given planes, and in each case find a simultaneous solution of these equations and the given plane.)

14. Find the distance between the parallel planes $2x + y - z = 8$ and $4x + 2y - 2z = 21$.

15. Find equations in parametric form for the line of intersection of the planes $x + y + z = 10$ and $2x - 3y + 4z = 24$.

16. In each of the following find the intersection of the given plane and the given line, and illustrate.

(a) $2x - 3y + 2z = 12$; $x = 1 + t, y = 2 - 2t, z = 3 - t$.
(b) $3x - 2y + 2z = 24$; $(x - 2)/3 = (y + 2)/4 = (z - 3)/5$.

17. Find the equation of a plane that passes through the points $(1, 4, 9)$ and $(9, 4, 1)$ (cf. Problem 2a) and is parallel to the line whose equations are $x = 1 + t, y = 2 - 2t, z = 3 - t$, and illustrate.

18. Find the equation of a plane that contains the line of Problem 6a and is parallel to the line of Problem 17.

19. Find an equation for the family of all lines through $(3, -2, 7)$ that are parallel to the plane $x + y + z = 5$, and illustrate.

20. Find the intersection of each of the following triples of planes, and illustrate.

(a) $x + y + z = 3$, $x - y + z = 1$, $x + y - z = 1$.

(b) $2x - y + z = 3$, $x - 2y + z = 0$, $x + y + 2z = 9$.

(c) $x + y + z = 3$, $x + 2y + 2z = 4$, $2x + 3y + 3z = 7$.

(d) $x + y + z = 3$, $x + 2y + 2z = 4$, $x + y + z = 7$.

(e) $x + y + z = 3$, $x + y + z = 5$, $x + y + z = 7$.

(f) $x + y + z = 3$, $x + 2y + 3z = 6$, $3x + 2y + z = 12$.

21. Find the equation of the set of all points in $E3'$ that are equidistant from the points $(3, 4, 5)$ and $(7, 10, 7)$, and illustrate.

22. Find the (common perpendicular) distance between the line in $E3'$ that passes through the points $(4, 2, 6)$ and $(6, -3, 7)$, and the line in $E3'$ that passes through the points $(8, 2, 4)$ and $(4, -2, 10)$, and illustrate.

23 (Optional). Generalize 3f Problem 11 to $E3'$.

3m. DETERMINANTS

In this section, for the reader who has not studied determinants and by way of review for those who have, we shall consider determinants only to the very limited extent that is necessary for our purposes.

It turns out to be useful, in many mathematical situations, to use the symbol $\begin{vmatrix} a & b \\ c & d \end{vmatrix}$ to represent the expression $ad - bc$. We call $\begin{vmatrix} a & b \\ c & d \end{vmatrix}$ a *determinant*.

For example, $\begin{vmatrix} 11 & 7 \\ 1 & 2 \end{vmatrix} = 22 - 7 = 15$ and $\begin{vmatrix} 11 & -7 \\ 1 & 2 \end{vmatrix} = 29$.

It turns out to be equally useful to use the symbol

$$\begin{vmatrix} a & b & c \\ d & e & f \\ g & h & i \end{vmatrix}$$

(which is also called a determinant) to represent another special expression, that may be described as follows.

If we delete the row (i.e., the horizontal array) and the column (i.e., the vertical array) in which the term a of a determinant appears, the resulting determinant is called the *minor of a*. We shall denote the minor of a: M_a. Thus $M_a = \begin{vmatrix} e & f \\ h & i \end{vmatrix}$. Similarly, $M_b = \begin{vmatrix} d & f \\ g & i \end{vmatrix}$ and $M_c = \begin{vmatrix} d & e \\ g & h \end{vmatrix}$. Now we define:

$$\begin{vmatrix} a & b & c \\ d & e & f \\ g & h & i \end{vmatrix} = M_a a - M_b b + M_c c.$$

For example,

$$\begin{vmatrix} 1 & 2 & 3 \\ 7 & 8 & 9 \\ 1 & 2 & 3 \end{vmatrix} = \begin{vmatrix} 8 & 9 \\ 2 & 3 \end{vmatrix} 1 - \begin{vmatrix} 7 & 9 \\ 1 & 3 \end{vmatrix} 2 + \begin{vmatrix} 7 & 8 \\ 1 & 2 \end{vmatrix} 3$$

$$= 6 - 24 + 18$$

$$= 0.$$

Problems

1. Prove that each of the following equations is an equation of a line through the distinct points (a_1, a_2) and (b_1, b_2) in $E2'$.

$$\begin{vmatrix} x & y & 1 \\ a_1 & a_2 & 1 \\ b_1 & b_2 & 1 \end{vmatrix} = 0, \qquad \begin{vmatrix} x - a_1 & y - a_2 \\ b_1 - a_1 & b_2 - a_2 \end{vmatrix} = 0.$$

2. Use Problem 1 to do 3f Problems 1f, g, h.

3n. THE VECTOR PRODUCT OF TWO VECTORS

Suppose we are given two nonzero vectors of $E3'$. How can we find a vector perpendicular to both of the given vectors? In some cases, the problem is easily solved. For example, if i, j are the given vectors, then k is a vector that is clearly perpendicular to both. The following definition leads to a general solution of the problem (indeed, one that does give the result k when the given vectors are i and j).

3n1 (Definition). In $E3$ let v, w be vectors. If v, w are nonzero vectors, let θ be the angle between them ($0° \leq \theta \leq 180°$); otherwise, let $\theta = 0°$. Then we define $v \times w$ to be a vector of $E3$ such that:

(i) $|v \times w| = |v| \, |w| \sin \theta$.

(ii) If v, w are nonzero vectors, and $\sin \theta \neq 0$ then $v \times w$ is perpendicular to v and w, and $(v, w, v \times w)$ form a lefthanded system (see statement 2g2).

[*Note:* $v \times w$ (read "v cross w") is called the *vector product*, or the *cross product*, of v and w.]

There immediately follows:

3n2. In $E3'$, $i \times j = k$, $j \times i = -k$, $j \times k = i$, $k \times j = -i$, $k \times i = j$, $i \times k = -j$, and $i \times i = j \times j = k \times k = 0_V$ (see Fig. 3n1; Proofs?).

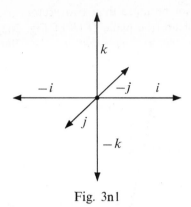

Fig. 3n1

Furthermore:

3n3. In $E3$ suppose v, w are vectors and s, t are scalars. Then:

(i) $v \times v = 0_V \times v = v \times 0_V = 0_V$.

(ii) $v \times w = -(w \times v)$.

(iii) $(sv) \times w = v \times (sw) = s(v \times w)$.

(iv) $(sv) \times (tw) = st(v \times w)$.

[Proofs? *Hint:* To prove (iii), consider the cases $s > 0$, $s = 0$, $s < 0$.]

Our next, very special result leads quickly to a much more general and useful consequence. (A statement of this sort, whose principal function is to help in the proof of another statement, is called a *lemma*.)

3n4. (Lemma). In $E3'$, $i \times (ai + bj + ck) = -cj + bk$.

Proof: If $b = c = 0$, the result follows quickly (?1). Otherwise, it is easy to see that both $-cj + bk$ and $cj - bk$ are nonzero vectors perpendicular to each of i and $ai + bj + ck$ (?2). Now suppose θ is the angle between i and $ai + bj + ck$, where $0° \leq \theta \leq 180°$ (see Fig. 3n2). Then $\cos \theta = a/\sqrt{a^2 + b^2 + c^2}$ (?3). Therefore

$$\sin \theta \overset{?4}{=} \sqrt{1 - \cos^2 \theta} \overset{?5}{=} \sqrt{b^2 + c^2}/\sqrt{a^2 + b^2 + c^2}.$$

Therefore

$$|i \times (ai + bj + ck)| \overset{?6}{=} 1\sqrt{a^2 + b^2 + c^2} \, (\sqrt{b^2 + c^2}/\sqrt{a^2 + b^2 + c^2})$$
$$= \sqrt{b^2 + c^2} = |-cj + bk| = |cj - bk|.$$

Since there cannot be more than two vectors of equal absolute value perpendicular to a plane (the plane OAB of Fig. 3n2), $i \times (ai + bj + ck)$ must equal *one* of the vectors $-cj + bk$, $cj - bk$. But which one?

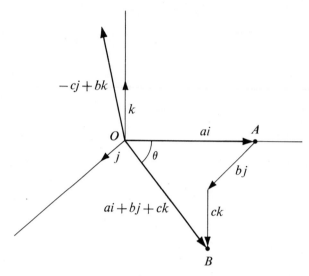

Fig. 3n2

If $b > 0$ (as in Fig. 3n2), then (see the description of a left-handed system in statement 2g2) $i \times (ai + bj + ck)$ must extend *upward*. But if $b > 0$, $-cj + bk$ extends upward and $cj - bk$ extends downward. Hence, in this case, $i \times (ai + bj + ck) = -cj + bk$.

It is left to the reader to prove that the same result holds if $b < 0$ or if $b = 0$. ‖

The preceding result enables us to prove the following important distributive law.

3n5. If u, v, w are vectors of $E3$, then

$$(i) \quad u \times (v + w) = u \times v + u \times w.$$

$$(ii) \quad (u + v) \times w = u \times w + v \times w.$$

Proof of (i): If $u = 0_V$, the result follows quickly (?1). Otherwise, we may choose a Cartesian coordinate system in $E3$ such that $u = i$ (see statement 2g2). Suppose that in this coordinate system $v = ai + bj + ck$

and $w = di + ej + fk$. Then

$$u \times (v + w) = i \times [(a + d)i + (b + e)j + (c + f)k]$$

$$\overset{?2}{=} -(c + f)j + (b + e)k = (-cj + bk) + (-fj + ek)$$

$$\overset{?3}{=} i \times (ai + bj + ck) + i \times (di + ej + fk)$$

$$= (?4). \quad \|$$

[*Proof of* (ii)?]

And now we can prove the principal result of this section:

3n6. In *E3'*,

$$(ai + bj + ck) \times (di + ej + fk) = \begin{vmatrix} i & j & k \\ a & b & c \\ d & e & f \end{vmatrix}.$$

Proof:

$$(ai + bj + ck) \times (di + ej + fk) \overset{?1}{=} ad(i \times i) + ae(i \times j) + af(i \times k)$$
$$+ bd(j \times i) + be(j \times j) + bf(j \times k)$$
$$+ cd(k \times i) + ce(k \times j) + cf(k \times k)$$

$$\overset{?2}{=} (bf - ce)i + (cd - af)j + (ae - bd)k$$

$$\overset{?3}{=} \begin{vmatrix} b & c \\ e & f \end{vmatrix} i - \begin{vmatrix} a & c \\ d & f \end{vmatrix} j + \begin{vmatrix} a & b \\ d & e \end{vmatrix} k$$

$$= \begin{vmatrix} i & j & k \\ a & b & c \\ d & e & f \end{vmatrix}. \quad \|$$

ILLUSTRATIVE EXAMPLE. Find an equation of the plane through the points $P = (1, 3, 1)$, $Q = (4, 0, 2)$, $R = (3, 8, -3)$.

Solution: Note first that $\overrightarrow{PQ} \times \overrightarrow{PR}$ is perpendicular to both $\overrightarrow{PQ}$ and $\overrightarrow{PR}$; hence $\overrightarrow{PQ} \times \overrightarrow{PR}$ is normal to plane *PQR*. (A vector perpendicular to two distinct vectors parallel to a plane is perpendicular to the plane.) But

$$\overrightarrow{PQ} \times \overrightarrow{PR} \overset{?1}{=} (3i - 3j + k) \times (2i + 5j - 4k)$$

$$= \begin{vmatrix} i & j & k \\ 3 & -3 & 1 \\ 2 & 5 & -4 \end{vmatrix}$$

$$= \begin{vmatrix} -3 & 1 \\ 5 & -4 \end{vmatrix} i - \begin{vmatrix} 3 & 1 \\ 2 & -4 \end{vmatrix} j + \begin{vmatrix} 3 & -3 \\ 2 & 5 \end{vmatrix} k$$

$$= 7i + 14j + 21k.$$

Hence direction numbers for a line normal to plane PQR are $(7, 14, 21)$. But then $\frac{1}{7}(7, 14, 21) = (1, 2, 3)$ are also direction numbers for a line normal to plane PQR (?2). Hence (?3) an equation of plane PQR is

$$x + 2y + 3z = 1 \cdot 1 + 2 \cdot 3 + 3 \cdot 1 = 10. \quad \|$$

Carrying out the preceding process in a less special setting leads to a very pretty solution of the general problem:

3n7. An equation of the plane through noncollinear points $P = (p_1, p_2, p_3)$, $Q = (q_1, q_2, q_3)$, $R = (r_1, r_2, r_3)$ is

(1)
$$\begin{vmatrix} x - p_1 & y - p_2 & z - p_3 \\ q_1 - p_1 & q_2 - p_2 & q_3 - p_3 \\ r_1 - p_1 & r_2 - p_2 & r_3 - p_3 \end{vmatrix} = 0.$$

Proof: Since $\overrightarrow{PQ} = (q_1 - p_1)i + (q_2 - p_2)j + (q_3 - p_3)k$, and $\overrightarrow{PR} = (r_1 - p_1)i + (r_2 - p_2)j + (r_3 - p_3)k$ (?1), a normal to plane PQR is

$$\overrightarrow{PQ} \times \overrightarrow{PR} \overset{?2}{=} \begin{vmatrix} i & j & k \\ q_1 - p_1 & q_2 - p_2 & q_3 - p_3 \\ r_1 - p_1 & r_2 - p_2 & r_3 - p_3 \end{vmatrix}$$

$$= \begin{vmatrix} q_2 - p_2 & q_3 - p_3 \\ r_2 - p_2 & r_3 - p_3 \end{vmatrix} i - (?3)j + (?4)k.$$

Hence (?5) direction numbers for a line normal to plane PQR are

$$\left(\begin{vmatrix} q_2 - p_2 & q_3 - p_3 \\ r_2 - p_2 & r_3 - p_3 \end{vmatrix}, -(?6), (?7) \right).$$

Hence (?8) an equation of plane PQR is

$$\begin{vmatrix} q_2 - p_2 & q_3 - p_3 \\ r_2 - p_2 & r_3 - p_3 \end{vmatrix} (x - p_1) - (?9)(y - p_2) + (?10)(z - p_3) = 0,$$

which is equivalent (?11) to Eq. (1). $\|$

(It is left to the reader to solve the Illustrative Example directly by means of statement 3n7.)

Problems

1. Find each of the following, and illustrate.

   (a) $i \times (3i + 4j)$.   (b) $(3i + 4j) \times i$.

   (c) $(i + j) \times (i - j)$.   (d) $(i + j) \times (i + j)$.

   (e) $(i + 2j + 3k) \times (2i - j + k)$.

2. Prove that the area of a triangle ABC in $E3'$ is $\frac{1}{2}|\vec{AB} \times \vec{AC}|$.

3. Use Problem 2 to find the area of triangle ABC in each of the following cases.

   (a) $A = (0, 0, 0)$, $B = (3, 0, 10)$, $C = (0, 6, 8)$.

   (b) $A = (1, 1, 1)$, $B = (4, 1, 11)$, $C = (1, 7, 9)$.

   (c) $A = (-4, 2, 3)$, $B = (2, 3, 4)$, $C = (2, -5, 5)$.

   (d) $A = (1, 2)$, $B = (5, -7)$, $C = (-3, 4)$. [*Hint:* These are points in $E2'$. The vector product of two vectors is defined only in $E3'$. But the area of this triangle ABC in $E2'$ is the same as that of the triangle in $E3'$ whose vertices are $(1, 2, 0)$, $(5, -7, 0)$, $(-3, 4, 0)$.]

4. Use Problem 2 to prove that the area of a triangle ABC in $E2'$ is the absolute value of

$$\frac{1}{2}\begin{vmatrix} x_A & y_A & 1 \\ x_B & y_B & 1 \\ x_C & y_C & 1 \end{vmatrix}.$$

   (*Hint:* See hint for Problem 3d.)

5. Use Problem 4 to find the area of triangle ABC in each of the following cases.

   (a) Problem 3d.

   (b) $A = (0, 0)$, $B = (3, 0)$, $C = (3, 4)$.

   (c) $A = (-1, 2)$, $B = (3, -4)$, $C = (4, 6)$.

   (d) $A = (-1, 2)$, $B = (3, -4)$, $C = (7, -10)$. (What is the significance of this result?)

6. Use the method of the Illustrative Example of this section to solve (a) 3l Problem 2c, (b) 3l Problem 2e.

7. Prove that the volume of a parallelepiped in $E3$, with edges AB, AC, AD, is $|(\vec{AB} \times \vec{AC}) \cdot \vec{AD}|$.

8. Use Problem 7 to find the volume of each of the following parallelepiped, with edges AB, AC, AD, and illustrate, given that A, B, C, D are respectively:

   (a) $(0, 0, 0)$, $(5, 0, 0)$, $(0, 4, 0)$, $(0, 0, 6)$.

   (b) $(0, 0, 0)$, $(8, 4, 0)$, $(4, 8, 0)$, $(10, 10, 10)$.

   (c) $(6, 8, 1)$, $(2, -4, 4)$, $(3, 4, 5)$, $(10, 0, 0)$.

   (d) $(6, 8, 1)$, $(2, -4, 4)$, $(3, 4, 5)$, $(7, 16, 2)$. (What is the significance of this result?)

9 (Optional).   Prove that if $u_1 = a_1 i + b_1 j + c_1 k$, $u_2 = a_2 i + b_2 j + c_2 k$, and $u_3 = a_3 i + b_3 j + c_3 k$, then

$$(u_1 \times u_2) \cdot u_3 = \begin{vmatrix} a_1 & b_1 & c_1 \\ a_2 & b_2 & c_2 \\ a_3 & b_3 & c_3 \end{vmatrix}.$$

10 (a)–(d).   Use Problem 9 to solve Problems 8a–d.

11 (Optional).   Prove that if u, v, w are vectors in $E3$, then:

(a) $(u \times v) \cdot w = u \cdot (v \times w)$.

(b) $(u \times v) \times w = (u \cdot w)v - (v \cdot w)u$.

(c) $u \times (v \times w) = (u \cdot w)v - (u \cdot v)w$.

Chapter 4

Algebraic Graphs in $E2'$

4a. FUNCTIONS OF ONE REAL VARIABLE

The set of all elements that a function assigns to the elements of its domain is called the *range* of the function.

A function whose domain and range both consist entirely of real numbers is called a *function of one real variable*. If f is a function of one real variable, then by the *graph of f* we shall mean simply the graph in $E2'$ of the equation $y = f(x)$.

For example, suppose f is the function whose domain is the set of all real numbers and whose action is given by the formula $f(x) = 7x + 11$. Then the graph of f is the graph in $E2'$ of the equation $y = 7x + 11$ (i.e., a straight line).

It is common practice in mathematical literature to refer to $f(x)$, or to an expression for $f(x)$ as the function f itself. We shall follow this practice. For example, we shall speak of "the function $7x + 11$" when what we mean is a function f with some specified domain whose action is given by the formula $f(x) = 7x + 11$. Following this practice, then, when we speak of the graph of $7x + 11$, we mean the graph in $E2'$ of the equation $y = 7x + 11$.

4b. POLYNOMIAL FUNCTIONS OF ONE REAL VARIABLE

Functions like $0, 7, x + 1, 2x, 1 - x, x^2 + 3x - 2, x^3$ are undoubtedly familiar to the reader. They are called *polynomial functions*, or often simply *polynomials*. They are, indeed, the most simple and basic of all functions of one real variable. We shall therefore consider graphs of polynomials before we consider other graphs in this chapter. But first, precise definitions are needed.

4b1 (Definitions).   A *polynomial function of one real variable* is a function p of one real variable whose action may be given by setting $p(x)$ equal to one of the following: (i) 0, (ii) a, (iii) $ax + b$, (iv) $ax^2 + bx + c$, (v) $ax^3 + bx^2 + cx + d$, etc., where $a, b, c, \ldots$ are real numbers and $a \neq 0$.

0, a, ax, b, ax^2, bx, c, ax^3, $\ldots$ are called the *terms* of their respective polynomial functions.

0, a, b, c, $\ldots$ are called the *coefficients* of their respective polynomial functions; also, a is called the *coefficient* of x in the term ax, b the *coefficient* of x^2 in the term bx^2, etc.

Except for terms with coefficient 0, every term of a polynomial function has assigned to it a number called its *degree* in the following way: If k is a nonzero real number, then the degree of a term k is 0; of a term kx, 1; of a term kx^n, n.

Except for case (i) above, every polynomial function also has a degree assigned to it. The *degree* of a nonzero polynomial function is the highest degree which any of its terms exhibits. Thus, since $a \neq 0$ in cases (ii)–(v), the degree of the polynomial function p in cases (ii)–(v) would be 0, 1, 2, 3 respectively.

Polynomial functions of type (i) or (ii) above are called *constant* polynomial functions; those of degrees 1, 2, 3, 4, 5 are called *linear, quadratic, cubic, quartic, quintic* polynomial functions respectively.

EXAMPLES.   In all of these examples of polynomial functions p of one real variable, we take the domain of p to be the set of all real numbers.

$p(x) = 0$ [falls under (i)]. $p(x) = 7$ [falls under (ii)].

$p(x) = 2x + 3$ [falls under (iii)].

$p(x) = x^2$ [falls under (iv), for this mapping *may* be given by
$\qquad p(x) = 1x^2 + 0x + 0$].

(In what follows we shall assume, unless otherwise noted, that the domain of each polynomial function of one real variable considered is maximal, i.e., that it is the set of *all* real numbers.)

Examples illustrating *degree* and *coefficients:*

(a) $p(x) = 3x^2 + 4x + 5$ defines a polynomial function of degree 2 (i.e., a quadratic function) with coefficients 3, 4, 5; 3 is said to be the coefficient of x^2 and 4 the coefficient of x; (5 is sometimes called the "constant" term).

(b) $2v - 7$, since it may be expressed as $2v + (-7)$, is a polynomial ("in v," we say) of the first degree (i.e., a linear polynomial); 2 is the coefficient of v, and -7 is the constant term of this polynomial.

(c) 11 is a zero-degree polynomial (i.e., a constant polynomial). [We have in mind, of course, the function p whose domain consists of the set of all real numbers and whose action is given by the equation $p(x) = 11$.]

(d) 0 is a constant polynomial also, but one to which we have assigned no degree (since to do so, in this text, would serve no useful purpose).

(e) $y - y^3$ is a cubic (i.e., a third-degree) polynomial in y, since $y - y^3 = (-1)y^3 + 0y^2 + 1y + 0$. (This equality is an *identity*, i.e., the two sides are defined and equal for all real numbers y.)

A polynomial expressed in one of the forms (i)–(v), etc., above will be said to be in *standard form*.

(*Note: In this text, "polynomial" will always mean "polynomial with real coefficients."*)

4c.   THE GRAPH OF A POLYNOMIAL $p(x)$

(*Note: In this section, all graphs are assumed to be in E2'.*)

The graph of an equation in the form $y = mx + b$, with m and b any real numbers, is a nonvertical straight line with slope m. If $m = 0$, the equation reduces to $y = b$, whose graph is a straight line with slope $m = 0$, i.e., a "horizontal" straight line. (See statements 3f4 and 3f5.)

We may therefore say that the graph of a function $mx + b$, where m and b are any real numbers, is always a straight line.

A constant polynomial function, i.e., one of no degree or else of degree 0, falls into the pattern $mx + b$, with $m = 0$. Therefore the graph of a constant polynomial is always a horizontal straight line.

For example, the graph of the polynomial 2, i.e., of the polynomial function $p(x) = 2$ and hence of the equation $y = 2$, is a line parallel to the X axis with Y-intercept 2.

A linear polynomial function, i.e., one of degree 1, falls into the pattern $mx + b$, with $m \neq 0$. Therefore the graph of a first-degree polynomial in x is always a straight line that is neither horizontal nor vertical.

For example, the straight line which is the graph of the polynomial $2x + 3$ is easily drawn either by the "slope–intercept" method ($m = 2$, $b = 3$) or by locating points $(0, 3)$, $(4, 11)$, for example, on that line (cf. Section 3f).

As far as the graphs of quadratic and higher-degree functions are concerned, we shall now make several definitions and statements, most of which, although they will be given roughly and intuitively and without proof, will nevertheless turn out to be helpful in drawing these graphs.

(i) A point on a graph that is higher than any "nearby" point is called a *maximum* point; a point on a graph that is lower than any nearby point is called a *minimum* point; an *extremum* is either a maximum or a minimum point.

The graph of a polynomial $p(x)$ of degree n has at most $n - 1$ extrema. Furthermore, the exact number of extrema differs from $n - 1$ by an even number. (See Fig. 4c1)

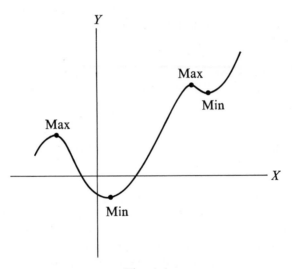

Fig. 4c1

(ii) The graph of a polynomial $p(x)$ is always "continuous"; that is to say, there are no "breaks" in the graph. Graphs of polynomials are also free of sharp points.

(Statements made in (i) and (ii) above are made more precisely and proved in courses in calculus, functions of a real variable, analysis, etc.)

(iii) The term of highest degree in a polynomial eventually "dominates" the polynomial. For example, in the polynomial $2x^4 - 7x^3 - x^2 - 2$, the term of highest degree is $2x^4$. For sufficiently large positive x, $2x^4$ will be very large positively—enough to outweigh the negative effect of the other terms. Therefore, in this case, after we have gone sufficiently far to the right, the graph simply continually rises. We say that on the right the graph eventually only rises. On the left, it is again the term of highest degree, examined this time for large *negative* values of x, which determines the behavior of a polynomial $p(x)$. In the case above, since $2x^4$ is positive when x is negative, the graph eventually only rises on the left also.

The graph of $-2x^4 + 6x^2 - 7$, however, will eventually only fall on both its left and right; the graph of $x^3 - 999$ will eventually only rise on the right and eventually only fall on the left; and the graph of $-2x^3 + 999$ will eventually only fall on the right and eventually only rise on the left.

(iv) Consider the graph G of the polynomial $p(x) = x^4 + x^2$. It happens that $(2, 20) \in G$. It follows that $(-2, 20) \in G$ also; for since only even exponents occur in $p(x)$, $p(-2) = p(2)$. Thus whenever $(a, b) \in G$, so is $(-a, b)$.

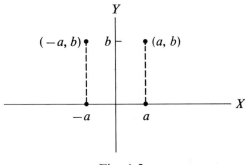

Fig. 4c2

But if the Y axis were a mirror, the points (a, b) and $(-a, b)$ would be each other's images (Fig. 4c2). For this reason, the points (a, b) and $(-a, b)$ are said to be *symmetric with respect to the Y axis*. And when it is true that for each point (a, b) on a graph, $(-a, b)$ is on the graph also, we say that the graph is symmetric to the Y axis. What we have remarked, then, is that the graph of $x^4 + x^2$ is symmetric to the Y axis. In fact:

The graph of a polynomial $p(x)$ is symmetric to the Y axis if and only if all the terms of $p(x)$ are of even degree.

(Note that a nonzero constant term has for its degree the even number 0.)

Suppose all the terms of a polynomial $p(x)$ are of odd degree, as, for example, in the case $p(x) = x^3 + x$. We note that $(1, 2)$ and $(-1, -2)$ are points of the graph of $x^3 + x$; in fact, it may be shown that whenever (a, b) is a point of the graph of $x^3 + x$, then so is $(-a, -b)$.

Points (a, b) and $(-a, -b)$ are said to be symmetric with respect to the origin (Fig. 4c3). And when it is true that for each point (a, b) on a graph, $(-a, -b)$ is on the graph also, we say that the graph is symmetric to the origin. Thus the graph of $x^3 + x$ is symmetric to the origin. In fact:

The graph of a polynomial $p(x)$ is symmetric to the origin if all the terms of $p(x)$ are of odd degree.

(v) Given an equation in x and y, the X-intercepts of its graph are the x values of the points of the graph for which $y = 0$, and, correspondingly, the Y-intercepts are the y values of the points of the graph for which $x = 0$.

Given a polynomial $p(x)$, the graph of $p(x)$ is, of course, the same as

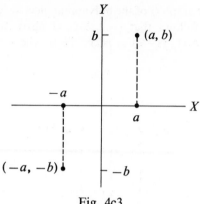

Fig. 4c3

that of the equation $y = p(x)$; here the X-intercepts are therefore simply the real roots of the equation $p(x) = 0$.

The graph of a polynomial $p(x)$ will always have just one Y-intercept, whose ordinate will be $y = p(0)$.

ILLUSTRATIVE EXAMPLE 1.   Sketch the graph G of $p(x) = x^3 - 8x$.

Solution: Note that:

(i) G has either two or zero extrema.

(ii) On the right G eventually only rises, and on the left G eventually only falls.

(iii) G is symmetric to the origin.

(iv) X-intercepts occur when $x^3 - 8x = 0$. The solution of this equation is $x(x^2 - 8) = 0$; $x = 0$, $\pm 2\sqrt{2}$;   or $x = 0$, ± 2.8, approximately. The unique Y-intercept is $y = p(0)$, or $y = 0$.

Since G is symmetric to the origin and since we already have $p(0)$, only the functional values for positive x must actually be computed in working out the following table of values.

x	-3	-2	-1	0	1	2	3
$p(x)$	-3	8	7	0	-7	-8	3

Using this information, we sketch the graph of $x^3 - 8x$ (see Fig. 4c4).   ‖

Before we proceed, we bring to the reader's attention the following intuitively plausible fact.

4c1.   Let p be a polynomial (or, indeed, any continuous function of one real variable), and suppose the numbers $p(a)$, $p(c)$ are opposite in sign. Then there is a real number b between a and c such that $p(b) = 0$.

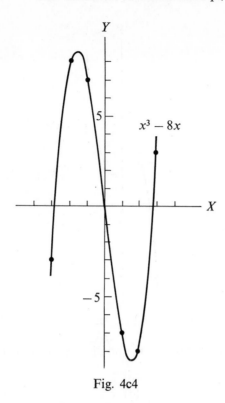

$x^3 - 8x$

Fig. 4c4

ILLUSTRATIVE EXAMPLE 2.   Sketch the graph G of $p(x) = x^3 - x + 2$.

Solution: Note that:
  (i) G has either two or zero extrema.
  (ii) G rises as we go far to the right and falls as we go far to the left.
  (iii) G is symmetric to neither the Y axis nor the origin.
  (iv) X-intercepts are not easily computed, but we note from the table of values below that one exists between $x = -2$ and $x = -1$ (?). The Y-intercept is at $y = p(0) = 2$.
    The table of values is computed as follows:

x	-2	-1	0	1	2
$p(x)$	-4	2	2	2	8

Using this information, we sketch the graph of $x^3 - x + 2$ (see Fig. 4c5).   ‖

Problems

1. Write out standard forms for quartic and quintic polynomials in x.
2. In each of the following cases state the degree (if any) and the type of

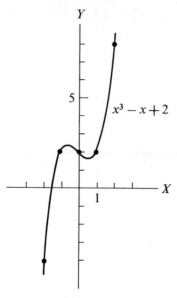

Fig. 4c5

the polynomial function given, and discuss and sketch its graph.

(a) 0.

(b) 7.

(c) $-\pi$.

(d) x.

(e) x^2.

(f) x^3.

(g) x^4.

(h) $2x$.

(i) $1 - x$.

(j) $2x^2$.

(k) $-2x^2$.

(l) $-x^3$.

(m) $-x^4$.

(n) $x^2 - x + 5$.

(o) $-x^2 + 2x + 1$.

(p) $x^3 - x^2 - 5$.

(q) $(x - 1)(x + 4)$.

(r) $x^2(x - 3)$.

(s) $-x^3 + x^2 + x + 1$.

(t) $(x - 2)(x + 1)(x + 3)$.

(u) $x^3 - x^2 - x + 1$.

(v) $x^3 - x^2 + x - 1$.

(w) $x^4 - x^2$.

(x) $x - x^4$.

3. (a) A single standard form for polynomials which includes the forms
    0, a, $ax + b$, $ax^2 + bx + c$, etc., as special cases in the following:

$$a_0x^n + a_1x^{n-1} + \cdots + a_{n-1}x + a_n,$$

where n is a nonnegative integer. For $n = 0$, this form is understood
to represent simply a_0x^0, or a_0; for $n = 1$, $a_0x + a_1$; for $n = 2$,
$a_0x^2 + a_1x + a_2$; etc. Write down what this form represents for
$n = 3$ and $n = 4$.

(b) In the case of each of the polynomials of Problem 2, identify n and $a_0, \ldots, a_n$ so that the new form given in part (a) expresses the given polynomial.

4. (a) Frame general definitions of symmetry with respect to lines and points. That is, given points P, P' and line l, under what circumstance will points P, P' be said to be symmetric with respect to line l? And given points P, P' and O, under what circumstances will points P, P' be said to be symmetric with respect to point O?

(b) Suppose (p, q) is a point in $E2'$. What point is symmetric to (p, q) with respect to each of the following lines?

(i) $y = x$.   (ii) $x = k$ (k any real number).
(iii) $x = p$.   (iv) $y = -x$.
(v) $y = mx + b$.

5. Why have we not discussed the symmetry of graphs of functions with respect to the X axis?

4d. RATIONAL FUNCTIONS OF ONE REAL VARIABLE

Roughly speaking, a rational function is the "ratio" of polynomial functions. More precisely:

(Definition). A *rational function of one real variable* is a function r of one real variable whose action may be given by

$$r(x) = \frac{p(x)}{q(x)},$$

where p and q are polynomial functions.

[$r(x)$ is said to be *in lowest terms* if $p(x)$ and $q(x)$ have no common factor.]

In what follows, unless otherwise noted, we shall assume that the domain of each rational function discussed is "maximal," i.e., that if $r(x)$ is as above, then the domain of r consists of all real numbers except those that are roots of the equation $q(x) = 0$.

Also, we shall refer to the rational function $1/x$, for example, when what we have in mind is the function r whose domain consists of all real numbers except 0 and whose action is given by $r(x) = 1/x$.

Similarly, we shall assume the domain of the rational function $(x + 1)/(x - 1)$ to be the set of all real numbers except 1, and the domain of the rational function $(x^2 + 1)/(x^2 - 1)$, to be the set of all real numbers except 1 and -1.

Note that every polynomial function is also a rational function, for the polynomial function $p(x)$ is identical with the rational function $p(x)/1$.

4e. THE GRAPH IN $E2'$ OF A RATIONAL FUNCTION $r(x)$

We shall now examine the graph in $E2'$ of the very simple rational function $1/x$.

According to our assumption concerning the domain of rational functions, the domain of the function $1/x$ consists of all real numbers except 0.

We construct the following table of values.

x	-4	-3	-2	-1	$-\frac{1}{2}$	$-\frac{1}{3}$	$-\frac{1}{4}$	0	$\frac{1}{4}$	$\frac{1}{3}$	$\frac{1}{2}$	1	2	3	4
$1/x$	$-\frac{1}{4}$	$-\frac{1}{3}$	$-\frac{1}{2}$	-1	-2	-3	-4		4	3	2	1	$\frac{1}{2}$	$\frac{1}{3}$	$\frac{1}{4}$

We then plot the indicated points, and through these points we draw a graph (see Fig. 4e1).

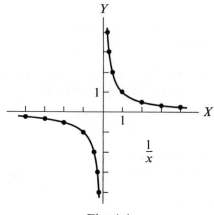

Fig. 4e1

The following facts are suggested by the graph and may be verified upon examining the function $1/x$.

(i) As x becomes large (either positively or negatively), the function $1/x$ approaches more and more nearly the value 0, but it never attains this value.

(ii) As x approaches the value 0 (either positively or negatively), the function $1/x$ becomes larger and larger (either positively or negatively).

In case (i) we may say that as x becomes large, our graph approaches but never reaches the straight line whose equation is $y = 0$. In case (ii) we may say that as x approaches 0, our graph approaches the vertical straight line whose equation is $x = 0$.

Straight lines that are approached (but not reached) by a graph as x or y becomes very large are called *asymptotes* for the graph. A bit more precisely:

(a) (Definition). Suppose a function $f(x) = a(x) + b(x)$ has the graph G, and the function $a(x)$ has for its graph the straight line l. Then l is said to be a (nonvertical) asymptote for G if $b(x)$ approaches (but never equals) 0 as x becomes large either positively or negatively (see Fig. 4e2).

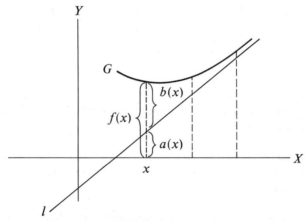

Fig. 4e2

For example, consider the function $f(x) = x + (1/x)$. Clearly, $b(x) = 1/x$ approaches but never equals 0 as x becomes large either positively or negatively. The graph of the function $a(x) = x$ is a straight line which is therefore approached by the graph of $x + (1/x)$ as we move far out both to the left and to the right.

[We shall further consider the function $x + (1/x)$ below.]

(b) (Definition). Suppose G is the graph of a function $f(x)$ and the vertical line l is the graph of the equation $x = k$. Then l is said to be a (vertical) *asymptote* for G if $f(x)$ becomes unboundedly larger and larger (positively or negatively) as x approaches the value k, either from the left or from the right or from both directions (see Fig. 4e3).

If $f(x)$ is a rational function in lowest terms, $f(x)$ will become unboundedly large whenever its denominator approaches 0. For example, the rational function $(x - 10)/(x - 2)$ becomes unboundedly large as x approaches 2, for as x approaches 2 the numerator and denominator of the function in question approach -8 and 0 respectively. Therefore the line

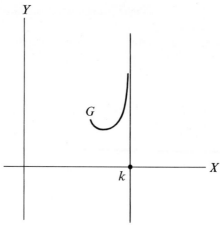

Fig. 4e3

whose equation is $x = 2$ is an asymptote for the graph of the function $(x - 10)/(x - 2)$. In fact:

If a rational function $p(x)/q(x)$ is in lowest terms, then whenever k is a root of $q(x) = 0$, $x = k$ will be the equation of a vertical asymptote for the graph of $p(x)/q(x)$.

As far as symmetry is concerned, considerations similar to those which obtained in the case of polynomials lead to the following rules.

If $r(x) = p(x)/q(x)$ is a rational function in lowest terms, then the graph G of $r(x)$ is symmetric to:
   (i) *The Y axis iff $p(x)$ and $q(x)$, in standard form, both involve only terms of even degree.*
   (ii) *The origin iff $p(x)$ and $q(x)$, in standard form, are such that one involves only terms of even degree and the other only terms of odd degree.*

ILLUSTRATIVE EXAMPLE 1.   Discuss and sketch the graph G of the rational function $r(x) = (x^2 + 1)/x$.

Solution: Note that:
   (i) The domain of $r(x)$ consists of all real numbers except $x = 0$.
   (ii) G has no X-intercept, for $r(x) = 0$ iff the numerator $x^2 + 1 = 0$; however, $x^2 + 1 = 0$ has no real roots. G has no Y-intercept, for $r(0)$ is not defined.
   (iii) G is symmetric to the origin.
   (iv) Since $r(x) = (x^2 + 1)/x = x + (1/x)$, the graph of the function x (as we have already noted) is an asymptote for G, approached both on the

right and left by G. Furthermore, since 0 is an immediate root of the equation that results from setting the denominator of $r(x)$ equal to 0, it follows that the vertical line whose equation is $x = 0$ (i.e., the Y-axis) is an asymptote for G.

With the help of the above information and the following table of values, we now sketch the graph G (see Fig. 4e4). ‖

x	-2	-1	$-\frac{1}{2}$	0	$\frac{1}{2}$	1	2
$r(x)$	-2.5	-2	-2.5		2.5	2	2.5

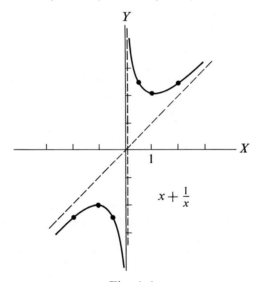

Fig. 4e4

ILLUSTRATIVE EXAMPLE 2.   Discuss and sketch the graph G of the function $r(x) = (x^2 - 3x)/(x^2 - 4)$.

Solution: Note that:

(i) The domain of $r(x)$ consists of all real numbers except $x = \pm 2$.

(ii) Solving $x^2 - 3x = 0$, we find that the X-intercepts of G are $x = 0, 3$. Since $r(0) = 0$, the Y-intercept of G is $y = 0$.

(iii) G is symmetric neither to the Y axis nor to the origin.

(iv) By long division $r(x) = 1 + [(4 - 3x)/(x^2 - 4)]$. As x becomes large, $(4 - 3x)/(x^2 - 4)$ approaches but never equals 0. Therefore the line that is the graph of the function 1 is an asymptote for G. Furthermore, since the roots of $x^2 - 4 = 0$ are $x = \pm 2$, the vertical lines with equations $x = \pm 2$ are also asymptotes for G.

With the help of the above information and the following table of values, we now sketch the graph of G (see Fig. 4e5).   ‖

x	-3	-2	-1	0	1	2	3
$r(x)$	3.6		$-\frac{4}{3}$	0	$\frac{2}{3}$		0

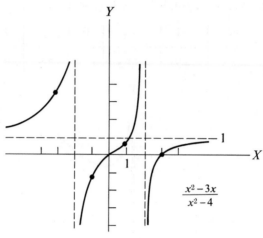

$$\frac{x^2 - 3x}{x^2 - 4}$$

Fig. 4e5

Problems

1.   Discuss and sketch the graph of each of the following rational functions.

(a) $\dfrac{12}{x}$.   (b) $-\dfrac{12}{x}$.   (c) $\dfrac{k}{x}$ (k a real number).

(d) $\dfrac{36}{x^2}$.   (e) $\dfrac{1}{x^2 - 1}$.   (f) $\dfrac{x}{x^2 - 1}$.

(g) $\dfrac{x^2}{x^2 - 1}$.   (h) $\dfrac{x^3}{x^2 - 1}$.   (i) $\dfrac{1}{x^2 + 1}$.

(j) $\dfrac{x}{x^2 + 1}$.   (k) $\dfrac{x^2}{x^2 + 1}$.   (l) $\dfrac{x^3}{x^2 + 1}$.

(m) $\dfrac{x^3 + 1}{x}$.   (n) $\dfrac{x - 1}{x^2 - 2x - 3}$.   (o) $\dfrac{x^2 + x - 2}{2x^2 + 1}$.

(p) $\dfrac{x^2 - 1}{x}$.   (q) $\dfrac{x - 1}{x + 1}$.   (r) $\dfrac{x + 3}{x^2 - 1}$.

(s) $\dfrac{x^2 - 1}{x^2}$.   (t) $\dfrac{3x^2 - 2}{x}$.   (u) $\dfrac{x^2 + 4}{x + 2}$.

(v) $\dfrac{x^2 + 4}{x - 2}$.   (w) $\dfrac{2x + 1}{x^2 - 2x - 3}$.   (x) $\dfrac{x^2 - 4}{x - 2}$.

2. Discuss and sketch the graph of each of the following equations. (*Hint:* Our discussion of rational functions applies, with the roles of x and y everywhere interchanged.)

(a) $x = \dfrac{y}{y^2 + 1}$.   (b) $x = \dfrac{y}{y^2 - 1}$.   (c) $x = \dfrac{y^2}{4y^2 - 1}$.

(d) $x = \dfrac{1}{y^3}$.   (e) $x = \dfrac{1}{y^3 + y}$.   (f) $x = \dfrac{1}{y^4 + y^2}$.

4f. THE GRAPH OF A POLYNOMIAL EQUATION IN TWO REAL VARIABLES

Functions are sometimes called *mappings*, and when a function f is such that $f(a) = b$, we say f *maps* (or *sends*) *a into b*.

The expression $x^2 + y$ may be used to define a function f which maps ordered pairs of real numbers into real numbers by specifying that $f(x, y) = x^2 + y$. This function f maps the ordered pair $(1, 2)$, for example, into the real number 3, and the ordered pair $(2, 1)$ into the real number 5.

We shall call a function whose domain consists of ordered pairs of real numbers a *function of two real variables*.

The simplest functions of two real variables are *polynomial* functions of two real variables. After several preliminary definitions, we shall define this class of functions.

(Definitions).   A *monomial function of two real variables* is a function m whose mapping may be given by

$$m(x, y) = kx^r y^s,$$

where k is any real number and r, s are any nonnegative integers.

k is called the *coefficient* of $x^r y^s$. If $k \neq 0$, the *degree* of m is defined to be $r + s$. (Following the usual practice, we understand the symbols x^0 and y^0 each to mean the real number 1 in the above contest.)

Two monomials are said to be *like* or *alike* if they are identical or if they differ only in their coefficients. For example, $2x^2y$ and $-2x^2y$ are like monomials.

Now suppose $m_1, \ldots, m_n$ are nonzero monomial functions of two real variables, no two of which are alike, and m is any monomial function of two real variables. Then we define a *polynomial function p of two real variables* to be a function whose mapping may be given by either

$$p(x, y) = m_1(x, y) + \cdots + m_n(x, y), \quad \text{or} \quad p(x, y) = m(x, y).$$

In the first case, $m_1(x, y), \ldots, m_n(x, y)$ are called the *terms* of $p(x, y)$, and and in the second, $m(x, y)$ is called the (single) *term* of $p(x, y)$.

In what follows we shall assume, unless otherwise noted, that the domain of each polynomial function of two variables considered is maximal, i.e., that it is the set of *all* ordered pairs of real numbers.

We shall follow the practice of referring to an expression such as $3x^2y^4$ as a monomial function, or even as just a "monomial," when what we have in mind, in the case of $3x^2y^4$, for example, is a monomial function m whose action is given by $m(x, y) = 3x^2y^4$; and similarly for polynomial functions.

EXAMPLES.   7, $2x$, $3y$, x^2y are monomials of degrees 0, 1, 1, 3 respectively "in x and y"; 7, $2x$, $7 + 2x$, and $2x + x^2y + 3y$ are polynomials in x and y.

Note that neither x nor y need necessarily appear in the expression of a polynomial in x and y; note further, however, that although neither x nor y appears in the polynomial 7, this polynomial may be written so that x and y do appear, namely in the form $7x^0y^0$.

Now we define a *polynomial equation* to be one in which a polynomial is set equal to zero. That is to say, if p is a polynomial in two variables, the equation $p(x, y) = 0$ is said to be a polynomial equation in two variables.

The equations whose graphs in $E2'$ we shall consider in this section are polynomial equations in x and y in which it is practicable to solve for x in terms of y, or for y in terms of x, or both.

ILLUSTRATIVE EXAMPLE 1.   Discuss and sketch the graph in $E2'$ of the equation $x^2y + y - 1 = 0$.

Solution: It is easy to solve for y, thereby arriving at the equivalent equation

$$y = \frac{1}{x^2 + 1}.$$

Now the graph of the equation $y = 1/(x^2 + 1)$ is the same as the graph of the rational function $1/(x^2 + 1)$, and we may proceed as before to find the graph of this function [4e Problem 1i].

However, some of the information which we seek with respect to the graph may be more easily derived directly from the original equation. Thus note that:

(i) *X*-intercepts may be found by letting $y = 0$ in the given equation and solving for x; *Y*-intercepts may be found by letting $x = 0$ and solving for y. In the case $x^2y + y - 1 = 0$, letting $y = 0$ leads to the impossibility $-1 = 0$; therefore the graph of $x^2y + y - 1 = 0$ has no *X*-intercept. Letting $x = 0$ leads to the *Y*-intercept $y = 1$.

(ii) In regard to symmetry, the following statements apply to the graph G in $E2'$ of a polynomial equation $p(x, y) = 0$.

(a) G is symmetric to the Y axis if x appears in the terms of $p(x, y)$ only with even exponents.

(b) G is symmetric to the X axis if y appears in the terms of $p(x, y)$ only with even exponents.

(c) G is symmetric to the origin if the terms of $p(x, y)$ are either all of even degree or all of odd degree.

It follows that the graph of $x^2y + y - 1 = 0$ is symmetric to the Y axis. [Here the terms of $p(x, y)$ are of degrees 3, 1, 0 respectively.]

(iii) We shall find it useful also to consider values of x and y that must be excluded because they lead to imaginary values of x or y and hence to ordered pairs (x, y) that are not ordered pairs of *real* numbers. (Recall that only ordered pairs of *real* numbers identify points in $E2'$.) Such values often arise when a solution for x or y involves an even root.

For example, solving the given equation for x, we have

$$x^2y = 1 - y$$

$$x = \pm\sqrt{\frac{1 - y}{y}} .$$

Now any value of y such that $(1 - y)/y$ is negative must be excluded. But $(1 - y)/y$ is negative if:

(1) $$1 - y < 0 \quad \text{and} \quad y > 0,$$

or

(2) $$1 - y > 0 \quad \text{and} \quad y < 0.$$

(1) is equivalent to $y > 1$ and $y > 0$, which in turn says no more than $y > 1$ (for if $y > 1$, then certainly $y > 0$). Similarly, (2) is equivalent to $y < 0$. Therefore all values of y such that $y > 1$ or $y < 0$ must be excluded, and the graph must be drawn in the unshaded region in Fig. 4f1.

[*Note:* The value $y = 0$ must also be excluded (Why?), but we shall usually not bother to mention such single points in our discussion of excluded values, since their existence, if they do exist, will generally be obvious.]

(iv) Since y approaches 0 as x becomes large positively or negatively, the line whose equation is $y = 0$ (i.e., the X axis) is an asymptote for the graph we seek.

The above information and the following table of values now enable us to sketch the graph (see Fig. 4f1). ‖

x	-3	-2	-1	0	1	2	3
y	0.1	0.2	0.5	1	0.5	0.2	0.1

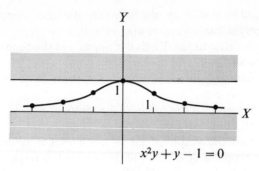

$$x^2y + y - 1 = 0$$

Fig. 4f1

ILLUSTRATIVE EXAMPLE 2.   Discuss and sketch the graph of the equation $x^2y^2 - 2x + 1 = 0$.

Solution: Note the following facts.

(i) For X-intercepts, letting $y = 0$, we have $-2x + 1 = 0$, or $x = \frac{1}{2}$. For Y-intercepts, letting $x = 0$, we have $1 = 0$; since this is impossible, there is no Y-intercept.

(ii) The graph is symmetric to the X axis, for y appears only with even exponents in the terms of the polynomial in question.

Further discussion is facilitated by solving the given equation for x and y. To solve for y, we proceed as follows:

$$x^2y^2 = 2x - 1$$

$$y^2 = \frac{2x - 1}{x^2}$$

$$y = \pm\sqrt{\frac{2x - 1}{x^2}} = \pm\frac{\sqrt{2x - 1}}{x}.$$

To solve for x, we make use of the quadratic formula ($a = y^2$, $b = -2$, $c = 1$):

$$x = \frac{-b \pm \sqrt{b^2 - 4ac}}{2a} = \frac{2 \pm \sqrt{4 - 4y^2}}{2y^2}$$

$$= \frac{2 \pm 2\sqrt{1 - y^2}}{2y^2}$$

$$= \frac{1 \pm \sqrt{1 - y^2}}{y^2}.$$

[Note that the solution for x is not quite equivalent to the given equation; the point $(\frac{1}{2}, 0)$ satisfies the given equation but not the solution for x.]

(iii) Examining the solution for x, values of y such that $1 - y^2 < 0$ must be excluded. But $1 - y^2 < 0$ is equivalent to $y^2 > 1$, which is true iff $y > 1$ or $y < -1$ [see 1d Problem 5(k)]. Similarly, we must exclude $2x - 1 < 0$, i.e., $2x < 1$, i.e., $x < \frac{1}{2}$. The graph must therefore be drawn in the unshaded region in Fig. 4f2.

(iv) Since we are not dealing with *rational* functions in this example, our preceding discussion of asymptotes will not apply here. The following modification will apply, however.

Examining our solution for y, we see that as x becomes large positively (Why positively?), y approaches 0. [For example, when $x = 50$, $y = \pm\sqrt{99/50} = \pm1/5$ (approximately); as x increases, x "overpowers" $\sqrt{2x - 1}$.] Therefore the line whose equation is $y = 0$ (i.e., the X axis) is an asymptote for the graph.

Using the information above and the following table of values, we sketch the graph (see Fig. 4f2). ‖

x	$\frac{1}{2}$	1	5	13
y	0	±1	±0.6	±0.4

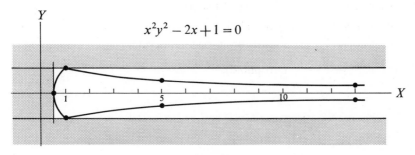

$$x^2y^2 - 2x + 1 = 0$$

Fig. 4f2

(*Note:* The types of functions and equations that we have dealt with in this chapter—polynomial and rational functions and polynomial equations—are called *algebraic* functions and equations, and their graphs are called *algebraic* graphs.)

Problems

1. Discuss and draw the graph of each of the following equations.

(a) $x + y + xy = 2$.

(b) $x + y = xy$.

(c) $y^2 - x^2 = x$.

(d) $x = x^2y^2 + 1$.

(e) $y^2 = x^3$.

(f) $y^2(4 - x) = x^3$.

(g) $x^2y + 4y - 8 = 0$.

(h) $y^2 = x/(x - 2)$.

(i) $y^2 = x^2/(4 - x^2)$.

(j) $y^3 = x^2$.

(k) $x^2y - 2x^2 - 16y = 0$.

(l) $x^3 - x^2y + y = 0$.

(m) $x^3 + 4x^2 + xy^2 - 4y^2 = 0$.

(n) $y^2 = x^2(x - 2)$. [Note the "isolated" point $(0, 0)$.]

(o) $y^2 = x(x - 2)^2$.

(p) $\sqrt{x} + \sqrt{y} = 1$.

(q) $\sqrt[3]{x} + \sqrt[3]{y} = 1$.

(r) $\sqrt[3]{x^2} + \sqrt[3]{y^2} = 1$.

(s) $y^2 = x(x - 2)(x + 2)$. [*Hint:* To determine excluded values of x, examine the sign of $x(x - 2)(x + 2)$ in the intervals $x < -2$, $-2 < x < 0, 0 < x < 2, x > 2$.]

2. Assuming that a is a positive real number, discuss and sketch the graph of each of the following equations. Use a scale on the X and Y axes in which the points $0, \pm a, \pm 2a$, etc. are marked, rather than the points $0, \pm 1, \pm 2$, etc.

(a) $y = \dfrac{1}{a^2} x^3$ (cubical parabola).

(b) $y^2 = \dfrac{1}{a} x^3$ (semicubical parabola).

(c) $x^2y = 4a^2(2a - y)$ (witch of Agnesi).

(d) $y^2(2a - x) = x^3$ (cissoid of Diocles).

(e) $\sqrt{x} + \sqrt{y} = \sqrt{a}$ (parabola).

(f) $\sqrt[3]{x^2} + \sqrt[3]{y^2} = \sqrt[3]{a^2}$ (four-cusped hypocycloid).

(g) $y^2 = \dfrac{x^2(a + x)}{a - x}$ (strophoid).

Chapter 5

Quadratic Graphs in $E_2{}'$

5a. INTRODUCTION

We have defined the degree of a monomial in two variables but not the degree of a polynomial in two variables or the degree of a polynomial equation in two variables. We do so now. (Actually, the first part of the following definition applies to polynomials in any number of variables.)

5a1 (Definition).   The *degree of a polynomial* is the maximum degree which any of its terms exhibits. The *degree of a polynomial equation* $f(x, y) = 0$ is the degree of the polynomial f.

Thus, since the degrees of the terms of the polynomial in two variables $1 + x + 2y - x^2y + 7x^3y^5$ are 0, 1, 1, 3, 8 respectively, it follows that $1 + x + 2y - x^2y + 7x^3y^5$ is a polynomial of degree 8 "in the variables x and y." Hence $1 + x + 2y - x^2y + 7x^3y^5 = 0$ is a polynomial equation "in x and y" of degree 8.

A polynomial equation in x and y of degree 1 would contain at least one term of degree 1 and might contain a term of degree 0. The following is a standard form for all polynomial equations of degree 1 in x and y

$$Ax + By + C = 0,$$

where A, B, C are real numbers and A, B are not *both* 0.

A polynomial equation in x and y of degree 2 (also called a *quadratic equation in x and y*) would contain at least one term of degree 2 and possibly other terms of lesser degree. The following is a standard form for all polynomial equations of degree 2 in x and y:

$$Ax^2 + Bxy + Cy^2 + Dx + Ey + F = 0,$$

where $A, \ldots, F$ are real numbers and A, B, C are not all 0.

113

We have already studied the graphs in $E2'$ that may arise from a first-degree equation (see statement 3f12), and, in fact, we may say this: *The graph of an equation is a straight line if and only if the equation is equivalent to a first-degree equation.*

Now we are ready to make a two-pronged advance. From the algebraic point of view, knowing all about the graph in $E2'$ of a *first-degree equation*, the next step would be to consider the graphs in $E2'$ that may arise from a *second-degree equation*. From the geometric point of view, knowing all about the equation of a *straight line*, it would be natural to go on to consider the equation of the next most familiar curve, the *circle*.

As a matter of fact, the two approaches complement each other nicely, for it turns out that every circle has an equation of the second degree. The converse is not true, however: not all second-degree equations have graphs that are circles. Indeed, we shall make our main goal in this chapter the determination of all graphs in $E2'$ that may arise from second-degree equations. (We shall call such graphs *quadratic* graphs.)

5b. THE CIRCLE

When we speak of a circle C of radius r and center Q, we shall mean the set of all points in a given plane whose distance from Q is r, where r is a nonnegative real number.

Suppose C is a circle in $E2'$ of radius r and center Q (see Fig. 5b1). We seek the equation of C. That is to say, we seek an equation in x and y which is satisfied by each point of C and by no other points in $E2'$.

Suppose (a, b) is a point of C, and (h, k) is the center Q of C. Then, by our definition of C, the distance from (a, b) to (h, k) must be r. That is,

$$\sqrt{(a - h)^2 + (b - k)^2} = r,$$

so that

$$(a - h)^2 + (b - k)^2 = r^2.$$

In other words, each point of C satisfies the equation

(1) $$(x - h)^2 + (y - k)^2 = r^2.$$

But before we can say that Eq. (1) is the equation of C, we must show that *no other* points in $E2'$ satisfy Eq. (1), i.e., that each point in $E2'$ that satisfies Eq. (1) must be in C.

Suppose, then, that $A = (u, v)$ satisfies Eq. (1). Then

$$(u - h)^2 + (v - k)^2 = r^2.$$

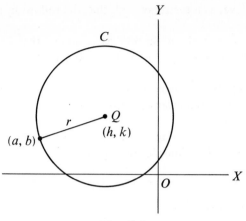

Fig. 5b1

We note that since r is the radius of a given circle, r must be a nonnegative real number. Therefore $\sqrt{r^2} = r$. Therefore

$$\sqrt{(u - h)^2 + (v - k)^2} = \sqrt{r^2} = r,$$

i.e., dis$(A, Q) = r$. But this means that A must be in C. We have proved:

5b1. The equation of a circle C in $E2'$ with center (h, k) and radius r is

$$(x - h)^2 + (y - k)^2 = r^2.$$

As a corollary, we note that the equation of a circle in $E2'$ with center at the origin and radius r is

$$x^2 + y^2 = r^2.$$

Thus $x^2 + y^2 = 25$ is the equation of a circle of radius 5 with center at the origin. The equation of a circle of radius 5 with center at $(-2, 3)$ is

$$(x + 2)^2 + (y - 3)^2 = 25.$$

This last equation may be transformed into an equivalent equation of somewhat different appearance by "squaring out" and simplifying:

$$x^2 + 4x + 4 + y^2 - 6y + 9 = 25$$
$$x^2 + y^2 + 4x - 6y - 12 = 0,$$

which the student will note is a second-degree equation in x and y.

In general, it is easily seen that every equation $(x - h)^2 + (y - k)^2 = r^2$ is equivalent to a second-degree equation in x and y, in fact, to one in which the coefficients of x^2 and y^2 are each 1 and in which there is no xy term.

We may prove, as a matter of fact, that the following statement is true.

5b2. Using the notation of Section 5a, suppose that in a given second degree equation we have $A = C$ and $B = 0$. Then one of the following must be true:
   (i) The graph of the given equation contains no points whatever.
   (ii) The graph of the given equation is a circle.

The method illustrated in the following example leads to a general proof of statement 5b2. Consider the equation

(1) $$4x^2 + 4y^2 - 4x + 12y - 15 = 0.$$

We first divide both sides by 4:

$$x^2 + y^2 - x + 3y - \tfrac{15}{4} = 0.$$

Then we collect x terms together and y terms together, and bring the constant term to the right:

$$(x^2 - x \qquad) + (y^2 + 3y \qquad) = \tfrac{15}{4}.$$

The space we have left within each parenthesis is for "completing the square." That is to say, we make use of the fact that $x^2 + kx + (k/2)^2 = [x + (k/2)]^2$. Also, to arrive at an equivalent equation, we add the same quantities to *both* sides of our equation:

$$[x^2 - x + (\tfrac{1}{2})^2] + [y^2 + 3y + (\tfrac{3}{2})^2] = \tfrac{15}{4} + \tfrac{1}{4} + \tfrac{9}{4},$$

which is equivalent to

(2) $$(x - \tfrac{1}{2})^2 + (y + \tfrac{3}{2})^2 = \tfrac{25}{4}.$$

Comparing this with the general equation of a circle,

$$(x - h)^2 + (y - k)^2 = r^2,$$

we see that the values $h = \tfrac{1}{2}$, $k = -\tfrac{3}{2}$, $r = \tfrac{5}{2}$ will make the general equation coincide with Eq. (2). The graph of Eq. (2), and hence of the equivalent Eq. (1), is therefore a circle with center $(\tfrac{1}{2}, -\tfrac{3}{2})$ and radius $\tfrac{5}{2}$ (see Fig. 5b2).
   If we had arrived, let us say, at the equation $(x - \tfrac{1}{2})^2 + (y + \tfrac{3}{2})^2 = 0$, our circle would have had center $(\tfrac{1}{2}, -\tfrac{3}{2})$ and radius 0—i.e., our graph would have consisted of the single point $(\tfrac{1}{2}, -\tfrac{3}{2})$; and if we had arrived at the equation $(x - \tfrac{1}{2})^2 + (y + \tfrac{3}{2})^2 = -1$, our graph would have been a *null graph*, i.e., a graph containing no points whatever—for a sum of squares of real numbers must be nonnegative, and therefore can never equal -1.

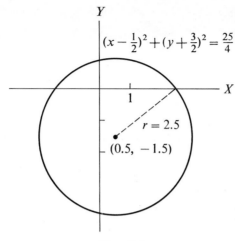

$$\left(x - \tfrac{1}{2}\right)^2 + \left(y + \tfrac{3}{2}\right)^2 = \tfrac{25}{4}$$

$r = 2.5$

$(0.5, -1.5)$

Fig. 5b2

Problems

1. Write the equations of and draw the circles whose centers and radii are respectively:

(a) $(1, 2)$; 3.   (b) $(-1, 2)$; 3.   (c) $(1, -2)$; 3.
(d) $(-1, -2)$; 3.   (e) $(3, 4)$; 5.   (f) $(-3, 4)$; 5.
(g) $(3, -4)$; 5.   (h) $(-3, -4)$; 5.   (i) $(0, 0)$; 7.
(j) $(3, 4)$; 0.   (k) $(0, 0)$; 0.   (l) $(5, 5)$; 5.

2. Draw the graph (if it exists) of each of the following equations.

(a) $x^2 + y^2 = 9$.   (b) $x^2 + y^2 = 16$.
(c) $x^2 + y^2 = 0$.   (d) $x^2 + y^2 = 10$.
(e) $y = \pm\sqrt{25 - x^2}$.   (f) $x = \pm\sqrt{36 - y^2}$.
(g) $y = \sqrt{25 - x^2}$.   (h) $y = -\sqrt{25 - x^2}$.
(i) $x = \sqrt{25 - y^2}$.   (j) $x = -\sqrt{25 - y^2}$.
(k) $(x - 2)^2 + (y - 3)^3 = 25$.   (l) $(x - 2)^2 + (y + 3)^2 = 36$.
(m) $(x + 2)^2 + (y - 3)^2 = 16$.   (n) $(x + 2)^2 + (y + 3)^2 = 20$.
(o) $x^2 + y^2 - 2x + 10y + 1 = 0$.
(p) $x^2 + y^2 + 6x - 12y + 20 = 0$.
(q) $x^2 + y^2 = 8x + 8y$.
(r) $x^2 + y^2 = 20x - 75$.
(s) $x^2 + y^2 + 7x + 3y - 10 = 0$.
(t) $4x^2 + 4y^2 + 28y + 13 = 0$.
(u) $4x^2 + 4y^2 - 60x - 20y + 225 = 0$.

(v) $y = -5 \pm \sqrt{24 + 2x - x^2}$.   (w) $y = -5 + \sqrt{24 + 2x - x^2}$.

(x) $y = -5 - \sqrt{24 + 2x - x^2}$.   (y) $x = 1 + \sqrt{-y^2 - 10y}$.

(z) $x = 1 - \sqrt{-y^2 - 10y}$.   (z') $x^2 + y^2 + 1 = 0$.

3. (a) Write a standard form for a third-degree equation in two variables, x and y.
   (b) How would you define the degree of a monomial $kx^r y^s z^t$ in three variables, assuming $k \neq 0$ is a real number?
   (c) Write a standard form for a first-degree equation in three variables, x, y, and z.
   (d) Write a standard form for a second-degree equation in three variables, x, y, and z.

5c.   CIRCLES IN E2' SATISFYING CERTAIN CONDITIONS

A classical problem of geometry is to circumscribe a circle about a triangle, i.e., to find a circle passing through three given points.

We solve a problem of this sort analytically.

ILLUSTRATIVE EXAMPLE 1.   (a) Find the equation of a circle in $E2'$ passing through the points $(4, 1)$, $(1, 2)$, $(-2, -7)$.

Solution: We know that every circle in $E2'$ has an equation of the form $x^2 + y^2 + Dx + Ey + F = 0$. It is a question, then, of determining the particular values of D, E, F which will lead to a circle passing through the given points.

However, the given points will lie on the graph of a given equation iff they satisfy the equation. Therefore our problem is equivalent to that of solving the following sets of equations:

$$4^2 + 1^2 + D \cdot 4 + E \cdot 1 + F = 0,$$
$$1^2 + 2^2 + D \cdot 1 + E \cdot 2 + F = 0,$$
$$(-2)^2 + (-7)^2 + D(-2) + E(-7) + F = 0,$$

or

(1) $4D + E + F + 17 = 0,$

(2) $D + 2E + F + 5 = 0,$

(3) $-2D - 7E + F + 53 = 0.$

But these simultaneous equations are particularly easy to solve, since F may be eliminated by two subtractions:

(1) − (2) $3D - E + 12 = 0,$

(2) − (3) $3D + 9E - 48 = 0.$

Taking the difference of these two equations, we have

$$10E - 60 = 0, \qquad E = 6.$$

Substituting in (1) — (2), we have $D = -2$. Substituting in (1), we have $F = -15$. Therefore the required equation is

$$x^2 + y^2 - 2x + 6y - 15 = 0. \quad \|$$

(b) Find the center and radius of a circle passing through the three points given in (a) above.

Solution: We might proceed first as in part (a); then, having found the equation of the required circle as above, we might find its center and radius by the process of completing the square. [It turns out that this circle has center $(1, -3)$ and radius 5.]

[Alternatively, we might have begun with the other general equation for a circle: $(x - h)^2 + (y - k)^2 = r^2$, in which (h, k) represents the center and r the radius of the circle. This method involves a little more work than the first, however. $\|$

There are many other cases in which one wishes to determine a circle satisfying certain conditions. In all such problems it should be kept in mind that one or the other of two general equations for the circle may be utilized. It is important also to remember the following general principle.

Requiring that a point lie on a given graph is equivalent to requiring that the point satisfy the equation of the given graph.

ILLUSTRATIVE EXAMPLE 2.   Find a circle in $E2'$ that is tangent to the X axis and that passes through the points $(3, 1)$, $(4, 2)$.

Solution: First of all, we note that if a circle has center (h, k) and radius r, then tangency to the X axis is equivalent to the condition $k = \pm r$ (see Fig. 5c1). It would seem, then, that the form $(x - h)^2 + (y - k)^2 = r^2$ is best suited to this problem. We have

(1) $$(4 - h)^2 + (2 - k)^2 = r^2,$$
(2) $$(3 - h)^2 + (1 - k)^2 = r^2,$$
(3) $$r = |k|,$$

from which follows

(1) — (2) $$10 - 2h - 2k = 0$$
(4) $$h = 5 - k.$$

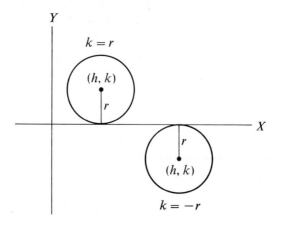

Fig. 5c1

Substituting Eqs. (3) and (4) in Eq. (2), we obtain

$$(3 - 5 + k)^2 + (1 - k)^2 = k^2$$
$$(k - 2)^2 + (1 - k)^2 = k^2$$
$$k^2 - 6k + 5 = 0$$
$$(k - 1)(k - 5) = 0.$$

Thus $k = 1, h = 4, r = 1$; or $k = 5, h = 0, r = 5$.

We see now that there are *two* solutions to the problem. One circle has center $(4, 1)$ and radius 1. The other has center $(0, 5)$ and radius 5. It is, of course, now easy to write the equations of these circles and to draw their graphs (see Fig. 5c2). ‖

A notable advantage of the analytic method is evident here: Its use greatly diminishes the likelihood that some of the possible solutions of a problem will be overlooked.

Problems

1. In each of the following cases find the equation of a circle that passes through the given triple of points. In each case find the center and radius of the circle and plot the given points and the required circle.

   (a) $(0, 0)$, $(0, 4)$, $(6, 0)$.
   (b) $(0, 0)$, $(8, 0)$, $(4, 8)$.
   (c) $(4, 2)$, $(5, 1)$, $(2, -2)$.
   (d) $(5, 6)$, $(4, -1)$, $(2, -3)$.
   (e) $(6, -2)$, $(4, 2)$, $(1, -7)$.
   (f) $(4, 1)$, $(3, 3)$, $(8, 0)$.
   (g) $(1, 5)$, $(3, 1)$, $(-2, 2)$.
   (h) $(2, 4)$, $(-2, 3)$, $(4, -1)$.
   (i) $(1, 2)$, $(3, 5)$, $(5, 8)$. (What is the trouble?)

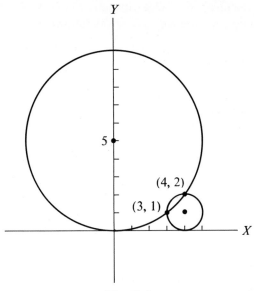

Fig. 5c2

2. In each of the following cases find the equation of a circle that satisfies the given conditions. In each case illustrate graphically.

   (a) Center $(-2, 1)$; passes through $(4, 5)$.
   (b) Center $(2, -3)$; tangent to the X axis.
   (c) Center $(2, -3)$; tangent to the Y axis.
   (d) Center $(2, -3)$; passes through the origin.
   (e) Center at the origin; tangent to $3x + 4y = 12$.
       (*Hint:* See Section 3g.)
   (f) Center at $(7, 11)$; tangent to $x = y$.

3. In each of the following cases find (algebraically; Why?) the points of intersection of the graphs of the given equations, and plot the graphs.

   (a) $3x - y = 5$, $x^2 + y^2 = 5$.
   (b) $x + y = 7$, $x^2 + y^2 = 25$.
   (c) $x^2 + y^2 = 11$, $x^2 + y^2 - 2x - 8 = 0$.
   (d) $x^2 + y^2 + 3x - 2y - 4 = 0$, $x^2 + y^2 - 2x - y - 6 = 0$.

4. A circle passes through the origin iff the point $(0, 0)$ satisfies its equation. If we write the equation in the form $x^2 + y^2 + Dx + Ey + F = 0$, then that circle will pass through the origin iff $0^2 + 0^2 + D \cdot 0 + E \cdot 0 + F = 0$, i.e., iff $F = 0$. Therefore the equation $x^2 + y^2 + Dx + Ey = 0$ is called a *general equation* for a circle that passes through the origin. Or, as before, we speak of the set of all circles which may arise from this

equation as the *family* of circles with equation $x^2 + y^2 + Dx + Ey = 0$. Write a general equation for each of the following.

(a) A circle passing through the origin (in terms of h, k).
(b) A circle tangent to the X axis.
(c) A circle tangent to the Y axis.
(d) A circle with center on the X axis.
(e) A circle with center on the Y axis.
(f) A circle tangent to the X axis at 0.
(g) A circle tangent to the Y axis at 0.
(h) A circle tangent to both the X axis and the Y axis.

5. Suppose (a, b) is a point on a circle with center at the origin and radius $r > 0$. Prove that the equation of a tangent line to the circle at the point (a, b) is $ax + by = r^2$.

5d. THE ELLIPSE

Throughout high school geometry and in this course also, the only curves we have studied in detail have been the straight line and the circle. Now, finally, we shall devote attention to several others of the countless interesting and important curves that occur in nature and science.

In this section we shall study a curve that may very easily be drawn. All that is necessary is a string fastened at two points F_1, F_2 on a sheet of paper (see Fig. 5d1).

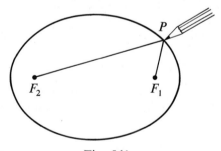

Fig. 5d1

Suppose we draw the string taut with a pencil point, and keeping the string taut, move the pencil so as to trace a curve, first on one side of the line F_1F_2 and then on the other. The resulting curve is called an *ellipse*. Each of the points F_1, F_2 is called a *focus* (plural: *foci*) of the ellipse.

It is traditional to denote the length of string between the foci by $2a$ and the distance between the foci by $2c$. (This choice of notation is for reasons of convenience which will soon become evident.) The ellipse may then be regarded as the set of all points (also called the *locus* of all points) P in the given plane such that $PF_1 + PF_2 = 2a$. [Note that in the preceding equation PF_1 and PF_2 are abbreviations for dis(P, F_1) and dis(P, F_2) respectively. We shall continue to make use of this notation in what follows.] We now make the following precise definition.

5d1 (Definition).   Let $a > c \geq 0$ be real numbers, and let F_1, F_2 be points in a given plane such that $F_1F_2 = 2c$. Then the set of all points P in the given plane such that $PF_1 + PF_2 = 2a$ is called an *ellipse*, with *foci* F_1, F_2.

If $c = 0$, then $F_1F_2 = 0$, so that $F_1 = F_2$. Physically, this would correspond to a situation in which both ends of our string are tied to the same point, so that our pencil would be constrained to trace a circle. Later on we shall prove mathematically that if $c = 0$, then our ellipse is a circle.

We proceed to study the ellipse *analytically*. Our first step will be to choose a convenient pair of coordinate axes, and then we shall derive a general equation for the ellipse.

If $F_1 \neq F_2$, the line F_1F_2 is a natural choice for the X axis. If $F_1 = F_2$, any line through F_1 may be chosen to be the X axis, but in both cases we make F_1 fall on the nonnegative side of the X axis (see Fig. 5d2).

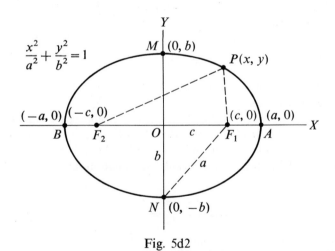

Fig. 5d2

If $F_1 \neq F_2$, let O be the midpoint of line segment F_1F_2. If $F_1 = F_2$, let $O = F_1$. In either case O is called the *center* of the ellipse.

And now it is natural to take a line perpendicular to the X axis at O as Y axis.

It follows that $OF_1 = OF_2 = c$, so that the coordinates of F_1, F_2 are $(c, 0)$, $(-c, 0)$ respectively.

Now suppose $P = (x, y)$ is any point on our ellipse. Then, by our definition of an ellipse,

(1) $$PF_1 + PF_2 = 2a.$$

From Eq. (1) we may successively derive the following equations (omitted steps are to be supplied by the reader):

(2) $$\sqrt{(x - c)^2 + y^2} + \sqrt{(x + c)^2 + y^2} = 2a,$$

(3) $$\sqrt{(x + c)^2 + y^2} = 2a - \sqrt{(x - c)^2 + y^2},$$

(4) $$(x + c)^2 + y^2 = 4a^2 - 4a\sqrt{(x - c)^2 + y^2} + (x - c)^2 + y^2,$$

(5) $$a\sqrt{(x - c)^2 + y^2} = a^2 - cx,$$

(6) $$a^2x^2 + a^2c^2 + a^2y^2 = a^4 + c^2x^2,$$

(7) $$x^2(a^2 - c^2) + a^2y^2 = a^2(a^2 - c^2).$$

But note that $a > c \geq 0$. Thus neither a^2 nor $a^2 - c^2$ nor $a^2(a^2 - c^2)$ can be zero, so that we may divide both sides of (7) by $a^2(a^2 - c^2)$:

(8) $$\frac{x^2}{a^2} + \frac{y^2}{a^2 - c^2} = 1.$$

Since $a^2 > c^2$, $a^2 - c^2$ is a positive real number, so that there exists a positive real number $\sqrt{a^2 - c^2}$, which we denote by b. Hence $b^2 = a^2 - c^2$, and Eq. (8) may be written in the more attractive form

(9) $$\frac{x^2}{a^2} + \frac{y^2}{b^2} = 1.$$

What we have shown, then, is that if (x, y) is a point on our ellipse, then Eq. (9) holds true.

To prove that Eq. (9) *is* the equation of our ellipse, we must now show conversely that if Eq. (9) holds true, then $P = (x, y)$ is a point of our ellipse. (We have relegated this part of the proof to the Appendix.)

Now we shall discuss the graph of equation $(x^2/a^2) + (y^2/b^2) = 1$. First of all, we solve for x and y:

$$\frac{x^2}{a^2} = 1 - \frac{y^2}{b^2} = \frac{b^2 - y^2}{b^2}$$

$$x^2 = \frac{a^2}{b^2}(b^2 - y^2)$$

$$x = \pm\frac{a}{b}\sqrt{b^2 - y^2}.$$

Similarly,

$$y = \pm\frac{b}{a}\sqrt{a^2 - x^2}.$$

We note the following facts.

(i) The intercepts are $x = \pm a$, $y = \pm b$.

(ii) The graph is symmetric to the X axis, Y axis, and origin.

(iii) For the excluded values we have $b^2 - y^2 < 0$, i.e., $y^2 > b^2$, i.e., $y > b$ and $y < -b$. Similarly, $x > a$ and $x < -a$ must be excluded.

The graph, of course, is that of Fig. 5d2.

Note that since we have defined b so that $b^2 = a^2 - c^2$, it follows that c may be computed once we know a and b. Note further that if $c = 0$, then $b^2 = a^2$, and the equation of our ellipse becomes $x^2 + y^2 = a^2$; i.e., if $c = 0$, then our ellipse is a circle of radius a.

In summary:

5d2. If a, b are real numbers such that $a \geq b > 0$, then

$$\frac{x^2}{a^2} + \frac{y^2}{b^2} = 1$$

is the equation of an ellipse with X-intercepts $\pm a$, Y-intercepts $\pm b$, and foci $(\pm c, 0)$, where $a^2 = b^2 + c^2$.

If we had interchanged our choices of X and Y axes, the effect would have been simply to interchange the roles of x and y, so that the following statement may be made (see Fig. 5d3).

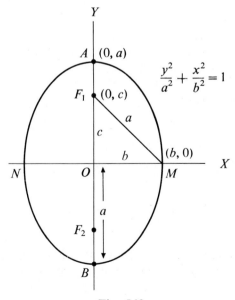

Fig. 5d3

5d3. If a, b are real numbers such that $a \geq b > 0$, then

$$\frac{y^2}{a^2} + \frac{x^2}{b^2} = 1$$

is the equation of an ellipse with X-intercepts $\pm b$, Y-intercepts $\pm a$, and foci $(0, \pm c)$, where $a^2 = b^2 + c^2$,

If $F_1 \neq F_2$, the points A, B in which line F_1F_2 intersects the ellipse are called the *vertices* of the ellipse. The line segment AB joining the vertices of the ellipse is called the *major axis* of the ellipse. The line segments OA and OB are called the *semimajor axes* of the ellipse. The points M, N in which the perpendicular bisector of line segment F_1F_2 intersects the ellipse are the endpoints of the *minor axis* of the ellipse. The line segments OM and ON are called the *semiminor axes* of the ellipse. Clearly, then, the major and minor axes of an ellipse are of lengths $2a$ and $2b$ respectively, and the semimajor and semiminor axes of an ellipse are of lengths a and b respectively.

Note that the line segment joining the end of a minor axis to a focus, e.g., line segment MF_1, has the length a also, for

$$MF_1 = \sqrt{(0 - c)^2 + (b - 0)^2} = \sqrt{b^2 + c^2} = \sqrt{a^2} = a.$$

That this is true may also be seen from the facts that since M is on the perpendicular bisector of line segment F_1F_2, $MF_1 = MF_2$; and since M is on the ellipse, $MF_1 + MF_2 = 2a$. Therefore $MF_1 + MF_1 = 2a$, $2(MF_1) = 2a$, $MF_1 = a$.

Thus we see that the foci of an ellipse lie on the major axis at a distance a from an end of the minor axis, so that, once the axes have been drawn, the foci of an ellipse may be easily located with a compass.

Note that each of the equations of the ellipses described in statements 5d2 and 5d3 is equivalent to an equation of the form

$$Ax^2 + Cy^2 + F = 0,$$

where A and C are of like sign and F is of opposite sign. Conversely, any equation in this form may easily be shown to be equivalent to one of the two equations given above for an ellipse.

ILLUSTRATIVE EXAMPLE 1. Plot the graph G of the equation $144 - 16x^2 - 9y^2 = 0$.

Solution: By the paragraph preceding this example, G is an ellipse with center at the origin and axes along the coordinate axes. Letting $x = 0$, we find the Y-intercepts of G are ± 4. Letting $y = 0$, we find the X intercepts of G are ± 3. The graph G is drawn in Fig. 5d4.

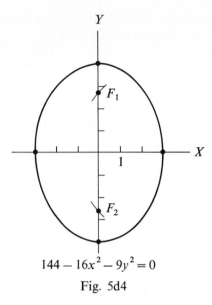

$$144 - 16x^2 - 9y^2 = 0$$

Fig. 5d4

The foci must be on the major axis at a distance of $c = \sqrt{a^2 - b^2} = \sqrt{7}$ from the center of the ellipse. They are more easily located, however, by opening a compass to a radius of 4 and, with center $(3, 0)$, swinging arcs which intersect the major axis at the foci. ‖

ILLUSTRATIVE EXAMPLE 2.   Find the equation of an ellipse that passes through the points $(1, -4)$, $(3, 2)$.

Solution: Actually, there are many ellipses that satisfy this condition, for there are ellipses (not yet considered) in a coordinate plane whose axes and centers are not the coordinate axes and the origin respectively.

We shall attempt, however, to find an ellipse of the type we *have* considered which passes through the given points. We begin, therefore, with a form equation for such an ellipse:

$$Ax^2 + Cy^2 + F = 0.$$

We must try to find values of A and C of like sign which result in an equation satisfied by the given points. We must therefore solve

(1)
$$A + 16C + F = 0,$$
$$9A + 4C + F = 0.$$

Subtracting, we find that $8A - 12C = 0$, or $A = \frac{3}{2}C$, is an equation that we wish to satisfy. Clearly, $C = 2$, $A = 3$ are convenient values that do the trick, and referring back to Eqs. (1), we see that $F = -A - 16C = -35$ is consistent with these values as a solution of Eqs. (1).

Substituting back in our form equation, we find that $3x^2 + 2y^2 - 35 = 0$ is the equation of an ellipse, is satisfied by our given points, and is therefore a solution of the problem.   ‖

5e.   THE ECCENTRICITY OF AN ELLIPSE

The real number $e = c/a$, called the *eccentricity* of the ellipse we have defined, is often used to tell something about the shape of the ellipse.

First of all, since $c \geq 0$ and $a > 0$, it follows that $c/a \geq 0$; and since $a > c$, it follows that $c/a < 1$. Thus if e is the eccentricity of an ellipse, $0 \leq e < 1$.

Now we consider extreme values of e.

At one extreme, suppose $e = 0$. Then $c/a = 0$, i.e., $c = 0$, and our ellipse is a circle.

If e is close to 0, we may expect the ellipse to be almost circular in shape. That this is true may be seen by dividing the equation $b^2 = a^2 - c^2$ by a^2:

$$\frac{b^2}{a^2} = 1 - \frac{c^2}{a^2} = 1 - e^2.$$

If e is close to 0, then b^2/a^2 is approximately 1 and hence b/a is approximately 1; the ratio of a major and minor axes is close to 1; i.e., the ellipse comes close to being a circle.

If e is close to 1, the equations above indicate that b/a is close to 0; i.e., b is small compared with a. Thus an ellipse for which e is close to 1 would look more like a cigar than a circle.

Problems

1.   Sketch the graph of each of the following equations, locating the foci and computing the eccentricity.

(a) $25x^2 + 9y^2 = 225$.   (b) $9x^2 + 25y^2 = 225$.
(c) $4x^2 + y^2 = 16$.   (d) $16x^2 + 25y^2 = 400$.
(e) $x^2 + 4y^2 = 4$.   (f) $25x^2 + 16y^2 = 400$.
(g) $x^2 + 2y^2 = 2$.   (h) $x^2 + y^2 = 25$.

2.   In each of the following find the equation of an ellipse passing through the given points.

(a) $(3, 4)$, $(5, 2)$.   (b) $(4, 1)$, $(3, 2)$.
(c) $(4, 3)$, $(3, 4)$.   (d) $(0, 7)$, $(11, 0)$.
(e) $(3, 4)$, $(2, 3)$. (What is the trouble?)

3. Find the equations of two ellipses each with major axis 8 and minor axis 4, and plot.

4. Find the equations of two ellipses each with major axis 10 and eccentricity 0.5, and plot.

5. Find the equation of an ellipse with minor axis 8 and foci at $(\pm 3, 0)$, and plot.

6. Find the eccentricity of an ellipse whose major axis is twice as long as its minor axis.

7. Find the eccentricity of an ellipse in which $F_1 F_2 M$ is an equilateral triangle, where M is an end of a minor axis.

8. An ellipse is to be drawn within a 6″ × 8″ rectangle, with vertices and ends of minor axes at midpoints of opposite sides. Where should the foci be placed, and what length of string should be used in drawing the ellipse?

9. Suppose a line through a focus F of an ellipse and perpendicular to its major axis meets the ellipse in points P, Q. Then line segment PQ is called the *latus rectum* of the ellipse.
   (a) What is the length of a latus rectum of an ellipse?
   (b) Show how knowing the fact of (a) is helpful in drawing an ellipse.

10. The possibility $a = c$, though physically feasible, was rejected in our definition of an ellipse, since the admission of this extreme possibility would have forced inelegant exceptions upon us in our later discussions of the ellipse and certain related curves. But suppose we *had* allowed the possibility $a = c$ in our definition of an ellipse. What would an ellipse in which $a = c$ turn out to be? (Consider two cases: $c = 0$ and $c > 0$.)

5f. THE HYPERBOLA

A variation upon the definition of an ellipse suggests itself: Suppose that instead of seeking all points in a plane the *sum* of whose distances from two fixed points is constant, we seek all points in a plane the *difference* of whose distances from two fixed points is constant. Then the resulting locus is called a *hyperbola*. More precisely (see Fig. 5f1):

5f1 (Definition).   Let $c > a > 0$ be real numbers and let F_1, F_2 be points in a given plane such that $F_1 F_2 = 2c$. Then the set of all points P in the given plane such that $PF_1 - PF_2 = \pm 2a$ is called a *hyperbola* with *foci* F_1, F_2.

Coordinate axes may be chosen exactly as in the case of the ellipse, so that if $P = (x, y)$ is a point of our hyperbola, then

$$(1) \qquad \sqrt{(x - c)^2 + y^2} - \sqrt{(x + c)^2 + y^2} = \pm 2a.$$

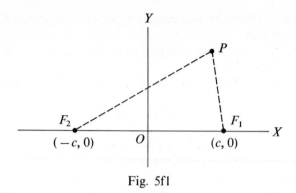

Fig. 5f1

By means of steps similar to those we followed in deriving the equation of an ellipse, it may be proved that Eq. (1) is equivalent to

(2)
$$\frac{x^2}{a^2} - \frac{y^2}{c^2 - a^2} = 1.$$

Since $c > a > 0$, we have that $c^2 > a^2$, so that the number $\sqrt{c^2 - a^2}$ is a real number, which we denote by b; i.e., $b = \sqrt{c^2 - a^2}$, and hence $b^2 = c^2 - a^2$, $a^2 + b^2 = c^2$. Equation (2) is then equivalent to

(3)
$$\frac{x^2}{a^2} - \frac{y^2}{b^2} = 1.$$

(Note that the relationship among a, b, c is not the same for the hyperbola as it is for the ellipse.)

Now we analyze the graph of Eq. (3). First we solve for x and y:

$$x = \pm \frac{a}{b} \sqrt{y^2 + b^2}, \qquad y = \pm \frac{b}{a} \sqrt{x^2 - a^2}.$$

We note the following facts.

(i) The X-intercepts are $\pm a$; there are no Y-intercepts.

(ii) The graph is symmetric to the X axis, Y axis, and origin.

(iii) For the excluded values, we see, from the solution for y, that there is no graph for $x^2 - a^2 < 0$, i.e., for $-a < x < a$. The solution for x reveals that no value of y need be excluded.

(iv) We shall prove that the straight lines whose equations are $y = \pm (b/a)x$ are asymptotes for our graph.

Proof: Because the hyperbola and the set of two lines $y = \pm(b/a)x$ are symmetric with respect to both coordinate axes, it will be sufficient to restrict our proof to the first quadrant.

We must show, then, that $(b/a)x - (b/a)\sqrt{x^2 - a^2}$ approaches but does not reach 0 as x becomes large. We "rationalize the numerator":

$$\frac{b}{a}x - \frac{b}{a}\sqrt{x^2 - a^2} = \frac{b}{a}(x - \sqrt{x^2 - a^2})$$

$$= \frac{b}{a}(x - \sqrt{x^2 - a^2})\left(\frac{x + \sqrt{x^2 - a^2}}{x + \sqrt{x^2 - a^2}}\right)$$

$$= \frac{b}{a} \cdot \frac{x^2 - x^2 + a^2}{x + \sqrt{x^2 - a^2}}$$

$$= \frac{ab}{x + \sqrt{x^2 - a^2}}.$$

And now it is clear that as x becomes large positively, $ab/(x + \sqrt{x^2 - a^2})$ approaches but never reaches 0. ‖

To draw the asymptotes of this hyperbola, it is convenient first to draw an "asymptote box" whose vertices are $(\pm a, \pm b)$; the asymptotes are then simply the extended diagonals of this box (see Fig. 5f2).

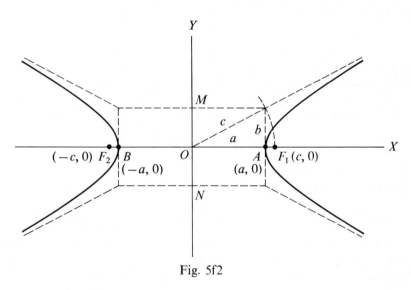

Fig. 5f2

In summary:

5f2. If a, b are positive real numbers, then

$$\frac{x^2}{a^2} - \frac{y^2}{b^2} = 1$$

is the equation of a hyperbola with X-intercepts $\pm a$, no Y-intercepts, asymptote box with vertices $(\pm a, \pm b)$, and foci $(\pm c, 0)$, where $c^2 = a^2 + b^2$.

Interchanging our choices of X and Y axes leads to the following statement.

5f3. If a, b are positive real numbers, then

$$\frac{y^2}{a^2} - \frac{x^2}{b^2} = 1$$

is the equation of a hyperbola with Y-intercepts $\pm a$, no X-intercepts, asymptote box with vertices $(\pm b, \pm a)$, and foci $(0, \pm c)$, where $c^2 = a^2 + b^2$.

The points A, B in which line F_1F_2 intersects the hyperbola are called the *vertices* of the hyperbola. The midpoint O of line segment F_1F_2 is called the *center* of the hyperbola. The line segment AB is called the *transverse axis*, and the line segments OA, OB the *semitransverse axes* of the hyperbola. (A *conjugate axis*, of length $2b$, perpendicular to line F_1F_2, and bisected by O, is sometimes defined, but we shall find no use for it here.) Clearly, the transverse axis is of length $2a$ and the semitransverse axes each of length a.

Note that a semidiagonal of an asymptote box has the length $\sqrt{a^2 + b^2} = \sqrt{c^2} = c$. The foci of a hyperbola may therefore be located by swinging an arc with center O, which passes through a vertex of the asymptote box, until it intersects the extended transverse axis in two places.

Note further that each of the equations of the hyperbolas described in the boxes above is equivalent to an equation of the form

$$Ax^2 + Cy^2 + F = 0,$$

where A and C are of opposite sign and $F \neq 0$. Conversely, any equation in this form is equivalent to one of the two equations given for a hyperbola.

ILLUSTRATIVE EXAMPLE.   Plot the graph G of $9y^2 - 16x^2 + 144 = 0$.

Solution: By the preceding paragraph, G is a hyperbola. Letting $x = 0$, we find no Y-intercept, but letting $y = 0$, we find X-intercepts ± 3. Therefore $a = 3$, and the vertices of the hyperbola are $(\pm 3, 0)$.

Now we transform the equation of G into "standard" form by dividing through by 144:

$$16x^2 - 9y^2 = 144$$

$$\frac{x^2}{9} - \frac{y^2}{16} = 1.$$

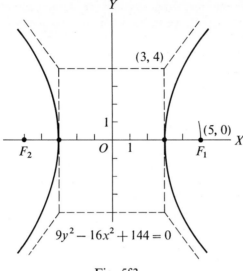

Fig. 5f3

Comparing this with Eq. (3) we see again that $a = 3$, but now also that $b = 4$. Furthermore, since $c^2 = a^2 + b^2$, $c = 5$. Thus the foci are at $(\pm 5, 0)$.

Now we draw asymptote box, asymptotes, and finally the hyperbola (see Fig. 5f3). Note that the hyperbola is tangent to the asymptote box at the vertices of the hyperbola.

5g. THE ECCENTRICITY OF A HYPERBOLA

In the case of the hyperbola, just as for the ellipse, we again define the real number $e = c/a$ to be the *eccentricity* of the curve. In the case of the ellipse we found that always $0 \leq e < 1$; in the case of the hyperbola, since $0 < a < c$, we see that always $e > 1$.

Here also the eccentricity tells us something about the shape of the curve, as we discover by examining extreme values of e.

At one extreme, suppose e is close to 1. We examine the curve $(x^2/a^2) - (y^2/b^2) = 1$ with asymptotes $y = \pm(b/a)x$. Since $c^2 = a^2 + b^2$, we have $(c/a)^2 = 1 + (b/a)^2$, i.e., $e^2 = 1 + (b/a)^2$. If e is close to 1, then b/a is close to 0, i.e., the slopes of the asymptote lines are numerically small; the hyperbola is pinched between lines which make a comparatively small angle with the transverse axis.

At the other extreme, suppose e is a very large number. Then from the equation $e^2 - 1 = (b/a)^2$, we see that b/a must be a very large number also. Thus the slopes of the asymptote lines are large numerically; i.e., the asymptotes rise very steeply and are close to being vertical. The hyperbola, approaching almost vertical lines, appears, near its center, almost like a pair of parallel lines.

5h.   RECTANGULAR HYPERBOLAS

A hyperbola whose asymptotes are perpendicular to each other is called a *rectangular* (i.e., a "right-angled") hyperbola.

Since the diagonals of a rectangle are perpendicular iff the rectangle is a square, a hyperbola is rectangular iff $a = b$. For this reason a rectangular hyperbola is also called an *equilateral* hyperbola. Now we investigate a case in which the equation of a rectangular hyperbola assumes a particularly simple form. Suppose we choose as foci the points (a, a), $(-a, -a)$ where $a > 0$. Then $2c = F_1 F_2 = 2a\sqrt{2}$. Therefore $c = a\sqrt{2}$. Since $c^2 = a^2 + b^2$, it follows that $a = b$. This hyperbola will therefore be rectangular. Furthermore, a point (x, y) will be on this hyperbola iff

$$\sqrt{(x - a)^2 + (y - a)^2} - \sqrt{(x + a)^2 + (y + a)^2} = \pm 2a.$$

We may proceed to derive an equivalent equation as before; in this case the final form turns out to be simply

$$xy = a^2/2.$$

If we had chosen as foci the points $(a, -a)$, $(-a, a)$, the equation of the hyperbola would have turned out to be

$$xy = -a^2/2.$$

We conclude, then, that

$$xy = k,$$

where k is any nonzero real number, is the equation of a rectangular hyperbola.

It is easily seen that the asymptotes of the hyperbola whose equation is $xy = k$ are simply the coordinate axes.

Problems

1. Identify by name and plot the graphs of the following equations; in each case find the foci and compute the eccentricity; if asymptotes

exist, find them.

(a) $9x^2 - 16y^2 = 144.$ (b) $9x^2 + 16y^2 = 144.$
(c) $16y^2 - 9x^2 = 144.$ (d) $16x^2 - 25y^2 = 400.$
(e) $4x^2 + y^2 = 64.$ (f) $4x^2 - y^2 = 64.$
(g) $y^2 - 4x^2 = 64.$ (h) $x^2 - 4y^2 = 64.$
(i) $25x^2 - 9y^2 = 225.$ (j) $9x^2 - 25y^2 = 225.$
(k) $4x^2 - y^2 = 16.$ (l) $x^2 - 4y^2 = 4.$
(m) $x^2 - y^2 = 25.$ (n) $y^2 - x^2 = 25.$
(o) $xy = 18.$ (p) $xy = -18.$
(q) $xy = 32.$ (r) $xy = -32.$
(s) $xy + 4 = 0.$ (t) $xy - 4 = 0.$

2. Find the equation of a hyperbola passing through each of the following pairs of points.

(a) $(3, 4), (1, 2).$ (b) $(2, 4), (3, 5).$
(c) $(2, 3), (3, 2).$ (d) $(1, 1), (2, 2).$

3. Find the equations and plot the graphs of hyperbolas satisfying the following conditions.

(a) Transverse axis $= 8$; $F_1F_2 = 10.$
(b) Transverse axis $= 6$; $e = 5/3.$
(c) Asymptotes $y = \pm 3x$; transverse axis $= 4.$
(d) Foci $(\pm 13, 0)$; passes through $(13, 28.8).$
(e) Vertices $(\pm 5, 0)$; passes through $(6, 2).$

4. Suppose a line through a focus of a hyperbola is perpendicular to the line F_1F_2 and intersects the hyperbola in points L, R. Then line segment LR is called a *latus rectum* of the hyperbola. Prove that a semi-latus rectum of a hyperbola is of length b^2/a, and show how this fact is useful in drawing the hyperbola.

5. Suppose $xy = k$ is the equation of a hyperbola H.

(a) If $k > 0$, where, in terms of k, are the vertices of H?
(b) If $k < 0$, where, in terms of k, are the vertices of H?
(c) What is the eccentricity of H?

5i. THE PARABOLA

In a first course in plane geometry one learns that the locus of points equidistant from *two distinct points A, B* is the perpendicular bisector of line segment *AB*, and the locus of points equidistant from *two distinct intersecting lines* is the pair of bisectors of the angles formed by these lines.

But what is the locus of points in a plane equidistant from a given line and a given point not on the line? It turns out to be something quite different from a straight line:

5i1 (Definition).   In a given plane let d be a line and F a point not on d. Then the set of points in the given plane equidistant from F and d is called a *parabola* with *focus F* and *directrix d*.

Now we proceed to study the parabola *analytically*. First of all, of course, we choose a pair of coordinate axes. We elect to utilize a line through F perpendicular to line d at point D as Y axis; and because it makes our final result especially simple, we use the perpendicular bisector of line segment FD as X axis (see Fig. 5i1).

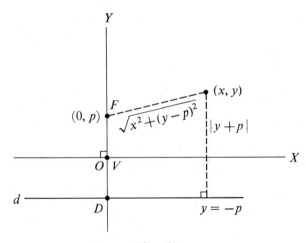

Fig. 5i1

Note that the midpoint of line segment FD is equidistant from focus and directrix. Therefore this midpoint is a point of the parabola and is called its *vertex V*. As we have chosen our coordinate axes, $V = (0, 0)$.

Let $F = (0, p)$; then the equation of line d is $y = -p$.

Now suppose (x, y) is a point of our coordinate plane. Then (see Section 3g) the distance from (x, y) to d is $|y + p|/\sqrt{0^2 + 1^2} = |y + p|$. Furthermore, the distance from (x, y) to F is $\sqrt{x^2 + (y - p)^2}$. Therefore (x, y) is on our parabola iff

$$|y + p| = \sqrt{x^2 + (y - p)^2}.$$

We successively transform the preceding equation into the following equations, each equivalent to the preceding equation:

$$(y + p)^2 = x^2 + (y - p)^2$$
$$4py = x^2$$
$$y = \frac{1}{4p} x^2.$$

If we let $a = 1/4p$, then $p = 1/4a$, and we conclude:

5i2. If $a \neq 0$, then $y = ax^2$ is the equation of a parabola with focus $(0, 1/4a)$, vertex $(0, 0)$, and directrix $y = -1/4a$.

As before, we may interchange the roles of x and y to arrive at the following statement.

5i3. If $a \neq 0$, then $x = ay^2$ is the equation of a parabola with focus $(1/4a, 0)$, vertex $(0, 0)$, and directrix $x = -1/4a$.

The line FV is called the *axis* of the parabola.

Note that the graph of $y = ax^2$ is symmetric to the Y axis, and if a is positive, then y is never negative, whereas if a is negative, then y is never positive; and analogously for the graph of $x = ay^2$.

ILLUSTRATIVE EXAMPLE 1. Discuss and draw the graph of $y = \frac{1}{4}x^2$.

Solution: The graph is a parabola which is symmetric to the Y axis; y is never negative; $V = (0, 0)$; $F = (0, 1)$; directrix: $y = -1$. We then determine a few actual points on the graph. In fact, it is usually easy to sketch the graph of a parabola simply from a well-chosen table of values. The graph is drawn in Fig. 5i2. ‖

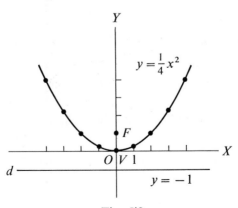

Fig. 5i2

ILLUSTRATIVE EXAMPLE 2.   Discuss and draw the graph of $y = -x^2$.

Solution: The graph is a parabola which is symmetric to the Y axis; y is never positive; $V = (0, 0)$; $F = (0, -\frac{1}{4})$; directrix: $y = \frac{1}{4}$. Utilizing a few points on the graph, we draw the graph as shown in Fig. 5i3.   ‖

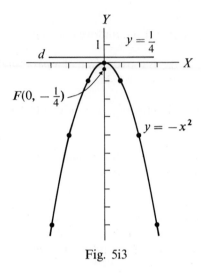

Fig. 5i3

ILLUSTRATIVE EXAMPLE 3.   Discuss and draw the graph of $x = -2y^2$.

Solution: The graph must be a parabola which is symmetric to the X axis; x is never positive; $V = (0, 0)$; $F = (-\frac{1}{8}, 0)$; directrix: $x = \frac{1}{8}$. Utilizing a few points on the graph, we draw the graph as shown in Fig. 5i4.   ‖

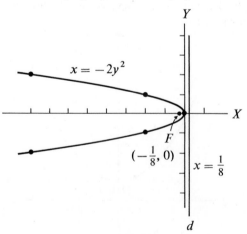

Fig. 5i4

Problems

1. Discuss and plot the graph of each of the following equations.

(a) $y = x^2$.　　　　　　(b) $y = 4x^2$.　　　　　　(c) $x = y^2$.
(d) $x = -y^2$.　　　　　(e) $y = 3x^2$.　　　　　　(f) $x = 3y^2$.
(g) $y = -3x^2$.　　　　(h) $x = -3y^2$.　　　　(i) $16y = x^2$.
(j) $16x - y^2 = 0$.　　(k) $16x + y^2 = 0$.　　(l) $16y + x^2 = 0$.

2. In each of the following cases write the equation of and plot the graph of a parabola satisfying the given condition or conditions.

(a) $F = (3, 0)$, $V = (0, 0)$.　　　　(b) $F = (0, 3)$, $V = (0, 0)$.
(c) $F = (-3, 0)$, $V = (0, 0)$.　　(d) $F = (0, -3)$, $V = (0, 0)$.
(e) Passes through $(7, 11)$.　　　　(f) $F = (4, 0)$, directrix: $x = 2$.
(g) $F = (0, 2)$, $V = (0, 4)$.

3. Find (algebraically) the points of intersection of each of the following pairs of curves and draw the curves.

(a) $y = x^2$, $x = y^2$.　　　　　(b) $y = 4x^2$, $x + 2y^2 = 0$.
(c) $y = x^2$, $y = x$.　　　　　　(d) $y = x^2$, $4x^2 + 9y^2 = 36$.
(e) $y = x^2$, $x + y = 6$.

4. A line segment through the focus of a parabola, perpendicular to line FD and terminated by the parabola, is called its *latus rectum*. Prove that the latus rectum of the parabola whose equation is $y^2 = 4px$ is of length $|4p|$; prove the same fact for the parabola whose equation is $x^2 = 4py$.

5j. TRANSLATION OF COORDINATE SYSTEMS

We recall (see Section 2g) that Cartesian coordinates for the points of a plane may be introduced by choosing unit orthogonal vectors i, j of the plane and a point O (the "origin") in the plane. If we use the same unit orthogonal vectors i, j, but different origins, say $O, \bar{O}$, we arrive at different coordinate systems for the same plane (see Fig. 5j1). Either is said to be derivable from the other by *translation* (since a translation, in the physical sense, is a motion that does not alter direction; note, for example, that the directions of the positive and negative coordinate axes with origin $\bar{O}$ are the same as the directions of the corresponding coordinate axes with origin O).

Clearly, if we translate the coordinate system from origin O to origin $\bar{O}$, the coordinates of a point will be changed. But exactly how?

For example, suppose that, with reference to a coordinate system

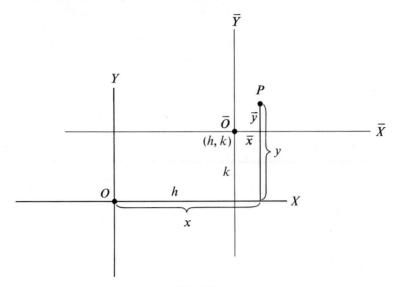

Fig. 5ji

(O, i, j), $\bar{O} = (h, k)$ and $P = (x, y)$. What will the coordinates of P be with reference to the coordinate system $(\bar{O}, i, j)$?

The answer is easily found. For

$$\overrightarrow{\bar{O}P} \overset{?1}{=} \overrightarrow{OP} - \overrightarrow{O\bar{O}} \overset{?2}{=} xi + yj - (hi + kj) \overset{?3}{=} (x - h)i + (y - k)j.$$

Therefore the coordinates of P, with respect to the coordinate system $(\bar{O}, i, j)$, are $(x - h, y - k)$ (?4).

Summarizing, we make the following statement.

5j1. Suppose the coordinate system (O, i, j) for a plane is translated to $(\bar{O}, i, j)$, where the coordinates of $\bar{O}$, with respect to (O, i, j), are (h, k). Let the "old" and "new" coordinates [i.e., with reference to (O, i, j) and $(\bar{O}, i, j)$ respectively] of a point in the plane be (x, y), $(\bar{x}, \bar{y})$. Then

(1) $$\bar{x} = x - h, \qquad \bar{y} = y - k.$$

The equations (1) above are called *equations of translation*.

Now we consider an application of the equations of translation. Suppose that in $E2'$ C is a circle whose center is $\bar{O} = (h, k)$ and whose radius is r, and suppose we translate so that the new origin is $\bar{O}$ (see Fig. 5j2). If P is a point of our coordinate plane whose coordinates in the original system are (a, b) and in the new system $(\bar{a}, \bar{b})$, we must have, by Eqs. (1),

$$\bar{a} = a - h, \qquad \bar{b} = b - k.$$

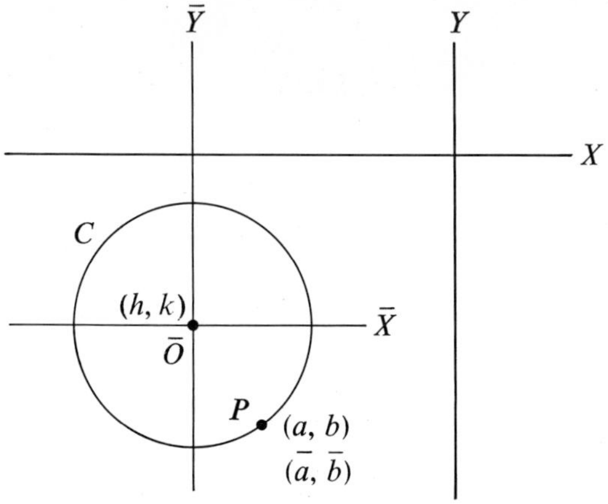

Fig. 5j2

Furthermore, since in the new system C is a circle with radius r and center at the origin, the equation of C in the new system is

$$\bar{x}^2 + \bar{y}^2 = r^2.$$

Hence point P belongs to circle C iff

$$\bar{a}^2 + \bar{b}^2 = r^2,$$

i.e., iff

$$(a - h)^2 + (b - k)^2 = r^2,$$

i.e., iff the original coordinates of P satisfy the equation

(2) $(x - h)^2 + (y - k)^2 = r^2.$

That is to say, Eq. (2) is the equation of C in the original coordinate system.

Of course, we know this already (see Section 5b). But exactly as in the special case of the circle, the next statement follows more generally.

5j2. Suppose the coordinate system (O, i, j) for a plane is translated to the system $(\bar{O}, i, j)$, where the coordinates of $\bar{O}$, with respect to (O, i, j), are (h, k). Then equations with respect to (O, i, j) of a graph may be derived from equations of the graph with respect to $(\bar{O}, i, j)$ simply by replacing each $\bar{x}$ by $x - h$, and each $\bar{y}$ by $y - k$.

ILLUSTRATIVE EXAMPLE 1.   Find the equation of a parabola with vertex $(3, 7)$ and focus $(3, 4)$ (see Fig. 5j3).

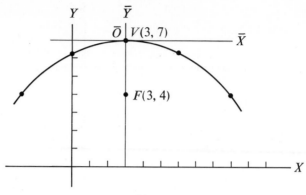

Fig. 5j3

Solution: We translate the axes to the new origin $\bar{O} = (3, 7)$, so that $h = 3$, $k = 7$. In the new system $F = (0, -3) = (0, 1/4a)$. Therefore $a = -1/12$. Hence the equation of the parabola in the new system is $\bar{y} = -(1/12)\bar{x}^2$. Therefore the equation of the parabola in the original system is $y - 7 = -(1/12)(x - 3)^2$. ‖

Just as we generalized from the case of a circle with center O to the case of a circle with center (h, k), using the equations of translation, so we may arrive at the following conclusions also.

(i) An equation of an ellipse in $E2'$ with center (h, k) and axes parallel to the coordinate axes is either

$$\frac{(x - h)^2}{a^2} + \frac{(y - k)^2}{b^2} = 1 \qquad \text{(major axis } \| X \text{ axis)}$$

or

$$\frac{(y - k)^2}{a^2} + \frac{(x - h)^2}{b^2} = 1 \qquad \text{(major axis } \| Y \text{ axis),}$$

where $2a = $ major axis and $2b = $ minor axis of the ellipse.

(ii) An equation of a hyperbola with center (h, k) and axes parallel to the coordinate axes is either

$$\frac{(x - h)^2}{a^2} - \frac{(y - k)^2}{b^2} = 1 \qquad \text{(transverse axis } \| X \text{ axis)}$$

or

$$\frac{(y - k)^2}{a^2} - \frac{(x - h)^2}{b^2} = 1 \qquad \text{(transverse axis } \| Y \text{ axis),}$$

where $2a = $ transverse axis of the hyperbola.

(iii) An equation of a parabola with vertex (h, k) and axis parallel to a coordinate axis is either

$$x - h = a(y - k)^2 \qquad (a \neq 0, \text{ axis} \parallel X \text{ axis})$$

or

$$y - k = a(x - h)^2 \qquad (a \neq 0, \text{ axis} \parallel Y \text{ axis}).$$

ILLUSTRATIVE EXAMPLE 2.   Plot the graph of the equation

(1) $$16x^2 - 9y^2 - 64x - 54y - 161 = 0.$$

Solution: We use the method of "completing the square":

(2) $$(16x^2 - 64x \quad) - (9y^2 + 54y \quad) = 161,$$
(3) $$16(x^2 - 4x \quad) - 9(y^2 + 6y \quad) = 161,$$
(4) $$16(x^2 - 4x + 4) - 9(y^2 + 6y + 9) = 161 + 64 - 81,$$
(5) $$16(x - 2)^2 - 9(y + 3)^3 = 144.$$

Now dividing both sides by 144, we have

(6) $$\frac{(x - 2)^2}{9} - \frac{(y + 3)^2}{16} = 1.$$

If we translate the coordinate axes so that the point $(2, -3)$ becomes the new origin, Eq. (6) becomes

(7) $$\frac{\bar{x}^2}{9} - \frac{\bar{y}^2}{16} = 1.$$

We have already drawn the *hyperbola* which is the graph of this equation (see Illustrative Example, Section 5f). The required graph is simply the graph of Eq. (7) drawn with respect to the *new* coordinate system (Fig. 5j4). $\parallel$

ILLUSTRATIVE EXAMPLE 3.   Plot the graph of the equation

$$x^2 - 6x + 12y - 75 = 0.$$

Solution:

$$x^2 - 6x = -12y + 75$$
$$x^2 - 6x + 9 = -12y + 75 + 9$$
$$(x - 3)^2 = -12y + 84$$
$$(x - 3)^2 = -12(y - 7)$$
$$y - 7 = -(1/12)(x - 3)^2.$$

In a translated system with origin $(3, 7)$, the equation of the required graph would be

$$\bar{y} = -(1/12)\bar{x}^2.$$

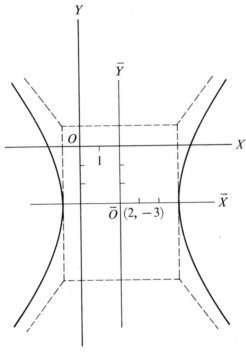

Fig. 5j4

This equation has been encountered in Illustrative Example 1 above, and its graph is drawn in Fig. 5j3. ‖

5k. THE GRAPH OF A SECOND-DEGREE EQUATION WITH xy TERM MISSING

We are not quite ready to settle completely the question of the graphs that may arise from a second-degree equation, but we are ready to take the major step toward that goal. We shall now consider the equation

(1) $Ax^2 + Cy^2 + Dx + Ey + F = 0$ (A, C not both 0),

i.e., the general second-degree equation in x and y with $B = 0$, and we shall determine all the graphs which may arise from equations of the form (1).

First of all, we note that we have already encountered the following as graphs of second-degree equations of the form (1).

(i) An *ellipse* (which may or may not be a *circle with nonzero radius*).
(ii) A *hyperbola*.
(iii) A *parabola*.
(iv) A single *point*. (Where?)
(v) A *null graph*. (Where?)

We now show that we may add to this list:

(vi) A single *line*.
(vii) A pair of $\neq$ *intersecting lines*.
(viii) A pair of $\neq$ *parallel lines*.

For example, consider the second-degree equation $x^2 = 0$. This is equivalent to the equation $x = 0$, whose graph is the Y axis, namely a *line*.

Next consider the second-degree equation $y^2 - x^2 = 0$. This is equivalent to $(y + x)(y - x) = 0$, which is satisfied if $y + x = 0$ or $y - x = 0$, and not otherwise. The points which satisfy $y + x = 0$ constitute one straight line, and the points which satisfy $y - x = 0$ constitute another, and the two straight lines intersect at $(0, 0)$. The graph of $y^2 - x^2 = 0$ is the set that consists of the graphs $y + x = 0$ and $y - x = 0$, i.e., a pair of $\neq$ *intersecting lines*.

Similarly, the graph of the second-degree equation $x^2 = 4x$ is the pair of $\neq$ *parallel lines* whose equations are $x = 0$, $x = 4$ [since $x^2 = 4x$ is equivalent to $x^2 - 4x = 0$, which in turn is equivalent to $x(x - 4) = 0$].

[A proof that *no other* graphs may arise from Eq. (1) above will be found in the Appendix.]

We are familiar with at least one type of second-degree equation in which the xy term is *not* missing, namely the equation $xy = k$, where $k \neq 0$. We know the graph of this equation to be a hyperbola, with transverse axis *not* parallel to a coordinate axis.

Actually, we shall prove in Section 5m that *the graph of any second-degree equation in x and y, even one whose xy term is not missing, must be one of the eight graphs listed above*. It will turn out that the effect of an xy term (i.e., $B \neq 0$) in our second-degree equation is to produce a graph whose axes of symmetry are generally not parallel to either coordinate axis, as is illustrated in the case of the equation $xy = k$, where $k \neq 0$.

A by-product of the analysis of this section is the following set of criteria.

The graph of a second-degree equation with xy term missing can be:

(a) A circle of nonzero radius only if $A = C$.
(b) An ellipse only if A and C are of like sign.
(c) A hyperbola only if A and C are of opposite sign.
(d) A parabola only if A or C is 0 (i.e., if x^2 or y^2 is missing).

It must be borne in mind, however, that even if these conditions hold, the graphs (iv)–(viii) listed above may occur also.

We say that the conditions given above are *necessary* but not *sufficient* for the graph to turn out as stated.

Problems

1. Identify, sketch, and find the foci of the graphs of each of the following equations.

   (a) $x^2 + 4y^2 - 2x + 16y + 13 = 0$.
   (b) $16x^2 - 9y^2 + 64x + 72y - 224 = 0$.
   (c) $2x^2 + 2y^2 - 4x + 8y + 5 = 0$.
   (d) $y = x^2 - 3x + 4$.
   (e) $9x^2 - 16y^2 - 18x - 64y - 199 = 0$.
   (f) $x = 2y^2 - 3y + 1$.
   (g) $16x^2 - 9y^2 + 90y - 81 = 0$.
   (h) $y^2 + 2x + 6y = 5$.
   (i) $4x^2 - 20x + 24y + 61 = 0$.
   (j) $9x^2 - 16y^2 + 18x + 64y + 89 = 0$.
   (k) $x^2 - 4x - 4y = 0$.
   (l) $9x^2 + 25y^2 - 108x - 250y + 724 = 0$.
   (m) $4x^2 - 9y^2 - 8x - 36y = 176$.
   (n) $x^2 - 4x + 3y = 7$.
   (o) $y = -x^2 - x + 6$.
   (p) $x = y^2 - 9$.
   (q) $y = x^2 - 9$.

2. Write the equation of the parabola with vertex at the point $(-4, 0)$ which passes through the ends of the major axis of the ellipse $9x^2 + 4y^2 = 36$.

3. What is the equation of the ellipse with center at $(2, 1)$, the end of an axis at $(0, 1)$, and passing through $(3, 4)$?

4. Find the equation of an ellipse or a hyperbola with foci $(1, 8)$ and $(1, -2)$ and vertices $(1, 7)$ and $(1, -1)$.

5. Find the equation of the hyperbola that has one vertex at $(1, 9)$, the corresponding focus at $(1, 7)$, and eccentricity equal to 2.

6. Find the equation of an ellipse that has one focus at $(2, -1)$ and an end of one axis at $(-1, 3)$.

7. Find the equation of a parabola with focus $(1, -7)$ and directrix $y = 3$.

8. A point moves in a plane so as to stay equidistant from the line $x = 4$ and the point $(7, 3)$. Find an equation satisfied by all points of its path.

9. Find the equation of the locus of all points the sum of whose distances from the points $(-2, 3)$ and $(4, 3)$ is 10.

10. What is the locus of all points the difference of whose distances from the points $(-2, 3)$ and $(4, 3)$ is 10?

11. Draw, or identify as null, each of the following graphs.

    (a) $xy = 0$.   (b) $x^2 - 2x + 1 = 0$.
    (c) $x^2 = -4$.   (d) $x^2 = 4x$.

(e) $x^2 + y^2 = 2y - 1$.   (f) $y^2 = 4x^2$.
(g) $xy + x + y + 1 = 0$.   (h) $x^3 - 9x = 0$.
(i) $9x^2 + 16y^2 = 0$.   (j) $9x^2 - 16y^2 = 0$.
(k) $x^2 + y^2 = 2y - 2$.   (l) $x^2 - 2xy + y^2 = 0$.

12 (Optional). We have found the loci of points which move in a plane so that in one case the sum and in another case the difference of their distances from two fixed points is kept constant. What about keeping the *ratio* of these distances constant? That is, suppose $F_1 \neq F_2$ are points in a plane and $a \geq 0$ is a real number. Find an equation in an appropriate coordinate system for the locus of all points P in the given plane such that $PF_1/PF_2 = a$. Show then that if $a = 1$, the locus is a straight line, the perpendicular bisector of line segment F_1F_2; and that if $a \neq 1$, the locus is a *circle* (called the *circle of Apollonius*).

51. ROTATION OF COORDINATE SYSTEMS

Suppose (O, i, j) and $(O, \bar{\imath}, \bar{\jmath})$ are coordinate systems in a plane such that the measure of the angle from i to $\bar{\imath}$ is θ. (Here we assume the measure of angles to be signed in the usual trigonometric sense—positive if counterclockwise, negative if clockwise.) Then we say that the "new" system $(O, \bar{\imath}, \bar{\jmath})$ may be derived from the "old" system (O, i, j) by rotating through the angle θ (see Fig. 5l1).

Now suppose P is a point in the given plane whose coordinates in the

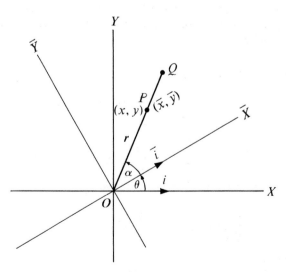

Fig. 5l1

old and new systems are (x, y) and $(\bar{x}, \bar{y})$ respectively. We seek relations among x, y, $\bar{x}$, and $\bar{y}$.

Let $OP = r$, let P lie on line segment OQ, and let the measure of the angle from i to $\overrightarrow{OQ}$ be α. Then directly from the definition of the trigonometric functions, we have

$$x = r \cos(\alpha + \theta), \qquad \bar{x} = r \cos \alpha,$$
$$y = r \sin(\alpha + \theta), \qquad \bar{y} = r \sin \alpha.$$

Therefore

$$x = r \cos \alpha \cos \theta - r \sin \alpha \sin \theta = \bar{x} \cos \theta - \bar{y} \sin \theta,$$
$$y = r \sin \alpha \cos \theta + r \cos \alpha \sin \theta = \bar{y} \cos \theta + \bar{x} \sin \theta.$$

Thus

(1)
$$x = \bar{x} \cos \theta - \bar{y} \sin \theta,$$
$$y = \bar{x} \sin \theta + \bar{y} \cos \theta.$$

The equations (1) above are called *equations of rotation*.

As in the case of translation, the following may be proved.

511. Suppose a coordinate system (O, i, j) for a plane is rotated through an angle θ to the system $(O, \bar{i}, \bar{j})$. Then equations with respect to $(O, \bar{i}, \bar{j})$ of a graph in the given plane may be derived from equations of the graph with respect to (O, i, j) simply by replacing x by $\bar{x} \cos \theta - \bar{y} \sin \theta$, and y by $\bar{x} \sin \theta + \bar{y} \cos \theta$.

ILLUSTRATIVE EXAMPLE.   Given the equation $xy = x^2 + y^2$ of a graph G in $E2'$, find the equation of G in a new system derived from the old by rotating through $45°$.

Solution: We have

$$x = \frac{\bar{x}}{\sqrt{2}} - \frac{\bar{y}}{\sqrt{2}} = \frac{1}{\sqrt{2}} (\bar{x} - \bar{y}),$$

$$y = \frac{\bar{x}}{\sqrt{2}} + \frac{\bar{y}}{\sqrt{2}} = \frac{1}{\sqrt{2}} (\bar{x} + \bar{y}).$$

The equation of G in the new system is therefore

$$\frac{1}{\sqrt{2}} (\bar{x} - \bar{y}) \cdot \frac{1}{\sqrt{2}} (\bar{x} + \bar{y}) = \left[\frac{1}{\sqrt{2}} (\bar{x} - \bar{y}) \right]^2 + \left[\frac{1}{\sqrt{2}} (\bar{x} + \bar{y}) \right]^2,$$

which reduces to

$$\bar{x}^2 + 3\bar{y}^2 = 0,$$

which is satisfied only if $\bar{x} = 0$, $\bar{y} = 0$. Therefore the graph G consists of only a single point, the origin of both coordinate systems. $\parallel$

5m. THE GRAPH OF THE GENERAL SECOND-DEGREE EQUATION (Optional)

We shall attempt, by rotating coordinate axes, to "eliminate" the xy term from the equation

(1) $Ax^2 + Bxy + Cy^2 + Dx + Ey + F = 0$ (A, B, C not all 0).

Suppose we rotate the axes through an angle θ (θ not yet determined). Then the new equation of the graph of Eq. (1) above will be

$$A(\bar{x} \cos \theta - \bar{y} \sin \theta)^2 + B(\bar{x} \cos \theta - \bar{y} \sin \theta)(\bar{x} \sin \theta + \bar{y} \cos \theta)$$
$$+ C(\bar{x} \sin \theta + \bar{y} \cos \theta)^2 + D(\bar{x} \cos \theta - \bar{y} \sin \theta)$$
$$+ E(\bar{x} \sin \theta + \bar{y} \cos \theta) + F = 0.$$

Collecting terms, we may write this equation in the form

(2) $\bar{A}\bar{x}^2 + \bar{B}\bar{x}\bar{y} + \bar{C}\bar{y}^2 + \bar{D}\bar{x} + \bar{E}\bar{y} + \bar{F} = 0.$

The coefficient of $\bar{x}\bar{y}$ in Eq. (2), as derived from the equation which precedes it, is

$$\bar{B} = -2A \sin \theta \cos \theta + B(\cos^2 \theta - \sin^2 \theta) + 2C \sin \theta \cos \theta,$$

or

(3) $\bar{B} = (C - A) \sin 2\theta + B \cos 2\theta.$

If $A = C$, then the coefficient $\bar{B}$ will be 0 if $\theta = 45°$. If $A \neq C$, then we solve

$$(C - A) \sin 2\theta + B \cos 2\theta = 0$$

$$\frac{\sin 2\theta}{\cos 2\theta} = -\frac{B}{C - A} = \frac{B}{A - C}$$

$$\tan 2\theta = \frac{B}{A - C}.$$

Since it is always possible to find a value of θ which will satisfy this last equation, it will in all cases be possible to find a value of θ which makes $\bar{B} = 0$.

We see, then, that by rotating the coordinate axes it is always possible to transform a second-degree equation into an equation of degree ≤ 2 with the xy term eliminated. (Actually, we shall show in one of the problems that the new equation is also of degree 2.)

Therefore the graphs which any second-degree equation in x and y may give rise to are exactly graphs (i)–(viii) of Section 5k in "oblique" position if the given equation contains an xy term.

In the Illustrative Example of the preceding section, $A = C$. It was for this reason that we elected to rotate the axes through 45° in that example.

ILLUSTRATIVE EXAMPLE.   Draw the graph of the equation

$$288x^2 + 168xy + 337y^2 = 3600.$$

Solution: Since $A \neq C$, we let

$$\tan 2\theta = \frac{B}{A - C} = \frac{168}{288 - 337} = -\frac{24}{7}.$$

We choose 2θ so that $\pi/2 < 2\theta < \pi$. Then $\cos 2\theta = -7/25$, $\pi/4 < \theta < \pi/2$, and

$$\sin \theta = \sqrt{\frac{1 - \cos 2\theta}{2}} = \sqrt{\frac{1 + 7/25}{2}} = \frac{4}{5};$$

therefore $\cos \theta = \sqrt{1 - \sin^2 \theta} = 3/5$.

Now we substitute into the original equation:

$$x = \tfrac{3}{5}\bar{x} - \tfrac{4}{5}\bar{y} = \tfrac{1}{5}(3\bar{x} - 4\bar{y}),$$
$$y = \tfrac{4}{5}\bar{x} + \tfrac{3}{5}\bar{y} = \tfrac{1}{5}(4\bar{x} + 3\bar{y}),$$

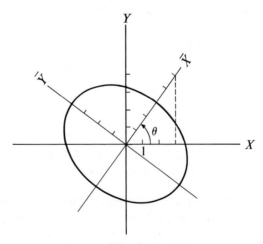

Fig. 5m1

arriving at

$$288[\tfrac{1}{5}(3\bar{x} - 4\bar{y})]^2 + 168 \cdot \tfrac{1}{5}(3\bar{x} - 4\bar{y}) \cdot \tfrac{1}{5}(4\bar{x} + 3\bar{y}) + 337[\tfrac{1}{5}(4\bar{x} + 3\bar{y})]^2 = 3600$$
$$288(3\bar{x} - 4\bar{y})^2 + 168(3\bar{x} - 4\bar{y})(4\bar{x} + 3\bar{y}) + 337(4\bar{x} + 3\bar{y})^2 = 25 \cdot 3600$$
$$10{,}000\bar{x}^2 + 5625\bar{y}^2 = 25 \cdot 3600$$
$$\frac{\bar{x}^2}{9} + \frac{\bar{y}^2}{16} = 1.$$

The graph is therefore an ellipse, which we plot as shown in Fig. 5m1. ‖

Problems

1. Identify, and, if it is not null, draw the graph of each of the following.
    (a) $xy = 12$. (Also find the equation arrived at when the xy term is eliminated in this example.)
    (b) $xy - 2x - 4y + 6 = 0$. [It is easily seen that this graph has asymptotes. Therefore the graph must be a (?). Also find the resulting equation when the xy term is eliminated in this example.]
    (c) $y^2 + 3xy - 3x^2 - 4 = 0$.
    (d) $2x^2 + y^2 - 3xy + 2x - y = 0$.
    (e) $x^2 + xy + y^2 = 1$.
    (f) $5y^2 + 4xy + 8x^2 - 9 = 0$.
    (g) $3y^2 - 10xy + 3x^2 + 32 = 0$.
    (h) $\sqrt{x} + \sqrt{y} = 1$. (*Hint:* Consider excluded values; then show that the graph is a part of a parabola by squaring the given equation, isolating the radical which appears, and squaring again.)
    (i) $x^2 - 2xy + 2y^2 = 0$.
    (j) $x^2 - 2xy + 2y^2 + 2 = 0$.

2. Referring to Eqs. (1) and (2) of Section 5m, we found, in Eq. (3), $\bar{B}$ in terms of coefficients of Eq. (1).
    (a) Similarly, find $\bar{A}$ and $\bar{C}$.
    (b) Show that under any rotation of the coordinate axes, $A + C$ is "invariant," i.e., $\bar{A} + \bar{C} = A + C$.
    (c) Show also that under any rotation of the coordinate axes, the "discriminant" $B^2 - 4AC$ of Eq. (1) is invariant.
    (d) Show, as follows, that Eq. (2) actually is of the second degree: Suppose, to the contrary, that $\bar{A} = \bar{B} = \bar{C} = 0$. Then from parts (b) and (c) above, $A + C = B^2 - 4AC = 0$. Deduce from this the contradiction that $A = B = C = 0$.
    (e) Prove that a necessary (but not a sufficient) condition for the graph of Eq. (1) to be:

      (1) An ellipse is: $B^2 - 4AC < 0$.
      (2) A parabola is: $B^2 - 4AC = 0$.

(3) A hyperbola is: $B^2 - 4AC > 0$. [*Hint:*   See Section 5k, (b)–(d). Assume that by rotating axes, Eq. (1) has been transformed into Eq. (2), with $\bar{B} = 0$. Then, by part (c) above, $B^2 - 4AC = -4\bar{A}\bar{C}$. Now complete the proof.]

(4) Prove that Eq. (1) is the equation of a circle of nonzero radius only if $A = C$ and $B = 0$.

3. Suppose that in an original Cartesian coordinate system a point $P = (x, y)$, and that in a new system derived from the original by rotating through an angle θ, $P = (\bar{x}, \bar{y})$. Derive the equations of rotation

$$\bar{x} = x \cos \theta + y \sin \theta,$$

$$\bar{y} = -x \sin \theta + y \cos \theta$$

in each of the following ways.

(a) Solve the simultaneous Eqs. 5l(1) for $\bar{x}$ and $\bar{y}$.

(b) Follow the method by which Eqs. 5l(1) were derived, but use α to denote the angle from i to $\overrightarrow{OQ}$.

(c) In Eqs. 5l(1) reverse the roles of (x, y) and $(\bar{x}, \bar{y})$; that is to say, think of $(\bar{x}, \bar{y})$ as the original coordinates of P, and (x, y) as the new coordinates of P, in a coordinate system derived from the original by rotating through an angle $-\theta$.

5n.   THE CONIC SECTIONS

We have seen (Section 5k) that the following are the only nonnull sets of points that may occur as graphs of second-degree equations.

   (i) A noncircular ellipse.
  (ii) A hyperbola.
 (iii) A parabola.
  (iv) A circle of nonzero radius.
   (v) A circle of zero radius (i.e., a point).
  (vi) A line.
 (vii) A pair of $\neq$ intersecting lines.
(viii) A pair of $\neq$ parallel lines.

It is a remarkable fact that these point-sets, besides being related *algebraically* in that they constitute all possible nonnull graphs of second-degree equations, are also related *geometrically* in that they represent all possible cross sections of the simplest types of cones and cylinders.

In order to clarify our last statement, we shall first define certain terms.

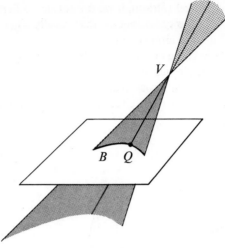

Fig. 5n1

5n1 (Definitions).   Let B be a curve in a plane and let V be a point not in the given plane. Then the set of all points on all lines VQ, where Q is a point of B, is called a *cone* with vertex V and base B (see Fig. 5n1).

Each line VQ is called an *element* of the cone.

The set of all points on all rays VQ is called a *nappe* of the cone. V and all the points of the cone not on the first nappe constitute another *nappe* of the cone.

If B is a circle of nonzero radius, then the cone is called a *circular cone*.

If B is a circle of nonzero radius and center O, and if line VO is perpendicular to the plane of B, then the cone is called a *right circular cone*.

5n2 (Definitions).   Let B be a set of points in a plane, and let L be a set of parallel lines not lying in the plane of B such that each line of L passes through a point of B and each point of B lies on a line of L. Then the set of all points on all lines in L is called a *cylinder* with base B.

Each line in L is called an *element* of the cylinder.

If B is a circle of nonzero radius, then the cylinder is called a *circular* cylinder.

If B is a circle of nonzero radius and the lines of L are perpendicular to the plane of B, then the cylinder is called a *right circular cylinder*.

5n3 (Definition).   A (planar) *cross section* of a set of points S is the intersection of a plane and S.

Now, as a matter of fact, of the graphs (i)–(viii) above, all but the last are cross sections of a right circular cone, and the last is a cross section of a right circular cylinder.

For it may be proved (although we do not do so here) that:

(i) An ellipse is the cross section that results when a plane intersects only one nappe of a right circular cone.

(ii) A hyperbola is the cross section that results when a plane intersects both nappes of a right circular cone but does not pass through its vertex.

(iii) A parabola is the cross section that results when a plane that is parallel to an element of a right circular cone intersects only one nappe of the cone. (See Fig. 5n2.)

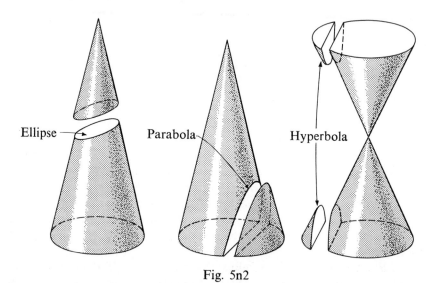

Fig. 5n2

It is left to the reader to show how the other second-degree graphs may be derived as cross sections of right circular cones or cylinders.

The nontrivial "conic sections," i.e., the ellipse, the parabola, and the hyperbola, have a long and interesting history and many practical applications. They were known and studied by the Greeks, who discovered them some 2500 years ago in the course of attempting to solve the "Three Famous Problems of Antiquity." First studied purely out of intellectual curiosity, the conic sections turned out later, as happens so often in mathematics, to be of the greatest practical importance. For it was discovered (empirically) by Johann Kepler, early in the seventeenth century, that the paths of the earth and the other planets about the sun are *ellipses*, with the sun at one focus; some 70 years later Isaac Newton proved this fact deductively, as a consequence of his law of gravitation.

Indeed, it has since turned out that not only ellipses, but parabolas and hyperbolas also, are paths that are traced by heavenly bodies.

The question of the path, or "trajectory," of a "projectile," i.e., an

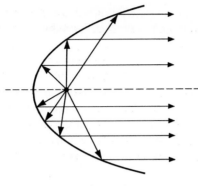

Fig. 5n3

object thrown like a baseball or fired like a bullet, is of the greatest importance, expecially militarily. The parabola has turned out to be important
in this connection since (neglecting relatively minor factors such as air
resistance) the trajectory of a projectile is parabolic.

The ellipse and parabola display interesting focal properties that have
been put to practical use. In the case of the ellipse, all rays emanating at one
focus and reflected from the ellipse will be reflected through the other focus.
This explains the phenomenon of the "whispering gallery," in which a
whisper emanating from one point may be heard clearly at a distance point
but not at intermediate points.

In the case of the parabola, rays emanating from its focus and reflected
from the parabola become rays parallel to its axis, so that these rays form a
powerful, unscattered beam (see Fig. 5n3). The principle finds application
in automobile headlights and aircraft beacons. Conversely, rays parallel
to an axis are reflected through the focus of a parabola. Solar furnaces make
use of this fact. (See, in this connection, the derivation of the word *focus*.)

Engineers employ conic sections in the building of bridges, for example;
in this connection it is interesting to note that when a bridge is uniformly
loaded, the cable by which it is suspended assumes the form of a parabola.

Finally, we mention that innumerable formulas in varied fields are of
the second degree and have graphs, therefore, which are of the type we have
been discussing. The curve the economist calls "the demand curve in the
case of unitary elasticity," for example, is simply the hyperbola whose
equation is $PQ = k$, where P is the price of an item, Q is the quantity
demanded at price P, and k is a real number.

Problems

1. (a) What condition on a cutting plane will guarantee that its intersection
       with a right circular cone will be a circle of nonzero radius? A
       point? A line? A pair of intersection lines?

(b) Which of the point-sets (i)–(viii) above are cross sections of a right circular cylinder, and how is each produced by a cutting plane?

2   (Optional). *Focus–directrix definition of certain conic sections.* The definitions we have given for the ellipse and the hyperbola are closely related to each other, but our definition of the parabola is of a different type. An approach that results in a more unified set of definitions is to define these curves as particular conic sections, but then our analytic treatment is made more difficult. A third type of definition, generalizing our definition of the parabola, will be considered in this problem.

The definition we have in mind stems from the following theorem.

Theorem.   Let F be a point, l a line not containing F, and e a positive real number. Let G be the locus of points P (in the plane determined by F and l) the ratio of whose distances to F and l (in that order) is e. Then:

(i) If $e = 1$, G is a parabola with focus F and directrix l.

(ii) If $e < 1$, G is a noncircular ellipse with focus F and eccentricity e.

(iii) If $e > 1$, G is a hyperbola with focus F and eccentricity e.

Proof: The proof of (i) is almost immediate (?1). For (ii) and (iii) proceed as follows (see Fig. 5n4): Use l as Y axis, a line through $F \perp l$ as X axis, and suppose $F = (k, 0)$, $k > 0$. Then (x, y) is a point of G iff

$$\frac{\sqrt{(x - k)^2 + y^2}}{|x|} = e.$$

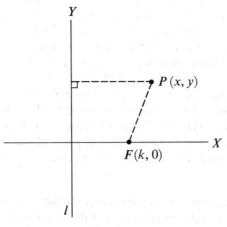

Fig. 5n4

From this derive the equivalent equation

$$(1 - e^2)x^2 + y^2 - 2kx + k^2 = 0,$$

from which show that if $e < 1$, G is an ellipse, and if $e > 1$, G is a hyperbola. Then complete the square and arrive at

(1)
$$\frac{\left(x - \dfrac{k}{1 - e^2}\right)^2}{k^2 e^2/(1 - e^2)^2} + \frac{y^2}{k^2 e^2/(1 - e^2)} = 1.$$

If $e < 1$, Eq. (1) is the equation of an ellipse in which

$$a^2 = \frac{k^2 e^2}{(1 - e^2)^2}, \qquad b^2 = \frac{k^2 e^2}{1 - e^2}.$$

Now show that $c^2 = a^2 - b^2 = k^2 e^4/(1 - e^2)^2$. [The fact that $a^2 - b^2$ is positive proves that we have identified a^2 and b^2 correctly in Eq. (1).] Hence

$$\frac{c}{a} = \frac{ke^2/(1 - e^2)}{ke/(1 - e^2)} = e.$$

Thus the eccentricity of G is e, as was to be proved.

Finally, the foci of Eq. (1) lie at

$$\left(\frac{k}{1 - e^2} \pm c, 0\right).$$

Show that one of these points is F. This completes the proof of (ii) above.

To complete the proof of (iii), we write Eq. (1) in the form

(2)
$$\frac{\left(x - \dfrac{k}{(1 - e^2)}\right)^2}{k^2 e^2/(1 - e^2)^2} - \frac{y^2}{k^2 e^2/(e^2 - 1)} = 1.$$

Then, since we are now assuming $e > 1$, Eq. (2) is the equation of a hyperbola with $a^2 = (?2)$, $b^2 = (?3)$, $c^2 = (?4)$. *It is left to the reader to complete the proof of* (iii).

Now, finally, if the theorem above is to supply a definition of the parabola, the noncircular ellipse, and the hyperbola, we must show that *every one* of these curves may be defined as in the theorem.

In the case of the parabola, the old and new definitions are trivially equivalent.

In the case of a noncircular ellipse, we proceed as follows: Suppose axes have been established so that the equation of the given ellipse is

(3)
$$\frac{x^2}{a^2} + \frac{y^2}{b^2} = 1.$$

We shall show that this equation may be written in the form of Eq. (1) after a translation of axes.

The fact that in our preceding development $a = ke/(1 - e^2)$ suggests that we now let $k = [a(1 - e^2)]/e$, where e is the eccentricity of the given ellipse. (This is permissible, for since our ellipse is noncircular, $e \neq 0$.) It follows that $a = ke/(1 - e^2)$, $a^2 = k^2e^2/(1 - e^2)^2$. Show that $b^2 = k^2e^2/(1 - e^2)$.

Now if we translate our axis to the new origin

$$\left(- \frac{k}{1 - e^2}, 0\right),$$

Eq. (3) becomes

(4)
$$\frac{\left(\bar{x} - \dfrac{k}{(1 - e^2)}\right)^2}{k^2e^2/(1 - e^2)^2} + \frac{\bar{y}^2}{k^2e^2/(1 - e^2)} = 1,$$

which is of the same form as Eq. (1).

Thus the given ellipse is the locus of points the ratio of whose distances to a certain point and a certain line is a positive real number $e < 1$.

Similarly, prove that any hyperbola has an equation of the form of Eq. (2), and therefore falls within the scope of our proposed new definition.

Up until now we have defined no eccentricity for the parabola. The preceding theorem suggests that we define *the eccentricity of a parabola to be* 1, and that we define the line *l* to be a *directrix* of the ellipse and hyperbola also. Considerations of symmetry show that actually the noncircular ellipse and the hyperbola each have *two* directrices.

As a final exercise, show that:
(a) The foci of an ellipse or a hyperbola are at a distance of ae from the center of each curve.
(b) The directrices of an ellipse or a hyperbola are at a distance of a/e from the center of each curve.

We have now proved the following definition to be equivalent to our original definition.

Definitions.   In a given plane let F be a point, *l* a line not containing F, and e a positive real number. Then the set of all points in the given plane the ratio of whose distances to F and *l* (in that order) is e is called a *noncircular ellipse* (if $e < 1$), a *parabola* (if $e = 1$), and a *hyperbola* (if $e > 1$.).

In each case F is called a *focus*, e the *eccentricity*, and *l* a *directrix* of the set of points defined.

Chapter 6

Transcendental Graphs, Parametric Equations, and Polar Coordinates

6a. INTRODUCTION

If the graph of a function is not "algebraic" (see Section 4*f*), then the graph and the function are said to be *transcendental*. The best-known transcendental functions are trigonometric functions, exponential functions, and logarithmic functions. In this chapter we shall consider graphs of these functions and graphs of certain simple combinations of these functions with each other and with algebraic functions.

6b. THE SINE FUNCTION

By the interval $[a, b]$, where $a < b$ are real numbers, we shall mean the set of all real numbers between a and b and including a and b. Since most statements in mathematical analysis that concern trigonometric functions are most easily expressed in terms of radian measure, from now on all our trigonometric statements will be assumed to be in terms of radian measure, unless otherwise noted. The reader will recall, then, that the graph of the function sin x in the interval $[0, 2\pi]$ is as in Fig. 6b1. The complete graph of sin x is related to this partial graph in the following way.

Suppose we were to move $\pi/6$ units to the right of the 2π mark on the X axis. Then, clearly, the height reached by the graph of sin x at this point, i.e., at the point $x = 13\pi/6$, is the same as the height reached by the same graph at $x = \pi/6$; for $\sin(13\pi/6) = \sin[(\pi/6) + 2\pi] = \sin(\pi/6)$. In fact, it is true, for any real number r, that $\sin r = \sin(r + 2\pi) = \sin(r - 2\pi)$.

Thus the pattern of y values exhibited by the graph of sin x between

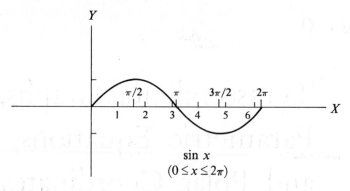

sin x
$(0 \leq x \leq 2\pi)$

Fig. 6b1

$x = 0$ and $x = 2\pi$ will be exactly repeated between $x = 2\pi$ and $x = 4\pi$, and also between $x = -2\pi$ and $x = 0$ (see Fig. 6b2).

The same process of reasoning may be repeated again and again; the whole graph of sin x is an endless repetition of that part of the graph which appears over *any* interval of length 2π on the X axis. Usually, however, we think of the sine graph as being generated by a repetition of the fundamental pattern of Fig. 6b1.

A number of important properties of the sine function are evident from its graph and may be rigorously proved:

(i) The maximum value achieved by the function sin x is 1, and this value is achieved only when $x = (\pi/2) + k \cdot 2\pi$, where k is any integer.

(ii) The minimum value achieved by the function sin x is -1, and this value is achieved only when $x = (3\pi/2) + k \cdot 2\pi$, where k is any integer.

(iii) The value 0 is achieved by the function sin x only when $x = k \cdot \pi$, where k is any integer.

(iv) The range of the sine function is the interval $[-1, 1]$. Therefore, for any real number x, it is always true that $-1 \leq \sin x \leq 1$.

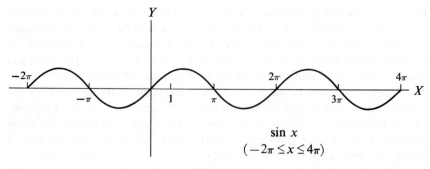

sin x
$(-2\pi \leq x \leq 4\pi)$

Fig. 6b2

(v) If the interval $[0, 2\pi]$ is divided into quarters, then the graph of sin x may be described as follows: In the first quarter the graph rises in a smooth curve from the axis to its maximum value; in the second quarter it falls from its maximum point back to the axis; in the third quarter it falls from the axis to its minimum point; in the last quarter it rises from its minimum point to the axis; and these four sections of the curve are all congruent.

If "quarter points" continue to be marked everywhere on the X axis, i.e., if we consider the values $x = k \cdot (\pi/2)$, where k is any integer, then the successive y values assumed at these x values run as follows (*max* and *min* are abbreviations for *maximum* and *minimum* respectively):

$$0, \text{max}, 0, \text{min}, 0, \text{max}, 0, \text{min}, \text{etc.}$$

But the most important property of the sine function which is evidenced by its graph is that which is known as *periodicity*.

Actually, we have been considering the property of periodicity but have fallen short of defining it. Roughly speaking, periodicity has to do with phenomena which occur over and over again at equally spaced intervals. The moon, for example, waxes and wanes in just this way. The waves of the sea rise up and down repeatedly. A pendulum swings back and forth continually. Business has its periodic ups and downs, and the seasons come and go in a predictable pattern.

But until we encounter the trigonometric functions in our study of mathematics, there is no function that displays this property of periodicity, and we are therefore severely limited in describing periodic phenomena mathematically. When we come to consider trigonometric functions, however, even in their definitions we observe that they repeat the same functional values over and over again at equally spaced intervals; and in the graphs of the trigonometric functions the property of periodicity is even more vividly evident.

Now, before we continue our discussion, we shall frame a precise definition of periodicity.

Let us consider the sine function. It has the property that if 2π is added to or subtracted from any real number, the sine of that number remains unchanged. That is, if x is any real number, then

$$\sin(x - 2\pi) = \sin x = \sin(x + 2\pi).$$

But 2π is not the only number that will do this trick. For example, if x is any real number, then

$$\sin(x - 4\pi) = \sin x = \sin(x + 4\pi).$$

We are led to make the following definition.

(Definition).   A function f with real domain is said to be *periodic* with *periodic number* k if the following are true:

(i) k is a positive real number.

(ii) Whenever x is in the domain of f, then so are $x - k$ and $x + k$, and $f(x) = f(x + k)$.

In the case of the sine function, the periodic number 2π plays a special role: It is the *smallest* of the periodic numbers of the sine function. We make the following definition.

(Definition).   If p is the smallest of the periodic numbers of a function f, then p is called the *period* of the function f.

(In certain applications it is also found convenient to include constant functions, with domain all real numbers, among the periodic functions and to define the period of such a constant function to be 0.)

Hence the period of the sine function is 2π.

In many practical applications, it is desirable to have a function similar to $\sin x$ whose maximum and minimum values are, however, not necessarily 1 and -1 respectively and whose period is not necessarily 2π.

Functions whose mappings are given by a formula $a \sin bx$, where a and b are nonzero real numbers, afford the desired flexibility with respect to extreme values and period. We may and shall take the domain of such a function to be the set of all real numbers, unless otherwise noted.

ILLUSTRATIVE EXAMPLE.   Plot the graph of the function $3 \sin 2x$ over the interval $[0, 2\pi]$.

Solution: We construct the following table of values

x	0	$\pi/4$	$\pi/2$	$3\pi/4$	π	$5\pi/4$	$3\pi/2$	$7\pi/4$	2π
$3 \sin 2x$	0	3	0	-3	0	3	0	-3	0

and then we plot the graph (see Fig. 6b3).

In this example, the period of the function is π; intuitively, this is easy to see—for when x "runs through" the interval $[0, \pi]$, $2x$ clearly runs through the interval $[0, 2\pi]$, and hence $\sin 2x$ through one "cycle."

The maximum value assumed by a function of the form $a \sin(bx + c)$ or $a \cos(bx + c)$, where a, b, c are real numbers, is called the *amplitude* of the function.

In the case of the function $3 \sin 2x$, the amplitude is 3. For when $x = \pi/4$, $3 \sin 2x = 3 \sin(\pi/2) = 3 \cdot 1 = 3$, so that 3 is a value of the function $3 \sin 2x$. Furthermore, for any value of x, $\sin 2x \leq 1$, so that

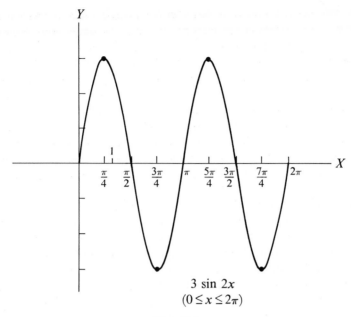

$$3 \sin 2x$$
$$(0 \le x \le 2\pi)$$

Fig. 6b3

$3 \sin 2x \le 3$; i.e., $3 \sin 2x$ never assumes a value greater than 3. Thus 3 actually is the amplitude of the function $3 \sin 2x$. ‖

Problems

Plot the graph of each of the following functions over the interval $[0, 2\pi]$. In each case tell what the period and amplitude of the function are.

1. $2 \sin 3x$.
2. $\sin 2x$.
3. $2 \sin 2x$.
4. $\sin 3x$.
5. $2 \sin 4x$.
6. $3 \sin 4x$.
7. $5 \sin x/2$.
8. $-2 \sin 3x$.
9. $2 \sin(-3x)$.
10. $-2 \sin(-3x)$.

6c. *APPLICATIONS OF THE SINE FUNCTION*

It is clear that since trigonometric functions have values that occur over and over again, these functions may be used to describe, at least roughly, natural phenomena that occur over and over again.

But it turns out that in many cases the description of periodic phenomena by means of trigonometric functions is actually not rough but quite precise; and it is this fact that explains the great importance we attach to the periodic property of trigonometric functions.

By way of illustration, we consider the phenomenon of musical sound. In general, a sound owes its existence to the fact that something—the plucked string of a banjo, for example, or the wing of a zooming fly—has set a surrounding mass of air into *vibration*. When the pulsating air reaches an auditor, his eardrum is set into vibration also; and if that vibration falls within a certain range (not too fast and not too slow), then it is transmitted to the brain as the sensation of sound.

A vibrating string and the eardrum which it excites to vibration both follow similar patterns: They move from a normal position to an extreme in one direction, back to normal, from there to an extreme in an opposite direction, and finally back to normal—after which the cycle is repeated over and over again.

But this is very much like the pattern of ordinates of the sine function's graph: 0, max, 0, min, etc. It would seem, then, that the sine function describes the behavior of a vibrating body at least approximately. The fact of the matter is that the description happens to be quite exact.

Suppose, for example, that we set the end of a tuning fork to vibrating vertically and that we plot the position of one moving endpoint on the fork above and below a normal position at times x beginning with $x = 0$. Then it is a consequence of the laws of physics that the resulting graph is *exactly* the graph of $a \sin bx$ (for some choice of real numbers a and b and neglecting the weakening of the vibration with the passage of time).

All musical tones have properties known as loudness, pitch, and quality. The first two are well known; the last is the property that enables us to distinguish between two notes of the same pitch and loudness played on different instruments.

A tuning fork, when struck, emits what is known as a *pure tone*. The loudness of the tone is related to the force with which it is struck, and the force determines the maximum distance that the vibrating end of the fork moves from its original position. As a consequence, the amplitude of the graph generated by the tuning fork is related to the loudness of the sound produced by the tuning fork: The louder the sound, the greater the amplitude of the graph.

The pitch of the tone produced by a tuning fork is related to the rapidity of its regular vibrations: The faster the vibration, the higher the pitch. But the faster the vibration, the shorter the time interval necessary for the completion of one cycle of vibration—hence the smaller the *period* of the graph generated by the tuning fork.

Now all sounds are simply combinations of pure tones. Along with every pure tone (called a "fundamental" or first "partial"), musical instruments produced "overtones" (also called second, etc., "partials" or "harmonics"), which are tones with periods which are one-half the period, one-third the period, one-fourth the period, etc., of the fundamental.

Different instruments are constructed so as to emphasize certain overtones and dampen others. It is the fundamental tone that determines the pitch of the note we hear; it is the arrangement of overtones that gives a note played on a particular instrument its characteristic quality.

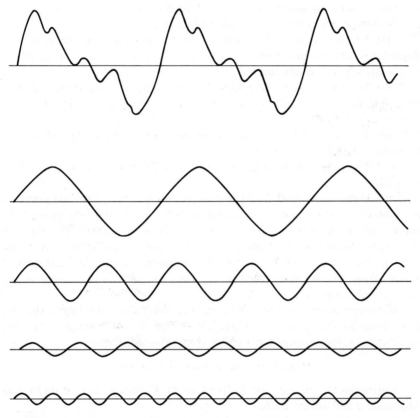

Fig. 6c1.   (From D. Blackwood and W. Kelly, *General Physics—A Textbook for Colleges*, 2nd ed., John Wiley and Sons, N.Y.)

In Fig. 6c1 we see a graph of a violin tone together with the graphs of four pure tones whose combination produces a close approximation to the illustrated violin tone. With the coordinate axes appropriately scaled, the functions whose graphs appear in Fig. 6c1 are:

First partial: $f_1(x) = 10 \sin x.$
Second partial: $f_2(x) = 5 \sin 2x.$
Third partial: $f_3(x) = 2 \sin 3x.$
Fourth partial: $f_4(x) = 2 \sin 5x.$
Composite tone (approximately): $f(x) = f_1(x) + f_2(x) + f_3(x) + f_4(x).$

We shall now consider the problem of drawing the graph of a function which, like $f(x)$ above, is the sum of functions of the form $a \sin bx$.

But first, we shall present a short-cut method for drawing the graph of a function of the form $a \sin bx$, where a and b are positive real numbers. The method is contained in statement (v) below; statements (i)–(v) below are consequences of statements (i)–(v) of Section 6b.

Assuming a and b to be positive real numbers, then:

(i) The maximum value assumed by the function $a \sin bx$ is a, and this value is achieved only when $bx = (\pi/2) + k \cdot 2\pi$, i.e., when $x = (\pi/2b) + k \cdot (2\pi/b)$, where k is any integer.

(ii) The minimum value achieved by the function $a \sin bx$ is $-a$, and this value is achieved only when $x = (3\pi/2b) + k \cdot (2\pi/b)$, where k is any integer.

(iii) The value 0 is achieved by the function $a \sin bx$ only when $x = k \cdot (\pi/b)$, where k is any integer.

(iv) The range of the function $a \sin bx$ is the interval of real numbers $[-a, a]$.

(v) If the interval $[0, 2\pi/b]$ is divided into quarters, then the graph of the function $a \sin bx$ may be described as follows: In the first quarter the graph rises in a smooth curve from the axis to its maximum value; in the second quarter it falls from its maximum point back to the axis; in the third quarter it falls from the axis to its minimum point; in the last quarter it rises from its minimum point to the axis; and these four sections of the curve are all congruent.

If quarter points continue to be marked everywhere on the X axis, i.e., if we consider the values $x = k \cdot (\pi/2b)$, where k is any integer, then the successive y values assumed at these x values run as follows:

$$0, \max, 0, \min, 0, \max, 0, \min, \text{etc.}$$

Furthermore, as may be induced from Problems 1–7, $a \sin bx$ has amplitude a and period $2\pi/b$.

ILLUSTRATIVE EXAMPLE 1.   Sketch one period of the graph of the function $3 \sin 2x$.

Solution: In this case $a = 3$ and $b = 2$, so that the amplitude of the required graph is 3 and the period is $2\pi/2$, or π. We divide the interval $[0, \pi]$ into quarters by the quarter points, 0, $\pi/4$, etc., and proceed as in statement (v) above. The graph is part of that drawn in Fig. 6b3. ‖

Now, we return to the problem of drawing the graph of a sum of functions of the form $a \sin bx$. A convenient way of accomplishing this is as follows: First, draw the graphs of each of the functions $a \sin bx$ on the same set of axes; then, at convenient points along the X axis, add the ordinates of the component graphs geometrically to form ordinates of the graph of $f(x)$, and thus locate points on the graph of $f(x)$. A curve drawn through the points located on the graph of $f(x)$ will, of course, be the graph we seek.

The method is illustrated below.

ILLUSTRATIVE EXAMPLE 2.   Sketch the graph of $f(x) = 3 \sin 2x + \sin x$.

Solution: We first sketch the graphs of $3 \sin 2x$ and $\sin x$ on the same set of axes over the interval $[0, 2\pi]$ (Why that interval?).

Then we add ordinates (taking *sign* into account) as shown in Fig. 6c2. One period of the graph of $f(x)$ is illustrated.   ‖

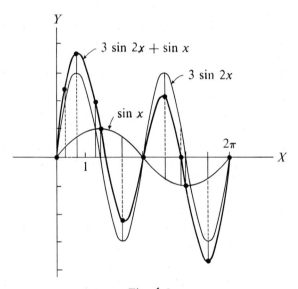

Fig. 6c2

We note finally that similar combinations of sine functions give precise descriptions and are of the greatest importance in the following cases also.

(i) *Alternating electric current.*   The electric current we are accustomed to using reverses its direction 120 times a second in the wires through which it passes. It describes, during each second, 60 cycles of the following type: In each one-sixtieth of a second it begins at zero strength, builds up to a maximum strength in one direction, falls to zero, builds up to a maximum in the opposite direction, and falls back to zero strength again.

(ii) *Light.*   The various colors that we recognize are described by "electromagnetic" waves of varying *periods.*

(iii) *Radio waves.* Our radios are calibrated to different *frequencies,* i.e., to different numbers of vibrations per second of radio waves. These frequencies are, of course, related to the *periods* of the waves: The larger the frequency, the smaller the period.

Problems

1. Draw one period of the graph of each of the following functions.

   (a) $\sin x + \sin 2x$.   (b) $2 \sin 2x + \sin x$.
   (c) $2 \sin x + \sin 3x$.   (d) $\sin 2x + \sin 3x$.
   (e) $2 \sin 2x + \sin 3x$.   (f) $3 \sin 2x + 2 \sin 3x$.
   (g) $4 \sin x - \sin 4x$.   (h) $\sin x + \sin 2x + \sin 3x$.

2. In Problem 1 above discuss the relative loudness and pitch of the component and composite tones described by the function in each case.
3. The following news item appeared in the *Springfield Republican* on September 18, 1955.

SOUND FIGHTS SOUND AND CREATES SILENCE

NEW YORK—*Chemical Engineering* magazine reports that the newest concept in the war against noise is fighting sound with sound. A machine has been developed that determines the frequency and character of an existing sound wave, then sends out its own sound of the same frequency but opposite phase. Interference results and the waves cancel each other, giving a localized cone of silence.

Write down two functions representing pure tones that "cancel each other" when combined. Draw their graphs and show how the addition of ordinates leads to a graph representing complete silence.

6d. *OTHER TRIGONOMETRIC GRAPHS*

Consider the function $f(x) = 3 \sin (\pi x + \pi)$. Since the sine of any number cannot exceed 1, $f(x)$ cannot exceed 3. Are there values of x for which $f(x) = 3$? The question is answered by solving the equation

$$3 \sin(\pi x + \pi) = 3,$$

i.e., $\sin(\pi x + \pi) = 1$. This equation has the solution:

$$\pi x + \pi = \pi/2 + k \cdot 2\pi$$
$$x + 1 = \tfrac{1}{2} + 2k$$
$$x = 2k - \tfrac{1}{2},$$

where k may be any integer. Thus $3 \sin(\pi x + \pi)$ attains a maximum value of 3 when $x = -\frac{1}{2}, 1\frac{1}{2}, 3\frac{1}{2}, \ldots$.

Similarly, we observe that $3 \sin(\pi x + \pi)$ attains a minimum value of -3 when

$$\pi x + \pi = (3\pi/2) + k \cdot 2\pi,$$

i.e., when

$$x + 1 = \frac{3}{2} + 2k,$$

i.e., when

$$x = 2k + \frac{1}{2},$$

for example, when $x = \frac{1}{2}, 2\frac{1}{2}, 4\frac{1}{2}, \ldots$.

Finally, $3 \sin(\pi x + \pi) = 0$ when $\pi x + \pi = k\pi$, i.e., when $x = k - 1$, for example, when $x = -1, 0, 1, \ldots$.

We use this information to draw (part of) the graph of the function $3 \sin(\pi x + \pi)$, (see Fig. 6d1)

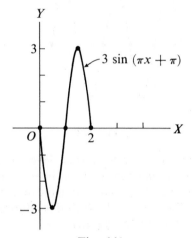

Fig. 6d1

In general, the graph of $a \sin(bx + c)$, where $a \neq 0$, $b \neq 0$, c are real numbers, resembles the graph we have drawn in Fig. 6d1. In fact, the following may be proved: If $a \neq 0$, $b \neq 0$, c are real numbers, then the graph of $a \sin(bx + c)$ is periodic with period $|2\pi/b|$ and maximum and minimum values $|a|$, $-|a|$ respectively. The pattern 0, max, 0, min, 0, max, 0, min, $\ldots$ is displayed by the graph at quarter-period intervals on the X axis.

A method of drawing graphs of functions of the form $a \sin(bx + c)$, then, is to find the values of x at which the function attains its maximum, and then to use the information of the preceding paragraph in drawing the graph.

ILLUSTRATIVE EXAMPLE.   Draw the graph of the function $-2 \sin(\pi - \pi x)$.

Solution: The given function attains a maximum value of 2 when

$$-2 \sin(\pi - \pi x) = 2$$
$$\sin(\pi - \pi x) = -1$$
$$\pi - \pi x = (3\pi/2) + k \cdot 2\pi$$
$$1 - x = \tfrac{3}{2} + 2k$$
$$-\tfrac{1}{2} - 2k = x,$$

where k is any integer. Here, in order to avoid values of x far out on the negative X axis, we let $k = 0, -1, -2$. Then the given function attains a maximum of 2 at $x = -\tfrac{1}{2}, 1\tfrac{1}{2}, 3\tfrac{1}{2}$.

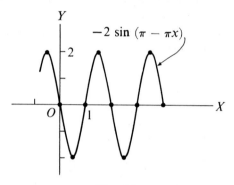

Fig. 6d2

Bisecting the interval between maxima gives us a point at which a minimum of -2 occurs; and bisecting the interval between maxima and minima gives us points at which zero ordinates occur (see Fig. 6d2). The period of this graph is $|2\pi/-\pi|$, or 2. With this information, the graph may be extended left or right as far as we please.   ‖

Problems

1.   Draw the graph of each of the following functions.

(a) $\sin \pi x$.

(b) $2 \sin \pi x$.

(c) $3 \sin 2\pi x$.

(d) $2 \sin \dfrac{\pi}{2} x$.

(e) $4 \sin\left(2\pi x + \dfrac{\pi}{2}\right)$.

(f) $3 \sin\left(\dfrac{\pi}{2} - 2\pi x\right)$.

(g) $-2 \sin(\pi x + \pi)$.

(h) $-3 \sin\left(\dfrac{\pi}{2} - 2\pi x\right)$.

(i) $-2 \sin\left(\dfrac{\pi}{2} x - \dfrac{\pi}{2}\right)$.

2. Draw the graph of each of the following functions.

(a) $-\sin x$.

(b) $\sin(-x)$.

(c) $2 \sin(2x + 1)$.

(d) $3 \sin(2x + \pi)$.

(e) $-\sin(\pi - x)$.

(f) $\tan x$.

(g) $\cot x$.

(h) $\sec x$.

(i) $\csc x$.

3. Graphs of equations of the form $a \cos(bx + c)$ may be handled by converting the cosine to a sine function, using the easily proved identity $\cos \theta = \sin(\theta + \pi/2)$. For example, $\cos x = \sin(x + \pi/2)$; to draw the graph of $\cos x$, we simply draw the graph of $\sin(x + \pi/2)$. Or alternatively, we may follow a method analogous to that by which we graphed sine functions, using principally the fact that $\cos \theta$ attains a maximum value of 1 when $\theta = 2k\pi$. Draw the graph of each of the following functions.

(a) $\cos x$.

(b) $2 \cos \pi x$.

(c) $3 \cos\left(\pi x - \dfrac{\pi}{2}\right)$.

(d) $-3 \cos\left(\pi x - \dfrac{\pi}{2}\right)$.

(e) $-2 \cos \dfrac{\pi}{2} x$.

(f) $2 \cos\left(\dfrac{\pi}{2} - x\right)$.

(g) $-2 \cos\left(\dfrac{\pi}{2} - \pi x\right)$.

(h) $-2 \cos \pi x$.

(i) $2 \cos(-\pi x)$.

4. Draw the graph of each of the following functions by the "addition of ordinates" method (see 6c Illustrative Example 2).

(a) $\sin \pi x + \sin 2\pi x$.

(b) $\sin x + 2 \sin x$.

(c) $2 \sin \pi x - \sin 2\pi x$.

(d) $\sin x + \cos x$.

(e) $\sin \pi x + \cos \pi x$.

(f) $3 \sin \dfrac{\pi}{2} x + 4 \cos \dfrac{\pi}{2} x$.

(g) $\sin \pi x - \cos \pi x$.

(h) $\sin x - \cos x$.

6e. INVERSE FUNCTIONS

It is often useful to have at hand a function that reverses the action of a given function. For example, the "cube" function assigns to the numbers 1, 2, 3, ... the numbers 1, 8, 27, ... respectively; the "cube root" function precisely reverses this action, assigning to the numbers $1, 8, 27, \ldots$ the numbers $1, 2, 3, \ldots$ respectively.

When we attempt to reverse the action of the sine function, however, we encounter a difficulty. The sine function assigns to the numbers $0, \pi, 2\pi, \ldots$ the number $0, 0, 0, \ldots$ respectively. How shall we reverse this action? Shall we assign to 0 the number 0, or the number π, or what? (Remember that a function must assign a unique object to each element in its domain.) This difficulty does not arise if the given function is "one–one."

6e1 (Definition).   A function f is said to be *one–one* if f never assigns the same object to two different elements in its domain. (If a function is not one–one, it is said to be *many–one*.)

Hence the sine function is many–one. However, it is possible, in a natural and simple way, to restrict the domain of the sine function, and thus to arrive at a new function, called the *principal sine function*, which *is* one–one, and which has the same range as the original sine function (namely the interval $[-1, 1]$.) We denote the principal sine function Sine, to distinguish it from the original sine function, sine (see Fig. 6e1).

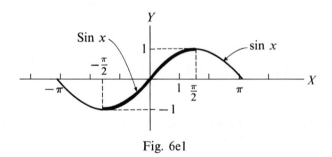

Fig. 6e1

6e2 (Definition).   The principal sine function, Sine (abbreviated Sin), is the one–one function whose domain is the interval $[-\pi/2, \pi/2]$, and whose action is given by the formula, Sin $x = \sin x$.

Now, there is no problem in reversing the action of the function Sin. In general, when the action of a one–one function is reversed, we arrive at a new one–one function, which is called the *inverse* of the original. More precisely:

6e3 (Definition).   Let f be a one–one function with domain A and range B. Then f^{-1} (read "f inverse") is defined to be the one–one function with domain B and range A such that $f^{-1}(b) = a$ iff $f(a) = b$.

EXAMPLES.   (Henceforth we shall denote the set of all real numbers R.)
If f is the well-known function with action $f(x) = x^3$, whose domain is R
and whose range is also R, then f^{-1} is the function with action $f^{-1}(x) = \sqrt[3]{x}$,
whose domain and range are each R; and since the domain and range of
the function Sin are the intervals $[-\pi/2, \pi/2]$ and $[-1, 1]$ respectively, it
follows that the domain and range of the function Sin^{-1} are the intervals
$[-1, 1]$ and $[-\pi/2, \pi/2]$ respectively.   Furthermore, Sin$^{-1} y = x$ iff
Sin $x = y$. Thus, since Sin$(\pi/6) = \frac{1}{2}$, it follows that Sin$^{-1}(\frac{1}{2}) = \pi/6$.

[*A note on notation:*   The reader is warned against the error of inter-
preting $f^{-1}(x)$ as the reciprocal of $f(x)$, $1/f(x)$. In fact, in the case of the
trigonometric functions, an alternate notation is often used which avoids
the possibility of this error. The notation Arcsin is used for Sin^{-1}, and
similarly for the other trigonometric functions.]

Now what about the graphs of inverse functions?

If (a, b) is a point on the graph of a function, then clearly (b, a) is a
point on the graph of its inverse. By reversing the coordinates of points on
the graph of a function, we may therefore arrive at points on the graph of
its inverse.

Thus, for example, since $(-\pi/2, -1)$, $(0, 0)$, and $(\pi/2, 1)$ are points on
the graph of the Sine function, it follows that $(-1, -\pi/2)$, $(0, 0)$, and
$(1, \pi/2)$ are points on the graph of the Arcsine function.

In fact, it may be proved that if $a \neq b$ are real numbers, then the line
whose equation is $y = x$ is the perpendicular bisector of the line segment
joining the points (a, b) and (b, a) (see Fig. 6e2); and, of course, if $a = b$,
then the point (a, b) is identical with the point (b, a) and lies on the line
whose equation is $y = x$.

The graph of an inverse function may therefore always be derived by
"reflecting" the graph of the given function in the line $y = x$.

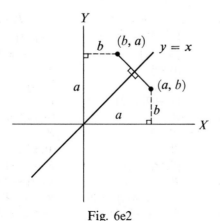

Fig. 6e2

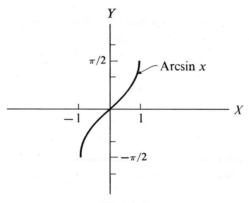

Fig. 6e3

For example, the graph of the function Arcsin x may be found by reflecting the graph of the function Sin x (Fig. 6e1) in the line $y = x$. In performing this reflection, it is helpful to have at hand a few points on the graph of Arcsin x. Here we have used the points $(-1, -\pi/2)$, $(0, 0)$, and $(1, \pi/2)$ obtained above. (See Fig. 6e3).

The other trigonometric functions may be similarly treated. We summarize in a table that makes use of the following notation.

6e4 (Definition). If A, B are sets, then $A - B$ (read "the complement of B in A") is defined to be the set of all elements of A that are not in B; and if $a < b$ are real numbers, then we define the intervals $(a, b] = [a, b] - \{a\}$, $[a, b) = [a, b] - \{b\}$, and $(a, b) = [a, b] - \{b\}$ (see Fig. 6e4).

	$[a, b]$		$[c, d)$		$(e, f]$		(g, h)	
a		b	c	d	e	f	g	h

Fig. 6e4

Function	Domain	Range
Sin	$[-\pi/2, \pi/2]$	$[-1, 1]$
Arcsin	$[-1, 1]$	$[-\pi/2, \pi/2]$
Cos	$[0, \pi]$	$[-1, 1]$
Arccos	$[-1, 1]$	$[0, \pi]$
Tan	$(-\pi/2, \pi/2)$	R
Arctan	R	$(-\pi/2, \pi/2)$
Cot	$(0, \pi)$	R
Arccot	R	$(0, \pi)$
Sec	$[0, \pi] - \{\pi/2\}$	$R - (-1, 1)$
Arcsec	$R - (-1, 1)$	$[0, \pi] - \{\pi/2\}$
Csc	$[-\pi/2, \pi/2] - \{0\}$	$R - (-1, 1)$
Arccsc	$R - (-1, 1)$	$[-\pi/2, \pi/2] - \{0\}$

ILLUSTRATIVE EXAMPLE (Optional).   Sketch the graph of the function $f(x) = 3 \cos x + 4 \sin x$.

Solution: The graph may be drawn by the "addition of ordinates" method, but the following is a better method which applies to all functions of the form $r \cos(vx + w) + s \sin(vx + w)$, where $r \neq 0$, $s \neq 0$, $v \neq 0$, w are real numbers.

Let $p = \text{Arcsin}(3/\sqrt{3^2 + 4^2}) = \text{Arcsin}(\tfrac{3}{5})$ (see Fig. 6e5). Then $\sin p = \tfrac{3}{5}$

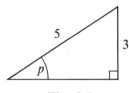

Fig. 6e5

and $\cos p = \tfrac{4}{5}$. Therefore $3 = 5 \sin p$, $4 = 5 \cos p$. Substituting in the given function, we have

$$f(x) = 5 \sin p \cos x + 5 \cos p \sin x$$
$$= 5(\sin p \cos x + \cos p \sin x)$$
$$= 5 \sin(p + x)$$
$$= 5 \sin(x + p).$$

The given function may therefore be written in the form $a \sin(bx + c)$, a form whose graph is familiar to us (see Section 6d).

In this case $f(x)$ has a maximum value of 5, which it attains when $x + p = (\pi/2) + k \cdot 2\pi$, i.e., when $x = (\pi/2) - p + k \cdot 2\pi$.

Since $\sin p = 0.6000$, we find, from trigonometric tables, that $p = 37°$ approximately; or, in terms of radians, $p = 37 \cdot \pi/180$, or $p = 0.2\pi$ approximately.

Maxima occur, therefore, when $x = 0.5\pi - 0.2\pi + k \cdot 2\pi = 0.3\pi + k \cdot 2\pi$; in particular, when $x = 0.3\pi$, 2.3π, i.e., when $x = 0.9$, 7.2 approximately.

The period of $5 \sin(x + p)$ is clearly $2\pi/1$, or 6.3 approximately. It is helpful to note that when $x = 0$, $f(x) = 3 \cos 0 + 4 \sin 0 = 3$. The graph is drawn in Fig. 6e6. ‖

Problems

1. Sketch the graph of each of the following.

  (a) Cos x; Arccos x.   (b) Tan x; Arctan x.
  (c) Cot x; Arccot x.   (d) Sec x; Arcsec x.
  (e) Csc x; Arccsc x.

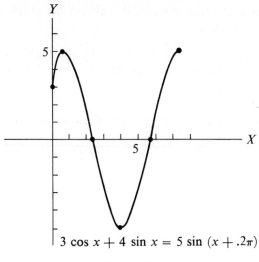

$$3 \cos x + 4 \sin x = 5 \sin (x + .2\pi)$$

Fig. 6e6

2 (Optional).   Sketch the graph of each of the following.

(a) $3 \cos x - 4 \sin x$.   (b) $\sin x + \cos x$.
(c) $\sin x - \cos x$.   (d) $\sin 2x + \cos 2x$.

6f.   EXPONENTIAL AND LOGARITHMIC GRAPHS

By means of a table of values, we may easily sketch a representative portion of the graph of the function 2^x, whose domain is the set of all real numbers, R (see Fig. 6f1). This function 2^x is called an *exponential function*.

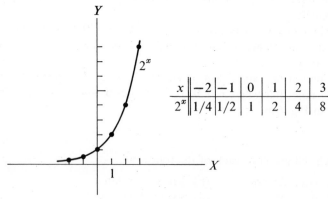

x	-2	-1	0	1	2	3
2^x	1/4	1/2	1	2	4	8

Fig. 6f1

More generally:

6f1 (Definition).   Let $a \neq 1$ be a real number. Then the *exponential function with base a* (abbreviated $\exp_a$) is defined to be the function with domain R and action $\exp_a x = a^x$ (read "exponent base a of x equals a to the x").

For example, $\exp_2 3 = 2^3 = 8$, $\exp_3 2 = 3^2 = 9$, and the graph drawn in Fig. 6f1 is the graph of $\exp_2 x$, since $\exp_2 x = 2^x$. In fact, it is easily seen that for any real number $a > 1$, the graph of $\exp_a x$ looks very much like the graph of $\exp_2 x$ (see Fig. 6f2).

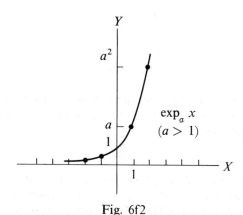

Fig. 6f2

The graph of $\exp_a x$ indicates (and it may be rigorously proved) that the function $\exp_a$ is one–one and that the range of $\exp_a$ is the set of all *positive* real numbers (which from now on we shall denote R^+).

Hence (see Section 6e) there is a function inverse to the function $\exp_a$:

6f2 (Definition).   The *logarithmic function with base a*, abbreviated $\log_a$ (read "log base a"), is defined to be the one–one function with domain R^+ and range R that is the inverse of the function $\exp_a$.

Since $\exp_a x = a^x$ and $\log_a$ is the inverse of $\exp_a$, it immediately follows (from the definition of *inverse function*) that

(1) $\log_a(a^x) = x.$

For example, $\log_2 32 = \log_2(2^5) = 5$.

Suppose N is a positive real number. Then again from the fact that $\log_a$ and $\exp_a$ are inverses of each other,

(2) $\log_a N = x$ iff $\exp_a x = N.$

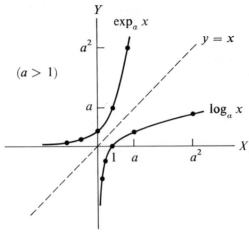

Fig. 6f3

Since $\exp_a x = a^x$, we have, by substitution into Eq. (2), the following important statement, which enables us to transform logarithmic to exponential expressions and vice versa:

(3) $$\log_a N = x \quad \text{iff} \quad a^x = N.$$

That is to say, $\log_a N$ is the (unique) *exponent* whose application to the base a yields the number N. For example, since the exponent 3 applied to the number 2 yields the number 8 ($2^3 = 8$), it follows that $\log_2 8 = 3$. And to find $\log_{10} 100$, we seek the exponent which when applied to the base 10 will yield the number 100. Clearly, then, $\log_{10} 100 = 2$.

We recall (see Section 6e) that the graphs of inverse functions (whose domains and ranges are subsets of R) are symmetric with respect to the line $y = x$. Hence we may easily derive the graph of $\log_a x$ from the graph of $\exp_a x$ (see Fig. 6f3).

Problems

1. Find each of the following.

    (a) $\log_2 \frac{1}{8}$.
    (b) $\log_2 \frac{1}{4}$.
    (c) $\log_2 \frac{1}{2}$.
    (d) $\log_2 1$.
    (e) $\log_2 2$.
    (f) $\log_2 4$.
    (g) $\log_2 8$.
    (h) $\log_2 0$.
    (i) $\log_2 -1$.
    (j) $\log_{10} 0.001$.
    (k) $\log_{10} 0.01$.
    (l) $\log_{10} 0.1$.
    (m) $\log_{10} 1$.
    (n) $\log_{10} 10$.
    (o) $\log_{10} 100$.
    (p) $\log_{10} 1000$.
    (q) $\log_{10} 0$.
    (r) $\log_{10} -1$.

2. Translate each of the following into a logarithmic statement.

(a) $10^x = 5$. (b) $2^{10} = 1024$.
(c) $10^{0.3010} = 2$ (approx.). (d) $2^{0.5000} = 1.414$ (approx.).

3. Translate each of the following into an exponential statement.

(a) $\log_{10} 3 = 0.4771$ (approx.). (b) $\log_{10} 5 = 0.6990$ (approx.).
(c) $\log_{10} x = y$. (d) $\log_2 x = y$.

4. Sketch a representative portion of the graph of each of the following functions, and name the (maximal) domain and the range of each of these functions.

(a) 10^x; $\log_{10} x$. (b) 3^x; $\log_3 x$.
(c) 4^x; $\log_4 x$. (d) 8^x; $\log_8 x$.
(e) $(1/2)^x$; $\log_{(1/2)} x$. (f) $(1/3)^x$; $\log_{(1/3)} x$.
(g) 2^{-x}. (h) 3^{-x}.
(i) $2 \cdot 2^x$. (j) $2 \cdot 2^{-x}$.
(k) $-3 \cdot 2^x$. (l) $2^{x^2} [= 2^{(x^2)}]$.
(m) 2^{-x^2} ("Bell curve"). (n) $2^x + 2^{-x}$.
(o) $2^x - 2^{-x}$. (p) $3 \log_2 x$.
(q) $(0.1) \log_{10} x$. (r) $\log_2 (x/4)$.
(s) $\log_{10} 5x$. (t) $\log_2 x^2$.
(u) $(\log_2 x)^2$. (v) $\log_2 x + \log_2(1/x)$.

5. Suppose a is a positive real number such that $a < 1$. Sketch a representative portion of the graph of a^x and a representative portion of the graph of $\log_a x$.

6. Suppose $f(x) = 2^x + 2^{-x}$ and $g(x) = 2^x - 2^{-x}$. Find each of the following.

(a) $f(x) + g(x)$. (b) $f(x) - g(x)$.
(c) $f(x) \cdot g(x)$. (d) $[f(x)]^2$.
(e) $[g(x)]^2$. (f) $[f(x)]^2 + [g(x)]^2$.
(g) $[f(x)]^2 - [g(x)]^2$.

7. Prove each of the following.

(a) $a^{\log_a N} = N$. (b) $(\log_a b)(\log_b a) = 1$.
(c) $\log_b N = (\log_a N)/(\log_a b)$.

6g. PARAMETRIC EQUATIONS

Among the most important of all physical problems are those that involve "compound motion." The following is an example of one such problem.

ILLUSTRATIVE EXAMPLE 1.   Suppose that while H. G. Wells' "Invisible Man" walks straight down a street at a rate of 3 feet per second, a fly alights upon his back and proceeds to crawl straight upward at a rate of 6 inches per second. To a startled spectator, along what path would the fly seem to be crawling?

Solution: We construct the following "mathematical model": Let the point at which the fly alights be the origin of a coordinate system whose positive X axis is a ray along which the invisible man moves towards increasing x values. Then when t seconds have elapsed, the invisible man has moved $3t$ feet along the X axis and the fly $\frac{1}{2}t$ feet upward, as illustrated in Fig. 6g1. The point (x, y) reached by the fly t seconds after it alights is such

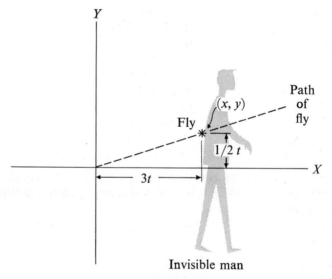

Fig. 6g1

that $x = 3t$, $y = \frac{1}{2}t$. But no matter what real number t is, if these equations hold true, then $y = \frac{1}{2}(x/3) = x/6$.

The points which the fly passes in its trip therefore satisfy the equation $y = x/6$. But, as we have seen, this is the equation of a straight line, and clearly it passes through the origin and has a slope of $\frac{1}{6}$. To a spectator, then, the fly would seem to be climbing in space along a straight line which rises with a slope of $\frac{1}{6}$.

We digress for a moment to remark that in similar fashion the scientist is enabled to predict the paths in the heavens taken by the earth and the sun and the planets and comets; the paths of satellites, both real and man-made, in space; the paths of electrons in an atom and of projectiles fired from stationary or moving vehicles—and these are only a few of the countless important instances of compound motion which occur all about us.

Returning to our fly and our invisible man, we observe once more that t seconds after a certain moment the fly will be found to be at a point (x, y) in $E2'$, where x and y are given by the formulas

$$x = 3t,$$
$$y = \tfrac{1}{3}t.$$

Each real value of t, in this case, determines a point in $E2'$. For example, the value $t = 4$ determines the point $(12, 2)$. The set of all such points is called *the graph of the given pair of equations*.

In general, suppose that f and g are functions whose domain and ranges are sets of real numbers. Then the pair of equations

$$x = f(t),$$
$$y = g(t)$$

is called a pair of *parametric* equations, with *parameter t*. The graph in $E2'$ of such a pair of parametric equations is defined to be the set of all points (x, y), where $x = f(t)$, $y = g(t)$, and t belongs to the domains of both f and g.

To distinguish between parametric equations of a graph and the equations $f(x, y) = g(x, y)$ whose graphs we have been considering, we shall call the latter *Cartesian* equations.

Now in the case of the parametric equations $x = 3t$, $y = \tfrac{1}{3}t$, we have already shown that any point (x, y) satisfying these conditions also satisfies $y = x/6$, so that each point of the graph of the parametric equations is also a point of the straight line whose equation is $y = x/6$.

It may also be shown that if all real values of t are used, then every point on the graph of $y = x/6$ is also on the graph of the parametric equations above. Therefore the graph of the parametric equations is, in this case, exactly the same as the graph of the equation which results from the elimination of t algebraically from the pair of parametric equations.

However, if negative time is not allowed, then the graph of the parametric equations above is only the part of the line $y = x/6$ not in the third quadrant, as indicated in Fig. 6g1. ‖

It is not feasible in every case to eliminate the parameter from a given set of parametric equations. We therefore often resort to our old standby, a table of values, in order to sketch the graph of a pair of parametric equations. In this process a *three*-column table of values is necessary. We *assign* values to t, *compute* associated values of x and y, and *plot* the points determined by corresponding values of x and y.

Unless otherwise noted, the domains of f and g above will be taken maximally; thus if we are given, for example, that $f(t) = t + 1/t$, we shall assume that the domain of f consists of all real numbers except 0.

ILLUSTRATIVE EXAMPLE 2.   Plot the graph G of the parametric equations $x = t^2 - 4$, $y = t^3 - 4t$, and find a Cartesian equation for G.

Solution: The table of values and graph are found in Fig. 6g2.

Note that the points of the graph are connected in an order determined by the order of the t's; i.e., the point associated with $t = -3$ is connected to the point associated with $t = -2$, which in turn is connected to the point associated with $t = -1$, etc.

This method of connecting points is always applicable when f and g above are polynomial functions, but the method must sometimes be modified in the case of rational or trigonometric functions. In these cases certain real numbers may be missing from the domains of f and g, which causes the sequential connection of points to take place in intervals rather than throughout the graph.

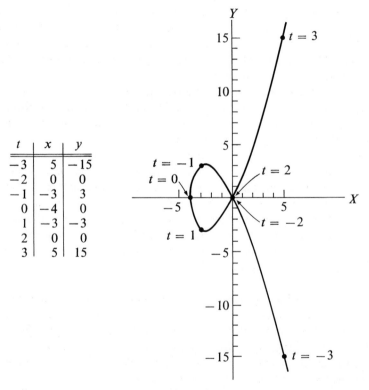

t	x	y
-3	5	-15
-2	0	0
-1	-3	3
0	-4	0
1	-3	-3
2	0	0
3	5	15

Fig. 6g2

Now, as for a Cartesian equation for the graph G: If (x, y) is a point of G, then there must exist a real number t such that

$$y = t(t^2 - 4) = tx.$$

Squaring, we have

$$y^2 = t^2 x^2 = (x + 4)x^2 = x^3 + 4x^2;$$

i.e., each point of the graph satisfies the Cartesian equation $y^2 = x^3 + 4x^2$.

Actually, $y^2 = x^3 + 4x^2$ *is* the Cartesian equation of F. But to prove that it is, we must show further that every point (x, y) which satisfies this equation is in G (see Appendix).   ‖

Another type of physical problem which very naturally leads to parametric equations is that which has to do with the path of projectiles.

ILLUSTRATIVE EXAMPLE 3.   A plane flying eastward at a speed of 300 miles per hour drops a bomb. Describe the path of the bomb.

Solution: The bomb's motion, like that of the fly in Illustrative Example 1, may be regarded as a combination of two motions: The bomb *moves forward* at a speed of 300 miles per hour (or $300 \cdot 5280/3600$ feet per second). The bomb *drops* (physicists tell us) approximately $16t^2$ feet in t seconds.

Suppose we choose the origin of $E2'$ as the position of the plane at the time that the bomb is dropped, and we introduce an X axis whose positive side is directed eastward and a Y axis whose positive side is vertically upward (see Fig. 6g3).

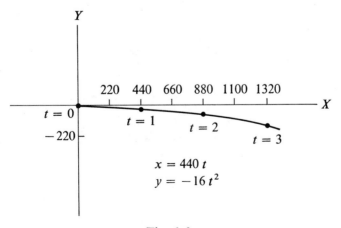

Fig. 6g3

Then the position (x, y) of the bomb t seconds after it drops from the plane is given by the equations

$$x = 440t,$$
$$y = -16t^2.$$

(Here x and y are measured in feet.)

Eliminating t, $y = [-16/(440)^2]x^2$. Thus the path of this projectile is an arc of a parabola (Why?). ‖

Parametric equations also arise naturally in many geometric situations. An important case is that of the circle.

ILLUSTRATIVE EXAMPLE 4.   Find parametric equations for a circle C of radius $r > 0$ and with center at the origin of $E2'$.

Solution: Suppose $P = (x, y)$ is a point of C (see Fig. 6g4) and the counterclockwise angle from the vector i to ray OP is θ. Then, from trigonometry, we have

(1) $$x = r \cos \theta,$$
$$y = r \sin \theta.$$

Now, each point on C satisfies Eq. (1), for some real value of θ. Conversely, if Eq. (1) is satisfied by a point $P = (x, y)$, for some real value of θ, then $\text{dis}(O, P) = \sqrt{x^2 + y^2} = \sqrt{r^2(\cos^2 \theta + \sin^2 \theta)} = \sqrt{r^2} = r$; i.e., P is on the given circle C.

The equations (1) are therefore parametric equations, with parameter θ, for a circle in $E2'$ with center O and radius r. ‖

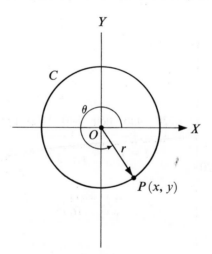

Fig. 6g4

ILLUSTRATIVE EXAMPLE 5.   When a circle rolls on a straight line, the path traced by a point on that circle is called a *cycloid*. Find parametric equations for a cycloid.

Solution: Suppose that we have a circle of radius r and with center at the point $(0, r)$ in $E2'$, and that the point P is fixed on the circle and at the moment is at the origin $(P_0 = O)$.

Now suppose the circle rolls on the positive X axis to a new position as indicated in Fig. 6g5.

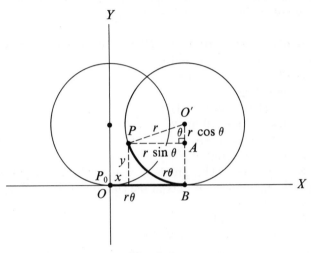

Fig. 6g5

With the notation of the figure, we use the measure θ (in radians) of $\sphericalangle PO'B$ as parameter, and we interpret the physical description of this situation to mean that the length of the heavily shaded arc PB is equal to the length of the line segment OB.

Now, to find the parametric equations (with parameter θ) of the path of P means, assuming $P = (x, y)$, that we must find equations for x in terms of θ and for y in terms of θ.

First of all, we note that the length of the shaded arc PB (by a well-known formula of trigonometry) is $r\theta$. Therefore $OB = r\theta$. Also, it is easy to see that $PA = r \sin \theta$ and $O'A = r \cos \theta$.

Now we see in Fig. 6g5 that

$$x = OB - PA = r\theta - r \sin \theta,$$
$$y = O'B - O'A = r - r \cos \theta.$$

Although we have leaned heavily upon a diagram in which P occupies a special position (e.g., $\sphericalangle PO'B$ is acute), it may be proved that these equations hold in all positions of P. Hence parametric equations, with parameter θ, for the cycloid described above are

$$x = r(\theta - \sin \theta),$$
$$y = r(1 - \cos \theta). \quad \|$$

Problems

1. Plot the graph of each of the following parametric equations as in Illustrative Example 1. Where feasible, eliminate the parameter to find the Cartesian equation of the graph.
    (a) $x = 4(\theta - \sin \theta)$, $y = 4(1 - \cos \theta)$.
    (b) $x = t + 1$, $y = t^2$.
    (c) $x = 10 \cos p$, $y = 10 \sin p$. (*Hint:* To eliminate p, solve for $\cos p$ and $\sin p$, square, and add.)
    (d) $x = 10 \cos p$, $y = 5 \sin p$.
    (e) $x = \sin p + \cos p$, $y = \sin p$.
    (f) $x = t + (1/t)$, $y = t - (1/t)$.
    (g) $x = 10 \sin u$, $y = 10 \sin 2u$.
    (h) $x = \sin^2 u$, $y = \cos^2 u$.
    (i) $x = \cos^3 u$, $y = \sin^3 u$
    (j) $x = t^2$, $y = t^2$. (The graph is not a whole straight line, even though eliminating t results in the equation $y = x$. Why not?)
    (k) $x = t + 1$, $y = t^2 - 1$.
    (l) $x = t^2 + 1$, $y = t^3 - t$.
    (m) $x = 4/(t^2 + 1)$, $y = (t^3 - t)/10$.

2. *Parametric equations for an ellipse.* Suppose (x, y) is a point on the ellipse whose equation is $(x^2/a^2) + (y^2/b^2) = 1$. Let the point $P = (x/a, y/b)$, and let θ be the angle from the positive X axis to the ray OP.
    (a) Show that $\text{dis}(O, P) = 1$.
    (b) Show therefore that

    (1)
    $$x = a \cos \theta,$$
    $$y = b \sin \theta.$$

    The Eqs. (1) are actually parametric equations for an ellipse with semiaxes a and b. For we have shown above that every point of the ellipse whose equation is $(x^2/a^2) + (y^2/b^2) = 1$ satisfies Eqs. (1). Conversely:
    (c) Show that if (x, y) is a point which satisfies Eqs. (1), then (x, y) satisfies $(x^2/a^2) + (y^2/b^2) = 1$.

3. *Parametric equations for a hyperbola.* Show that

    $$x = a \sec \theta,$$
    $$y = b \tan \theta$$

is a set of parametric equations for the hyperbola whose equation is $(x^2/a^2) - (y^2/b^2) = 1$. [*Hint:* In analogy with Problem 2 above, let $P = (a/x, ay/bx)$. Show then that dis$(O, P) = 1$. Let θ be as in Problem 2. Etc.]

4 (Optional). *The hypocycloid.* When a circle rolls upon and within the circumference of another circle, the path traced by a fixed point on the rolling circle is called a *hypocycloid.* If the radius of the fixed circle is *n* times the radius of the rolling circle (where *n* is a positive integer), the hypocycloid is called a *hypocycloid of n cusps.* We consider here a hypocycloid of three cusps.

Suppose, then, that our smaller circle has a radius of *r* and our larger circle a radius of $3r$. We choose a Cartesian coordinate system with origin at the center of the larger circle, and roll the smaller circle, with original point of tangency at $(3r, 0)$, so that the point of tangency moves in a clockwise direction along the larger circle. We trace the path of *P* (see Fig. 6g6).

Suppose that the center of the rolling circle has reached the point *Q*, that the point of tangency has reached *T*, and that *P* has simultaneously reached the point (x, y). Translate the original coordinate system to one with origin *Q*, let the *clockwise* angle from the original positive *X* axis to ray *OT* be θ, and let the *counterclockwise* angle from the new *X* axis to ray *OP* be ϕ.

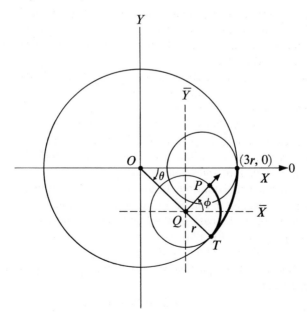

Fig. 6g6

Then the lengths of arc unrolled on the two circles are $3r\theta$ and $r(\phi + \theta)$, and they are equal. Hence $\phi = 2\theta$.

Furthermore, if $P = (\bar{x}, \bar{y})$ in the new system, then $\bar{x} = r \cos 2\theta$, $\bar{y} = r \sin 2\theta$, and if $Q = (h, k)$ in the original system, then $h = 2r \cos \theta$, $k = -2r \sin \theta$.

Now show that $x = r \cos 2\theta + 2r \cos \theta$, $y = r \sin 2\theta - 2r \sin \theta$. Hence parametric equations, with parameter θ, for the hypocycloid described above, are

$$x = r(\cos 2\theta + 2 \cos \theta),$$
$$y = r(\sin 2\theta - 2 \sin \theta).$$

Now:

(a) Plot the graph of the set of parametric equations above, using any convenient value for r.

(b) Derive, as above, a set of parametric equations for a hypocycloid of four cusps. Show, using trigonometric identities, that these equations are equivalent to

$$x = 4r \cos^3 \theta,$$
$$y = 4r \sin^3 \theta.$$

Show that these equations are equivalent to the Cartesian equation

$$x^{2/3} + y^{2/3} = (4r)^{2/3}.$$

(See the graphs of Problem 1i above and 4f Problem 2f.)

(c) What would a hypocycloid of two cusps be? That is, what path would be traced by a point on a circle of radius r rolling within a circle of radius $2r$?

(d) Find a Cartesian equation of the hypocycloid of three cusps whose parametric equations are given above.

5 (Optional). *The epicycloid.* When a circle rolls upon and outside the circumference of another circle, the path traced by a fixed point on the rolling circle is called an *epicycloid.* If the radius of the fixed circle is n times the radius of the rolling circle, where n is a positive integer, the epicycloid is called an *epicycloid of n cusps.*

(a) Find parametric equations of an epicycloid generated by a point on a circle of radius r rolling on a circle of radius r. [*Hint:* Follow the method in the case of the hypocycloid; here arcs of lengths $r\theta$ and $r[\pi - (\phi + \theta)]$ play roles analogous to those of lengths $3r\theta$ and $r(\phi + \theta)$ in Problem 4 above.]

Show that the parametric equations for this epicycloid may be expressed as

$$x = r(2 \cos \theta - \cos 2\theta),$$
$$y = -r(2 \sin \theta + \sin 2\theta).$$

(b) Choose a convenient value of r, and plot the graph of the epicycloid whose equations are given above.

6 (Optional). A man stands on a ladder, one of whose ends rests on level ground, the other on a vertical wall. Show that if the ladder slips, the man travels along a path which is part of an ellipse whose semiaxes are the segments into which the man separates the ladder.

6h. POLAR COORDINATES

The reader will recall that a Cartesian coordinate system in a plane is a system for identifying each point of that plane by means of an ordered pair of real numbers. It happens that there are other systems which serve the same purpose. Of particular importance is the *polar* coordinate system.

[Before describing that system, we note, first of all, that in this section (and in the next), for reasons of familiarity, we shall revert to the *degree* system of measurement of angles, except where otherwise noted. Secondly, in $E2'$, if the angle from the positive X axis to a ray OP is p, then the ray OP will be labeled p. Thus the $0°$ ray is the positive X axis, the $180°$ ray is the negative X axis, the negative Y axis may be labeled $270°$ and, in fact, also $-90°$, $630°$, etc.]

Now suppose that P is a point $\neq 0$ in $E2'$ and that ray OP is labeled p (see Fig. 6h1). Then, given $r_P = \mathrm{dis}(O, P)$ and p, the point P is uniquely determined. For example, given that $p = 30°$, $r_P = 2$, we may locate the point P by first locating the unique ray labeled $30°$, and then on that ray the unique point P whose distance from the origin O is 2.

The ordered pair of numbers (r_P, p), then, may be used to identify P

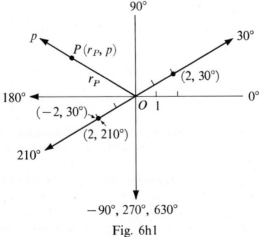

Fig. 6h1

(r_P and p are called the *polar* coordinates of the point P). The point P of the preceding paragraph may, for example, be labeled (2, 30°).

If $P = 0$, then we may identify P as the point for which $r_P = 0$ on *any* ray in $E2'$ with vertex 0. That is to say, if k is any real number, then (0, $k°$) are polar coordinates that identify the origin O.

Immediately we observe a distinction between Cartesian and polar coordinates: In Cartesian coordinates each point has a unique label. This is not true in polar coordinates, where, for example, the point (2, 30°) may also be labeled (2, 390°), (2, −330°), etc.

In fact, it is usual to introduce a convention that allows points to have different r_P values as well as different p values. What we have said so far has the consequence that r_P values are never negative. We shall now agree to allow negative r_P values, with this interpretation: When p and a negative value of r_P are given, then we shall mean that the point P lies on the ray that is the extension through O of the ray labeled p, at a distance of $|r_P|$ from O.

Thus the point (−2, 30°) is identical with the point (2, 210°) (see Fig. 6h1), and for any point (a, $b°$) in polar coordinates, (a, $b°$) and (−a, $b°$ + 180°) denote the same point.

It is customary in mathematics texts to use the letters "r" and "θ" to denote what we have called "r_P" and "p" respectively. We shall follow this practice. Thus when we refer in polar coordinates to the point $P = (r, \theta)$, we shall mean that $r_P = r$ and $p = \theta$.

In polar coordinate systems, the origin is sometimes referred to as the *pole*, and the $O°$ ray as the *polar axis* of the system.

Now, given an equation involving r or θ or both, the set of all points (r, θ) satisfying the equation is called the *polar graph* of the given equation.

ILLUSTRATIVE EXAMPLE 1.   Plot the graph of the equation $r = 10 \cos \theta$.

Solution: Again, a table of (occasionally approximate) values is our mainstay (see below).

θ	0	30°	45°	60°	90°	120°	135°	150°	180°
r	10	8.7	7	5	0	−5	−7	−8.7	−10

[It will be found that the points of the graph obtained for $180° < \theta < 360°$ duplicate those found for $0° < \theta < 180°$; for example, the point (210°, −8.7) is identical with (30°, 8.7).]

The graph (see Fig. 6h2) appears to be a circle of diameter 10. That this is actually the case is suggested by the fact that an angle inscribed in a semi-circle is a right angle. In fact, we shall prove in the next section that the graph of $r = 2k \cos \theta$ is a circle with center (k, $0°$) and radius k.   ‖

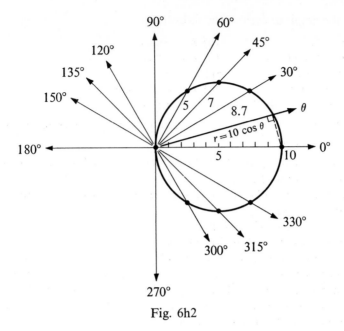

Fig. 6h2

ILLUSTRATIVE EXAMPLE 2.   The graph of $r = 5$ is easily seen to consist of all points at a distance of 5 units from O; i.e., the graph of $r = 5$ is a circle of radius 5 with center at O.

In fact, for any real number k, the graph of $r = k$ is a circle with center O and radius $|k|$.

ILLUSTRATIVE EXAMPLE 3.   The graph of $\theta = 30°$ is easily seen to consist of all points on the line made up of the *two* rays labeled 30° and 210° respectively; for each point $(c, 210°)$ may also be labeled $(-c, 30°)$, and therefore satisfies the equation $\theta = 30°$.

In fact, for any real number k, the graph of $\theta = k$ is a straight line through the origin.

Problems

1. Locate each of the following points in a polar coordinate system, and in each case identify the given point by two other labels. Choose labels with r's of opposite sign (if possible).

(a) $(3, 30°)$.   (b) $(0, 30°)$.   (c) $(0, 0°)$.
(d) $(4, 90°)$.   (e) $(-4, 90°)$.   (f) $(-3, 120°)$.
(g) $(5, 700°)$.   (h) $(-2, 0°)$.   (i) $(-2, 270°)$.

2.   Plot the graph of each of the following.

(a) $r = 5$. (b) $r = -5$.
(c) $r = 5/\sin \theta$. (d) $r = 5/\cos \theta$.
(e) $\theta = 45°$. (f) $\theta = \pi$.
(g) $r = 10 \sin \theta$. (h) $r = 4/(2 + \cos \theta)$.
(i) $r = 4/(1 + \sin \theta)$. (j) $r = 4/(1 + 2 \cos \theta)$.

3.   Plot the graph of each of the following, choosing convenient nonzero values for a and b.

(a) $r = a \sin 2\theta$. (Four-leaved rose. Hint: $\theta = k \cdot 45°$, k any integer, are important.)

(b) $r = a \sin 3\theta$. (Three-leaved rose. Hint: $\theta = k \cdot 30°$, k any integer, are important.)

(c) $r = a \cos 2\theta$. (Four-leaved rose.)

(d) $r = a \cos 3\theta$. (Three-leaved rose.)

(e) $r = b + a \cos \theta$. [Limaçon; (if $|b| = |a|$, cardioid; choose values such that $|b| > |a|$, then values such that $|b| = |a|$, and then values such that $|b| < |a|$. In the last watch out for a loop in the graph!)]

(f) $r^2 = a^2 \cos 2\theta$. (Lemniscate.)

(g) $r^2 = a^2 \sin 2\theta$. (Leminiscate.)

(h) $r = a/\theta$. (Hyperbolic spiral.)

(i) $r = a\theta$. (Archimedean spiral.)   Use radian measure.

(j) $r^2 = a^2/\theta$. (Lituus or trumpet.)

(k) $r = a \sec \theta + b$. [Conchoid; consider cases as in (e) above, including cases in which a, b are of opposite sign.]

4   (Optional). *Conic sections in polar coordinate systems.* In this problem we consider a conic (i.e., a conic section) C with positive eccentricity e. The conic C (see 5n Problem 2) may then be considered to be the locus of points P in the plane of C, the ratio of whose distances to $C's$ focus F and C's directrix l (which does not contain F) is e.

Let the distance from F to l be $k > 0$, and choose a Cartesian coordinate system whose origin is at F and whose X axis is perpendicular to l, so that the equation of l is $x = k$ (see Fig. 6h3).

If P is a point of this system and P lies on a ray labeled θ_P, then the distance from P to F is r_P, and the distance from P to l (see Section 3g) is $|x_P - k| = |r_P \cos \theta_P - k|$.

Therefore P lies on C iff

(1)
$$\frac{r_P}{|r_P \cos \theta_P - k|} = e;$$

i.e., the equation of C in polar coordinates is

(2)
$$\frac{r}{|r \cos \theta - k|} = e.$$

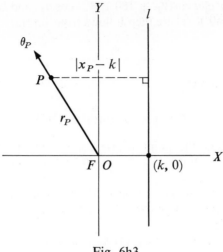

Fig. 6h3

It may now be proved that Eq. (2) is equivalent to

(3)
$$\frac{r}{k - r \cos \theta} = e.$$

In order to prove that Eq. (2) is equivalent to Eq. (3), it is sufficient to show that every point P which satisfies Eq. (2) satisfies Eq. (3), and vice versa. We shall show the first part below; it will be left to the reader to show that every point which satisfies Eq. (3) satisfies Eq. (2).

Suppose, then, that P is a point which satisfies Eq. (2); i.e., suppose that Eq. (1) is true. We consider two cases.

CASE 1. $r_P \cos \theta_P - k < 0$. Then

$$|r_P \cos \theta_P - k| = -(r_P \cos \theta P - k) = k - r_P \cos \theta_P,$$

so that there follows from Eq. (1)

(4)
$$\frac{r_P}{k - r_P \cos \theta_P} = e,$$

but this means that P satisfies Eq. (3).

CASE 2. $r_P \cos \theta_P - k \geq 0$. Then

$$|r_P \cos \theta_P - k| = r_P \cos \theta_P - k,$$

so that there follows from Eq. (1)

(5)
$$\frac{r_P}{r_P \cos \theta_P - k} = e,$$

Now show that $\cos(\theta_P + 180°) = -\cos\theta_P$, *and hence that* $\cos\theta_P = -\cos(\theta_P + 180°)$. There then follows from Eq. (5)

(6)
$$\frac{r_P}{-r_P \cos(\theta_P + 180°) - k} = e,$$

From which follows

(7)
$$\frac{-r_P}{k - (-r_P)\cos(\theta_P + 180°)} = e.$$

This means that the point whose coordinates are $(-r_P, \theta_P + 180°)$ satisfies Eq. (3). But $(-r_P, \theta_P + 180°)$ are coordinates for P. Therefore P satisfies Eq. (3).

The reader may now complete the proof that Eqs. (2) and (3) are equivalent equations by proving that every point P which satisfies Eq. (3) satisfies Eq. (2).

Then proceed to solve Eq. (3) for r, arriving at the following equation in polar coordinates for a conic section with eccentricity e:

(8)
$$r = \frac{ek}{1 + e\cos\theta}.$$

Similarly it may be proved that the following are equations for conic sections with eccentricity e:

(9)
$$r = \frac{ek}{1 - e\cos\theta}.$$

(10)
$$r = \frac{ek}{1 + e\sin\theta}.$$

(11)
$$r = \frac{ek}{1 - e\sin\theta}.$$

The directrices of Eqs. (8), (9), (10), and (11) have the equations $x = k$, $x = -k$, $y = k$, $y = -k$ respectively.

Identify and plot the graph of each of the following equations, and locate a directrix in each case.

(a)
$$r = \frac{4}{2 + 3\cos\theta}.$$

[*Hint:*

$$r = \frac{2}{1 + \frac{3}{2}\cos\theta}.$$

Comparing with Eq. (8) above, $e = \frac{3}{2}$, $ek = 2$; therefore $k = 2/e = \frac{4}{3}$. Since $e > 1$, the graph is a hyperbola. The directrix is the line $x = \frac{4}{3}$.

Make a table of values and plot.]

(b)
$$r = \frac{4}{3 - 2 \cos \theta}.$$

(c)
$$r = \frac{1}{1 + \sin \theta}.$$

(d)
$$r = \frac{2}{1 - \sin \theta}.$$

6i. CONVERSION FROM POLAR TO CARTESIAN COORDINATES AND VICE VERSA

Suppose that the point P in $E2'$ is identified by the Cartesian (or "rectangular") coordinates (x, y) and the polar coordinates (r, θ). Then (as illustrated for a special case in Fig. 6i1)

(1)
$$x = r \cos \theta,$$

(2)
$$y = r \sin \theta,$$

(3)
$$\tan \theta = \frac{y}{x} \quad (\text{if } x \neq 0),$$

(4)
$$x^2 + y^2 = r^2.$$

These equations may be used:

(i) To find polar coordinates of a point, given the rectangular coordinates of the point.

(ii) To find rectangular coordinates of a point, given the polar coordinates of the point.

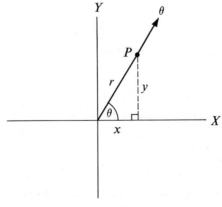

Fig. 6i1

(iii) To find the polar equation of a graph, given its rectangular equation.
(iv) To find the rectangular equation of a graph, given its polar equation.

ILLUSTRATIVE EXAMPLE 1. Find the rectangular coordinates of the point whose polar coordinates are $(-10, 60°)$.

Solution: Using Eqs. (1) and (2), we have

$$x = -10 \cos 60° = -5,$$
$$y = -10 \sin 60° = -5\sqrt{3}.$$

If $(r, \theta) = (-10, 60°)$, then $(x, y) = (-5, -5\sqrt{3})$ uniquely.   ‖

ILLUSTRATIVE EXAMPLE 2. Find polar coordinates of the point whose rectangular coordinates are $(5, -5\sqrt{3})$.

Solution: With positive r, $\tan \theta = y/x = -\sqrt{3}$ leads to $\theta = 300°$ (as one possibility); from Eq. (4), $r^2 = 25 + 75$, so that $r = 10$.
If $(x, y) = (5, -5\sqrt{3})$, then $(r, \theta) = (10, 300°)$, but not, of course, uniquely; $(10, 660°)$ and $(-10, 120°)$ identify the same point.   ‖

ILLUSTRATIVE EXAMPLE 3. Convert the following polar equation to a Cartesian equation:

$$(5) \qquad\qquad\qquad r = 2k \cos \theta.$$

Solution: From Eq. (1), $\cos \theta = x/r$, substituting into Eq. (5), we have

$$(6) \qquad\qquad\qquad r = 2k \cdot \frac{x}{r},$$

from which

$$(7) \qquad\qquad\qquad r^2 = 2kx.$$

Now, using Eq. (4), there follows from Eq. (7)

$$(8) \qquad\qquad\qquad x^2 + y^2 = 2kx.$$

The required Cartesian equation is Eq. (8). The equations (8) and (5) are equivalent in the sense that they have the same graph. Any point whose polar coordinates satisfy Eq. (5) has Cartesian coordinates which satisfy Eq. (8), and vice versa.

[The substitution $\cos \theta = x/r$ is valid only if $r \neq 0$. Actually, we may check independently that the origin O satisfies both Eqs. (5) and (8), and then note that the steps above guarantee that all *other* points which satisfy Eq. (5) satisfy Eq. (8), and vice versa.]

Using the method of completing the square, Eq. (8) may be transformed into the equivalent equation

(9) $(x - k)^2 + y^2 = k^2,$

which we recognize as the equation of a circle whose center (in Cartesian coordinates) is $(k, 0)$ and whose radius is k.

We have proved, then, that the graph of the polar equation $r = 2k \cos \theta$ is a circle of radius k with center at $(k, 0°)$ (see Fig. 6i2).   ‖

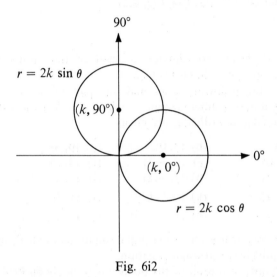

Fig. 6i2

ILLUSTRATIVE EXAMPLE 4.   Convert the following Cartesian equation to a polar equation:

(10) $x^2 + (y - k)^2 = k^2.$

Solution: Clearly, Eq. (10) is equivalent to

(11) $x^2 + y^2 - 2ky = 0.$

Using Eqs. (4) and (2), there follows from Eq. (11).

(12) $r^2 - 2kr \sin \theta = 0,$

and dividing by r, we have

(13) $r - 2k \sin \theta = 0,$

from which

(14) $r = 2k \sin \theta.$

[Actually, factoring the left side of Eq. (12), we see that a point (r, θ) satisfies Eq. (12) either if $r = 0$ or if $r - 2k \sin \theta = 0$. The only point which satisfies $r = 0$ is the origin; but the origin happens to satisfy $r - 2k \sin \theta = 0$ also. The equation $r = 0$ is therefore redundant here and may be discarded. Thus, in this case, no harm has been done by dividing both sides of an equation by r.]

We see, then, that $r = 2k \sin \theta$ is the polar equation of a circle whose radius is k and whose center is at $(0, k)$ in Cartesian coordinates, i.e., at $(k, 90°)$ in polar coordinates (see Fig. 6i2). ‖

Problems

1. Find the Cartesian coordinates of each of the points whose polar coordinates are given in 6h Problem 1.
2. In each of the following cases find one pair of polar coordinates in which $r \geq 0$ and a different pair in which $r \leq 0$, to identify the point whose Cartesian coordinates are given.

   (a) $(0, 0)$.   (b) $(3, 0)$.   (c) $(0, 3)$.
   (d) $(-3, 0)$.   (e) $(0, -3)$.   (f) $(2, 2)$.
   (g) $(-2, 2)$.   (h) $(2, -2)$.   (i) $(-2, -2)$.
   (j) $(1, \sqrt{3})$.   (k) $(-1, \sqrt{3})$.   (l) $(\sqrt{3}, -1)$.
   (m) $(-1, -\sqrt{3})$.   (n) $(1, -\sqrt{3})$.   (o) $(-\sqrt{3}, 1)$.

3. (a)–(j). Transform each of the polar equations in 6h Problem 2(a)–(j) into an equivalent Cartesian equation.
4. (a)–(g). Transform each of the polar equations in 6h Problem 3(a)–(g) into an equivalent Cartesian equation.
5. (a) Find the polar equations of the straight lines whose Cartesian equations are $x = a$ and $y = b$.
   (b) Plot the graph of the equation $r = 2a(\sin \theta + \cos \theta)$, and prove, by transforming the given equation into a Cartesian equation, that the graph is a circle.
   (c) Plot the graph of the equation $r = 10/(\sin \theta + \cos \theta)$; identify the graph and prove that your identification is correct.
6. From the equation of a line l in normal form (see 3f Problem 11) derive the polar equation of l: $r \cos(\theta - \alpha) = d$.

Chapter **7**

Surfaces in $E3'$

7a. INTRODUCTION

(*Note: All graphs in this chapter will be assumed to be in E3', unless otherwise noted.*)

In general (although not always), the graph of an equation in x, y, z is a *surface*. For example, the graph of the equation $2x + 3y + 4z = 5$ is a surface called a *plane*. The graph of the equation $x + y = 10$ is a plane also. (Note that this equation may be regarded as an equation in x, y, z, for it may be written $x + y + 0z = 10$.) However, the graph of the equation $x^2 + y^2 + z^2 = 0$ is not a surface, but only a single point (Which?).

7b. SPHERES

Much of what we do in $E3'$ is a natural extension of what we do in $E2'$. For example, in our discussion of spheres in $E3'$ we may closely parallel our treatment of circles in $E2'$ (see Section 5b):

7b1 (Definition). When we speak of a sphere S with radius r and center Q, we shall mean the set of all points in $E3$ whose distance from Q is r, where r is a nonnegative real number.

The reader may now write a discussion analogous to that preceding statement 5b1, leading to the following statement.

7b2. The equation in $E3'$ of a sphere S with center (h, k, l) and radius r is

$$(x - h)^2 + (y - k)^2 + (z - l)^2 = r^2.$$

As a corollary, we note that the equation of a sphere in $E3'$ with center at the origin and radius r is

$$x^2 + y^2 + z^2 = r^2.$$

Again, a discussion exactly analogous to that which led to statement $5b2$ leads to the following statement.

7b3. The graph in $E3'$ of an equation of the form

$$x^2 + y^2 + z^2 + ax + by + cz + d = 0,$$

where a, b, c, d are real numbers, is either null or a sphere.

ILLUSTRATIVE EXAMPLE. Sketch the graph in the "first octant" (i.e., the region of $E3'$ in which x, y, z are nonnegative) of the equation

$$x^2 + y^2 + z^2 - 10x + 9 = 0,$$

and shade the portion of the graph such that $2 \leq x \leq 5$.

Solution: By the process of completing the square, the given equation is equivalent to

$$(x - 5)^2 + y^2 + z^2 = 16.$$

Hence the required graph is a sphere, with center $(5, 0, 0)$ and radius 4. For the rest, see Fig. 7b1. ‖

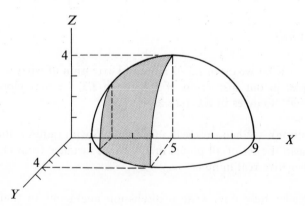

Fig. 7b1

7c. CYLINDERS

We know that the graph in $E2'$ of the equation $x^2 + y^2 = 25$ is a circle of radius 5 whose center is at the origin (see Section 5b). But what would be the graph of the same equation in $E3'$?

First of all, note that $(3, 4, 0)$ satisfies the given equation; but so indeed does $(3, 4, 1)$, and $(3, 4, -7)$, and $(3, 4, \sqrt{2})$, and $(3, 4, -\pi)$, and, in fact, $(3, 4, c)$, where c is any real number. That is to say, all the points on a line through $(3, 4, 0)$, parallel to the Z axis, are in the graph in $E3'$ of the equation $x^2 + y^2 = 25$.

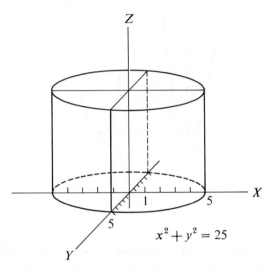

Fig. 7c1

More generally, if B represents the circle in the XY plane whose equation is $x^2 + y^2 = 25$, then each point in each line in $E3'$ that is parallel to the Z axis and that passes through a point of B is in the graph in $E3'$ of the equation $x^2 + y^2 = 25$, and no other points are in that graph. Hence (see definitions 5n2) the graph in $E3'$ of $x^2 + y^2 = 25$ is a circular cylinder whose *trace* (i.e., cross section) in the XY plane has the equation $x^2 + y^2 = 25$ and whose elements are parallel to the Z axis (see Fig. 7c1).

More generally:

7c1. The graph in $E3'$ of an equation $f(x, y) = 0$ is a cylinder whose trace in the XY plane is the graph in that plane of the equation $f(x, y) = 0$ and whose elements are parallel to the Z axis; and similarly for $f(x, z) = 0$ and $f(y, z) = 0$.

ILLUSTRATIVE EXAMPLE.   Describe and sketch a representative portion of the graph in $E3'$ of the equation $y^2 = 4z$.

Solution: The graph is a cylinder whose trace in the YZ plane is the parabola whose equation in that plane is $y^2 = 4z$. The elements of the cylinder are parallel to the X axis. In Fig. 7c2 there is sketched a representative portion of the required graph.   ‖

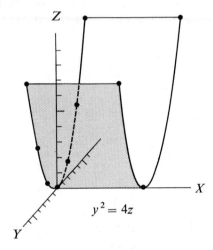

$$y^2 = 4z$$

Fig. 7c2

Problems

1. Sketch the graph (or a representative portion of the graph) in the first octant in $E3'$ of each of the following equations, and shade the indicated part of the graph.

    (a) $x^2 + y^2 + z^2 = 25;\ 2 \le z \le 4.$
    (b) $x^2 + y^2 + z^2 - 10x = 0;\ 0 \le x \le 5.$
    (c) $x^2 + y^2 + z^2 - 10x - 10y + 25 = 0;\ x \ge 5, y \ge 5.$
    (d) $y^2 + z^2 = 25;\ x \le 10.$
    (e) $x^2 + z^2 = 25;\ y \le 10.$
    (f) $x^2 = 4y;\ z \le 10.$
    (g) $y^2 = 9 - z;\ x \le 10.$
    (h) $x^2 + z = 16;\ y \le 10.$
    (i) $x^2 + y^2 + z^2 - 2x - 4y - 6z + 14 = 0.$
    (j) $x^2 + y^2 + z^2 - 2x - 4y - 6z + 15 = 0.$
    (k) $x^2 = y^2.$
    (l) $x^2 + y^2 = 0.$
    (m) $x^2 - 2xy + y^2 = 0;\ z \le 10.$

2. Find an equation of each of the following surfaces in $E3'$.

(a) A sphere with center $(1, 2, -3)$ and radius 4.

(b) A sphere with center at the origin and tangent to the plane $x + y + z = 10$.

(c) The cylinder formed by rotating the line $x = 5$, $z = 0$ about the Y axis.

(d) The cylinder whose elements are parallel to the Z axis and whose base is an ellipse with vertices $(\pm 4, 0, 0)$, $(0, \pm 3, 0)$.

7d. QUADRIC SURFACES

In this section we note, without proof, a number of important facts about the graph in $E3'$ of a second-degree equation. Such graphs are called *quadric surfaces*. Apart from "degenerate" cases (a null graph, a point, a line, a plane, or a pair of planes), the following seven types of quadric surfaces may be distinguished.

(i) *A right cylinder whose base is a conic section* (see Section 7c).

(ii) *A right cone whose base is an ellipse.* For example, consider the equation $4x^2 + 9y^2 - z^2 = 0$. The equations of the traces of its graph in the XY, XZ, and YZ planes are $4x^2 + 9y^2 = 0$, $4x^2 - z^2 = 0$, and $9y^2 - z^2 = 0$ respectively. Hence the first trace is simply the origin, the second is the pair of lines $z = \pm 2x$ in the XZ plane, and the third is the pair of lines $z = \pm 3y$ in the YZ plane. Two more traces, in planes parallel to the XY plane, will be helpful in drawing the graph—we choose $z = \pm 6$, in both of which planes the trace is the ellipse $4x^2 + 9y^2 = 36$, with vertices $(0, \pm 2)$ and $(\pm 3, 0)$. With this information, we sketch the surface (see Fig. 7d1) that is the graph of the equation $4x^2 + 9y^2 - z^2 = 0$.

In general, *the graph of any equation in the form* $Ax^2 + By^2 + Cz^2 = 0$, *where two of the coefficients* A, B, C *are of like sign and the other is of opposite sign, is a right cone with an elliptic base.*

(iii) *An ellipsoid.* Consider the equation $4x^2 + 9y^2 + z^2 = 36$. The equations of the traces of its graph in the XY, XZ, and YZ planes are $4x^2 + 9y^2 = 36$, $4x^2 + z^2 = 36$, and $9y^2 + z^2 = 36$ respectively. Hence its traces in all three coordinate planes are easily drawn ellipses. The graph itself (an *ellipsoid*) is sketched in Fig. 7d2.

In fact, *we define an ellipsoid to be the graph of any equation in the form* $Ax^2 + By^2 + Cz^2 = D$, *where the coefficients* A, B, C, D *are all positive.*

Note that a sphere is a special case of an ellipsoid (Occurring when?). Note also that when two of the coefficients A, B, C are equal, there is a straight line l (actually one of the coordinate axes) such that each cross

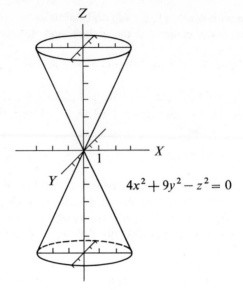

$$4x^2 + 9y^2 - z^2 = 0$$

Fig. 7d1

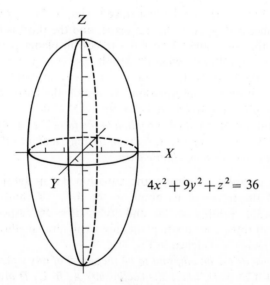

$$4x^2 + 9y^2 + z^2 = 36$$

Fig. 7d2

section of the ellipse perpendicular to l is a circle whose center is on l. In this case the ellipsoid is called an *ellipsoid of revolution*; and similarly for any surface that has such a set of circular cross sections.

(iv) *A hyperboloid of one sheet.* Consider the equation $4x^2 + 9y^2 - z^2 = 36$. With respect to the traces of its graph in coordinate planes, two are hyperbolas and the third is an ellipse. In sketching the graph (a *hyperboloid of one sheet*), it is also useful to sketch two more elliptic cross sections. We choose the cross sections $z = \pm 8$, and sketch the part of the graph between these cross sections in Fig. 7d3.

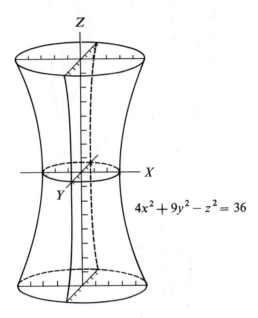

$$4x^2 + 9y^2 - z^2 = 36$$

Fig. 7d3

In fact, *we define a hyperboloid of one sheet to be the graph of any equation in the form $Ax^2 + By^2 + Cz^2 = D$, where D and two of the coefficients A, B, C are positive and the other coefficient is negative.*

(v) *A hyperboloid of two sheets.* The graph of the equation $4x^2 - 9y^2 - z^2 = 36$ also has, in the coordinate planes, two traces that are hyperbolas. The third, however, is null (Why?). Here the cross sections in the planes $x = \pm 5$ are useful in sketching the graph, for in both of these planes the cross section is the ellipse whose equation is $9y^2 + z^2 = 64$. The graph of $4x^2 - 9y^2 - z^2 = 36$ (called a *hyperboloid of two sheets*) is sketched in Fig. 7d4.

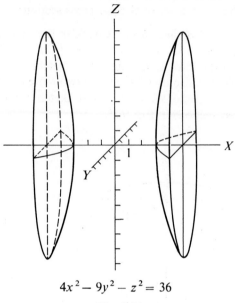

$$4x^2 - 9y^2 - z^2 = 36$$

Fig. 7d4

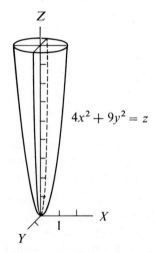

$$4x^2 + 9y^2 = z$$

Fig. 7d5

We define a hyperboloid of two sheets to be the graph of any equation in the form $Ax^2 + By^2 + Cz^2 = D$, where D and one of the coefficients A, B, C are positive and the other two coefficients are negative.

(vi) *An elliptic paraboloid.* An analysis similar to the preceding easily enables us to sketch the graph (called an *elliptic paraboloid*) of the equation $4x^2 + 9y^2 = z$ (see Fig. 7d5).

We define an elliptic paraboloid to be the graph of any equation in the form $Ax^2 + By^2 = Cz$ (or $Ax^2 + Bz^2 = Cy$, or $Ay^2 + Bz^2 = Cx$), where A and B are positive and $C \neq 0$.

(vii) *A hyperbolic paraboloid (or "saddle surface").* Finally we sketch, by methods that are now familiar, the graph of the equation $4x^2 - 9y^2 = z$ (see Fig. 7d6).

We define a hyperbolic paraboloid to be the graph of any equation in the form $Ax^2 - By^2 = Cz$ (or $Ax^2 - Bz^2 = Cy$, or $Ay^2 - Bz^2 = Cx$), where A and B are positive and $C \neq 0$.

The treatment, given in Section 5j, of translation of coordinate systems in $E2'$ may easily be extended to $E3'$. For example, the graph in $E3'$ of the

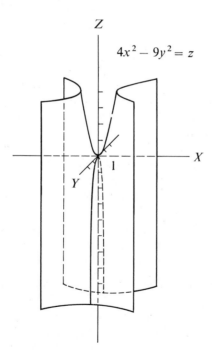

$$4x^2 - 9y^2 = z$$

Fig. 7d6

equation $4(x - 1)^2 + 9(y + 1)^2 + z^2 = 36$ is the ellipsoid whose equation is $4\bar{x}^2 + 9\bar{y}^2 - \bar{z}^2 = 36$ in a new coordinate system $(\bar{O}, i, j, k)$, where $\bar{O} = (1, -1, 0)$. (Cf. 5j Illustrative Examples 2 and 3.)

Problems

Identify the graph in $E3'$ of each of the following equations, state whether or not it is a surface of revolution, and sketch all or a representative part of the surface.

1. $4x^2 + 4y^2 + 9z^2 = 144.$ 2. $4x^2 - 4y^2 + 9z^2 = 144.$
3. $4x^2 - 4y^2 - 9z^2 = 144.$ 4. $4x^2 + 4y^2 - 9z^2 = 0.$
5. $4x^2 + 4y^2 = z.$ 6. $4x^2 - 4y^2 = z.$
7. $4x^2 + 9z^2 = 144.$ 8. $x^2 = 4y^2 + 9z^2.$
9. $x^2 = 4y^2 - 9z^2.$ 10. $x = 4y^2 + 9z^2.$
11. $x = 4y^2 - 9z^2.$ 12. $x^2 + y^2 + 9z^2 = 36.$
13. $y^2 + 9z^2 = 36 - x^2.$ 14. $y^2 + 9z^2 = 36 - x.$
15. $4x^2 + 4y^2 + 9z^2 - 8x - 16y - 54z - 43 = 0.$
16. $z = 4x^2 + 4y^2 - 16x - 16y + 32.$
17. $x^2 - 25y^2 - 25z^2 - 20x + 100 = 0.$
18. $x^2 - 3xy + 2y^2 = 0.$
19. $x^2 + y^2 + z^2 - 2x - 4y - 6z + 14 = 0.$
20. $x^2 + y^2 + z^2 - 2x - 4y - 6z + 15 = 0.$

7e. CYLINDRICAL AND SPHERICAL COORDINATES

Just as there exists in $E2$ at least one system of coordinates (polar coordinates) alternative to Cartesian coordinates and useful in many special situations, so there exist in $E3$ similarly useful coordinate systems different from the Cartesian system.

In fact, derived directly from polar coordinates in $E2$ are *cylindrical* coordinates in $E3$. Suppose a point P has the coordinates (x, y, z) in $E3'$, and the point in $E2'$ with Cartesian coordinates (x, y) has polar coordinates (r, θ). Then we define the ordered triple (r, θ, z) to be the *cylindrical* coordinates of P (Fig. 7e1).

Equations transforming cylindrical coordinates and equations to Cartesian, and vice versa, are already at hand [Eqs. 6i(1)–(4)].

Spherical coordinates in $E3$ are defined as follows: Suppose a point $P \neq 0$ has cylindrical coordinates (r, θ, z), the angle between $\overrightarrow{OP}$ and the vector k is ϕ, $(0 \leq \phi \leq \pi)$, and $\mathrm{dis}(O, P) = \rho$. Then we define the ordered triple (ρ, θ, ϕ) to be the *spherical* coordinates of P (Fig. 7e2).

Furthermore, we define *any* ordered triple $(0, \theta, \phi)$ to be spherical coordinates of the origin O; and, finally, we introduce a convention that permits ρ to be negative: If ρ is a negative real number, we define the point (ρ, θ, ϕ) to be identical with the point $(|\rho|, \pi + \theta, \pi - \phi)$. For example, in

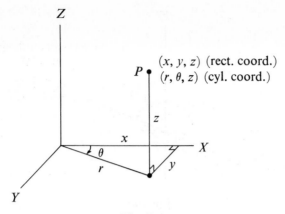

Fig. 7e1

spherical coordinates the point $(-5, \pi, 2\pi/3)$ is identical with the point $(5, 2\pi, \pi/3)$, which in turn coincides with the point $(5, 0, \pi/3)$ (see Fig. 7e3).

The following equations, which may be used to transform Cartesian coordinates and equations to the spherical type, and vice versa, are now easily derived (see Fig. 7e2).

(1) $$x = \rho \cos \theta \sin \phi.$$
(2) $$y = \rho \sin \theta \sin \phi.$$
(3) $$z = \rho \cos \phi.$$
(4) $$\rho^2 = x^2 + y^2 + z^2.$$
(5) $$\tan \theta = y/x.$$
(6) $$\cos \phi = z/\sqrt{x^2 + y^2 + z^2}.$$

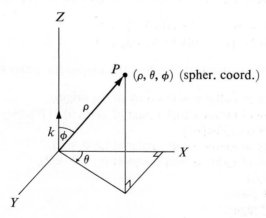

Fig. 7e2

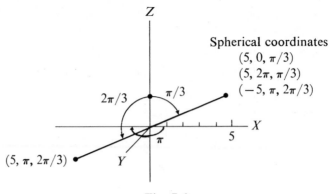

Fig. 7e3

Problems

1. Given the following points, expressed in Cartesian coordinates, find the cylindrical and the spherical coordinates of each point, and illustrate.

    (a) $(1, \sqrt{3}, 0)$.   (b) $(-1, 0, \sqrt{3})$.
    (c) $(1, 1, \sqrt{2})$.   (d) $(1, -1, \sqrt{2})$.

2. Given the following points, expressed in cylindrical coordinates, find the Cartesian and spherical coordinates of each point, and illustrate.

    (a) $(3, \pi/6, 7)$.   (b) $(-7, \pi, 11)$.
    (c) (π, π, π).   (d) $(10, \pi/4, 5\sqrt{2})$.

3. Given the following points, expressed in spherical coordinates, find the Cartesian and cylindrical coordinates of each point, and illustrate.

    (a) $(10, \pi/4, \pi/4)$.   (b) $(10, 3\pi/2, \pi/2)$.
    (c) $(6, 3\pi/4, 2\pi/3)$.   (d) $(-6, \pi/2, \pi/2)$.

4. In a spherical coordinate system find an equation for each of the following.

    (a) A sphere of radius a with center at the origin.
    (b) A sphere of radius a with center at $(a, 0, 0)$. (*Warning:* These are *spherical* coordinates!)
    (c) A sphere of radius a with center at $(a, 0, \pi/2)$.
    (d) A sphere of radius a with center at $(a, \pi/2, \pi/2)$.
    (e) The Z axis.
    (f) The XY plane.
    (g) The YZ plane.
    (h) The XZ plane.

5. The following are equations of graphs in spherical coordinates. In each case find the equation of the graph in Cartesian coordinates, and sketch the graph.

(a) $\phi = \pi/4$.   (b) $\rho = 10$.
(c) $\theta = \pi/4$.   (d) $\rho \cos \phi = 10$.
(e) $\rho \sin \phi = 10$.   (f) $\rho = 10 \cos \phi$.
(g) $\rho = 10 \sin \phi$.   (h) $\rho^2 \cos 2\phi = 100$.

6. The following are equations of graphs in cylindrical coordinates. In each case find the equation of the graph in Cartesian coordinates, and sketch the graph.

(a) $r = 5$.   (b) $\theta = \pi/6$.
(c) $z = 5$.   (d) $r^2 + z^2 = 9$.
(e) $r = 10 \sin \theta$.   (f) $r \sin \theta = 10$.
(g) $r = 2z$.   (h) $r^2 = 2z$.

7. The following are equations of graphs in $E3'$ in Cartesian coordinates. In each case find the equation of the graph in spherical coordinates and also in cylindrical coordinates, and sketch the graph.

(a) $x^2 + y^2 + z^2 = 9$.   (b) $x^2 + y^2 = 9$.
(c) $x = 9$.   (d) $x^2 - y^2 = 9$.
(e) $x^2 + y^2 = 8z$.   (f) $x^2 + y^2 = 9z^2$.
(g) $y = x$.   (h) $x^2 + y^2 + z^2 = 2z$.

Appendix

Proof of Statement 2a3. First of all, for each point Q in E, there exists a unique point Q' in E such that $\text{dir}(Q, Q') = \text{dir}(P, P')$ and $\text{dis}(Q, Q') = \text{dis}(P, P')$ (?1). Define function t with domain E such that $t(Q) = Q'$, for each point Q in E. Then, for each A, B in E, $\text{dir}(A, t(A)) \overset{?2}{=} \text{dir}(A, A') \overset{?3}{=} \text{dir}(P, P') \overset{?4}{=} \text{dir}(B, B') \overset{?5}{=} \text{dir}(B, t(B))$, and similarly $\text{dis}(A, t(A)) = \text{dis}(B, t(B))$ (?6). Therefore t is a translation of E (?7) such that $t(P) = P'$ (?8).

It remains only to prove that t is unique, i.e., that if u is also a translation of E such that $u(P) = P'$, then $t = u$. But $\text{dir } t \overset{?9}{=} \text{dir}(P, t(P)) \overset{?10}{=} \text{dir}(P, P') \overset{?11}{=} \text{dir}(P, u(P)) \overset{?12}{=} \text{dir } u$, and similarly $|t| = |u|$ (?13). Therefore $t = u$ (?14). ‖

Remark on Definition 2b1. Definition 2b1 uniquely defines, in fact, the sum $t + u$ of any two vectors t, u of E. For suppose $t = \overrightarrow{AA'}$ and $u = \overrightarrow{A'A''}$. Then $t + u = \overrightarrow{AA''}$ (?1). If our expressions for t, u are, on the other hand, $t = \overrightarrow{BB'}$ and $u = \overrightarrow{B'B''}$, then $t + u = \overrightarrow{BB''}$. But then $\overrightarrow{AA''} = \overrightarrow{BB''}$ (?2), justifying our assertion that definition 2b1 uniquely defines the sum $t + u$ of any two vectors t, u of E.

Proof of Statement 2b10. Let $v = \overrightarrow{AB}$ and $w = \overrightarrow{BC}$. Then $v + w = \overrightarrow{AC}$ (?1). But $\text{dir}(A, B) \overset{?2}{=} \text{dir } v \overset{?3}{=} \text{dir } w \overset{?4}{=} \text{dir}(B, C)$. Therefore $\text{dir}(v + w) \overset{?5}{=} \text{dir}(A, C) \overset{?6}{=} \text{dir}(A, B) \overset{?7}{=} \text{dir } v$, and $|v + w| \overset{?8}{=} \text{dis}(A, C) \overset{?9}{=} \text{dis}(A, B) + \text{dis}(B, C) \overset{?10}{=} |v| + |w|$. ‖

Remark on Definition 2c1. It easily follows, from statement 2a2, that $sv \in V$ is uniquely defined for each real number s and each $v \in V$; that is to

213

say, if $v = \overrightarrow{AB}$ and also $v = \overrightarrow{CD}$, then, from definition 2c1, $s \cdot \overrightarrow{AB} = s \cdot \overrightarrow{CD}$. (Proof?)

Proof of Statement 2d1. First of all, $|r(sv)| \overset{?1}{=} |r| \, |sv| \overset{?2}{=} |r| \, |s| \, |v| \overset{?3}{=} |rs| \, |v| \overset{?4}{=} |(rs)v|$.

Secondly, if $r = 0$ or $s = 0$, then dir $r(sv) = $ dir$(rs)v$ (?5). If $r < 0$ and $s < 0$, then $rs > 0$ (?6), so that dir $r(sv) \overset{?7}{=} -$dir$(sv) \overset{?8}{=} -(-$dir $v) \overset{?9}{=}$ dir $v \overset{?10}{=}$ dir$(rs)v$.

Completion of proof (?11). ‖

Proof of Statement 2d2.

CASE 1. $r = 0$ or $s = 0$ or $r + s = 0$. [Proof (?1)]

CASE 2. $r > 0$, $s > 0$. Then $r + s > 0$ (?2). Therefore $(r + s)v$, rv, sv, and $rv + sv$ all have the same direction as v (?3). Furthermore,

$$|(r + s)v| \overset{?4}{=} |r + s| \, |v| \overset{?5}{=} (r + s) \, |v| \overset{?6}{=} r \, |v| + s \, |v|$$
$$\overset{?7}{=} |r| \, |v| + |s| \, |v| \overset{?8}{=} |rv| + |sv| \overset{?9}{=} |rv + sv|.$$

Therefore $(r + s)v = rv + sv$ (?10).

CASE 3. $r < 0, s < 0$. [Proof (?11)]

CASE 4a. $r > 0, s < 0, r + s > 0$. Then $-s > 0$ (?12), and $(r + s)v \overset{?13}{=}$ $(r + s)v + [(-s)v + sv] \overset{?14}{=} [(r + s)v + (-s)v] + sv \overset{?15}{=} rv + sv$.

CASE 4b. $r > 0, s < 0, r + s < 0$. [Proof (?16)]

CASE 5. $r < 0, s > 0$. (Follows from Cases 4a and 4b by interchanging r and s.) ‖

Proof of Statement 2d3

CASE 1. $s = 0$. Proof (?1)

CASE 2. $s > 0$. Let $v = \overrightarrow{AB}$, $w = \overrightarrow{BC}$, $sv = \overrightarrow{A'B'}$, and $sw = \overrightarrow{B'C'}$. Then dir$(A', B') = $ dir(A, B), dis$(A', B') = s \cdot$ dis(A, B), dir$(B', C') = $ dir(B, C), and dis$(B', C') = s \cdot$ dis(B, C) (?2) (see Fig. A1). Now

$$\text{dir}(sv + sw) \overset{?3}{=} \text{dir}(A', C') \overset{?4}{=} \text{dir}(A, C) \overset{?5}{=} \text{dir } s(v + w),$$

and similarly $|sv + sw| \overset{?6}{=} |s(v + w)|$.

CASE 3. $s < 0$. Proof (?7) ‖

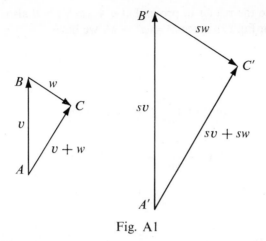

Fig. A1

Proof of Statement 2e2

CASE 1. *A, B, C, D* are not distinct. Proof (?1)

CASE 2. *A, B, C, D* are distinct. We have $\overrightarrow{AD} = r \cdot \overrightarrow{AB} + s \cdot \overrightarrow{AC}$ (?2). Let $r \cdot \overrightarrow{AB} = \overrightarrow{AE}$ and let $s \cdot \overrightarrow{AC} = \overrightarrow{AF}$. Then $\overrightarrow{AD} = \overrightarrow{AE} + \overrightarrow{AF}$, so that *A, D, E, F* are coplanar (?3), say *A, D, E, F* ∈ plane *H*. If $r = 0$, then $\overrightarrow{AD} = s \cdot \overrightarrow{AC}$ (?4); hence *A, C, D* are collinear (?5); hence *A, B, C, D* are coplanar (?6). Similarly, if $s = 0$, then *A, B, C, D* are coplanar (?7). If $r \neq 0$ and $s \neq 0$, then $\overrightarrow{AB} = (1/r)\overrightarrow{AE}$, and $\overrightarrow{AC} = (1/s)\overrightarrow{AF}$ (?8); hence $A \neq E$ and $A \neq F$ (?9); hence $B \in$ line *AE* and $C \in$ line *AF* (?10); hence *B, C* ∈ plane *H* (?11). But *A, D* already ∈ plane *H*. ‖

Remark on Definitions 4b1. Note that the definition of degree included here assumes that the action of a polynomial function *p* cannot be expressed by more than *one* of the forms (i)–(v), etc., with $a \neq 0$; otherwise this degree would not be "well defined." The uniqueness we have assumed can be proved, although we do not do so here.

Completion of Proof That 5d(9) Is the Equation of the Ellipse Defined in 5d1. Assuming Eq. (9) to be true, we shall first prove that $a - (cx/a) > 0$ and $a + (cx/a) > 0$.

Since the square of any real number is nonnegative, $y^2/b^2 \geq 0$. Therefore $-y^2/b^2 \leq 0$. Therefore $1 - (y^2/b^2) \leq 1$. Hence, from Eq. (9), $x^2/a^2 \leq 1$, from which follows $-1 \leq x/a \leq 1$ (see 1d Problem 5b).

Since $x/a \leq 1$, we have $cx/a \leq c$; and since $c < a$, we have $cx/a < a$, from which we have $a - (cx/a) > 0$.

It is left to the reader to prove that $a + (cx/a) > 0$ also.
Now from Eq. (9), since $b^2 = a^2 - c^2$, we have

(10)
$$\frac{x^2}{a^2} + \frac{y^2}{a^2 - c^2} = 1,$$

(11)
$$(a^2 - c^2)\frac{x^2}{a^2} + y^2 = a^2 - c^2,$$

(12)
$$x^2 - \frac{c^2 x^2}{a^2} + y^2 = a^2 - c^2,$$

(13)
$$a^2 + \frac{c^2 x^2}{a^2} = x^2 + y^2 + c^2.$$

Hence $PF_1 = \sqrt{(x - c)^2 + y^2} = \sqrt{x^2 + y^2 + c^2 - 2cx}$

$$= \sqrt{a^2 + (c^2 x^2/a^2) - 2cx} = a - (cx/a),$$

since $a - (cx/a) > 0$. It is left to the reader to show similarly that $PF_2 = a + (cx/a)$.

Finally, $PF_1 + PF_2 = a - (cx/a) + a + (cx/a) = 2a$, so that P *does* lie on our ellipse.

The proof that Eq. (9) is the equation of our ellipse is now complete.

Proof That No Graphs But Those Listed as 5k(i)–(viii) May Arise from Eq. 5k(1). Since A and C cannot both be 0, one of three cases must occur, and we shall consider each in turn.

CASE 1. $A \neq 0, C \neq 0$. In this case, just as we have done in particular cases, we may [unless the equation is already in the simpler form of Eq. (2) below] complete the square in Eq. (1) and translate to new axes to arrive at an equation in the simpler form:

(2)
$$A\bar{x}^2 + C\bar{y}^2 = K.$$

Throughout the rest of Case 1 we shall restrict ourselves to the new coordinate system, with which understanding we may omit the "bars" and write Eq. (2) as

(3)
$$Ax^2 + Cy^2 = K.$$

Now we consider the following subcases.

CASE 1a. A and C are of like sign. Then if K is of sign opposite to A

and C, our graph is *null*. For otherwise Eq. (3) would yield a nonnegative number equal to a negative number.

If $K = 0$, we note that only one point $(0, 0)$ fails to make the left side of Eq. (3) $\neq 0$. The graph consists of a single *point*.

If K is of the same sign as A and C, we have noted that the graph of Eq. (3) is an *ellipse*. (If, furthermore, $A = C$, the graph will be a *circle of nonzero radius*.)

CASE 1b. A and C are of opposite sign. Then if $K \neq 0$, we have noted that the graph of Eq. (3) is a *hyperbola*.

Suppose, then, that $K = 0$. The equation whose graph we seek becomes

$$(4) \qquad\qquad Ax^2 + Cy^2 = 0,$$

which is equivalent to

$$(5) \qquad\qquad y^2 + \frac{A}{C}x^2 = 0.$$

Since A and C are of opposite sign, the real number $-A/C$ is positive, so that there exists a real number $m = \sqrt{-A/C}$; hence $m^2 = -A/C$, $-m^2 = A/C$.

Therefore Eq. (5) is equivalent to

$$(6) \qquad\qquad y^2 - m^2x^2 = 0,$$

which in turn is equivalent to:

$$(7) \qquad\qquad (y + mx)(y - mx) = 0.$$

The graph of Eq. (7) is a pair of $\neq$ *intersecting lines*.

CASE 2. $A \neq 0$, $C = 0$. Then Eq. (1) is equivalent to

$$(8) \qquad\qquad Ax^2 + Dx + Ey + F = 0,$$

and unless Eq. (8) is already in the simpler form of Eq. (9) below, we may complete the square and translate, to arrive at the equation

$$(9) \qquad\qquad A\bar{x}^2 + E\bar{y} + R = 0.$$

If $E = 0$, Eq. (9) is equivalent to an equation $\bar{x}^2 = K$, whose graph will be either *null*, a *line*, or a pair of $\neq$ *parallel lines*, depending upon whether $K < 0$, $K = 0$, or $K > 0$ respectively.

If $E \neq 0$, then Eq. (9) is equivalent to the equation $\bar{y} + R/E = -(A/E)\bar{x}^2$, whose graph we have seen to be a *parabola*.

CASE 3. $A = 0$, $C \neq 0$. The situation here is simply that of Case 2 with the roles of x and y interchanged. Therefore no new types of graphs will occur in this case.

In 6g Illustrative Example 2, Completion of Proof That $y^2 = x^3 + 4x^2$ **Is the Cartesian Equation of** G. Suppose x, y are real numbers such that $y^2 = x^3 + 4x^2$. Then $y = x\sqrt{x+4}$ or $y = -x\sqrt{x+4}$.

CASE 1. $y = x\sqrt{x+4}$. If $x = 0$, then $\sqrt{x+4}$ is the real number 2. If $x \neq 0$, then $\sqrt{x+4}$ is the real number y/x. Throughout this case, then, $\sqrt{x+4}$ is a real number, which we denote by t. We have, then, $t = \sqrt{x+4}$, $t^2 = x+4$, $x = t^2 - 4$, $y = (t^2 - 4)t = t^3 - 4t$, so that (x, y) satisfies the given parametric equations and is in G.

CASE 2. $y = -x\sqrt{x+4}$. As above, $-\sqrt{x+4}$ is a real number in this case also, and we denote it by t. The rest of the proof is left to the reader.

Selected Answers

[*Note:* The notation "2bP7c" means, "At the end of Section 2b, Problem 7(c)"; and "P7c" means, "In this set of problems, Problem 7(c)."]

1b5. $(?)0_2 \in S$, and 0_1 is an additive identity in S.

1c2. i.e., if $a, b, c \in S$, then $(ab)c = a(bc)$.

1c3. i.e., there exists an element $1 \in S$ (called a *multiplicative identity*) such that, for each $a \in S$, $a \cdot 1 = a$, and $1 \cdot a = a$.

1c7. (vi)(?) $(a - d)v + (b - e)w + (c - f)x = 0$, and $(a - d)v = (e - b)w + (f - c)x$, etc.

(viii)(?) $w = (-b^{-1}a)v + (-b^{-1}c)x$.

1d10. (?1) 1d9. (?2) 1d4(ii). (?3) 1c7(i), (ii). (?4) 1d8. (?5) 1d9.

1d. PROBLEMS

1. (a) 7. (c) 0. (e) 2.
2. (a) $x = \pm 7$. (c) No solution. (e) $x = -2$ or 8.
   (g) $x = 0$ or a.
3. (a) $\mathrm{dis}(A, B) = |x_A - x_B|$.
   (b) (i) $\mathrm{dis}(A, B) = \mathrm{dis}(B, A) = 4$. (iii) $\mathrm{dis}(A, B) = 7$. (v) $\mathrm{dis}(B, A) = 14$.
4. (a) $A = B$. (b) $\mathrm{dis}(A, B) = \mathrm{dis}(B, A)$.
   (c) $\mathrm{dis}(A, B) + \mathrm{dis}(B,C) \geq \mathrm{dis}(A, C)$.
   (d) $\mathrm{dis}(A, B) + \mathrm{dis}(B, C) = \mathrm{dis}(A, C)$.
5. (a) $|a| = 0$ iff $\pm a = 0$ (by 1d9). But $\pm a = 0$ iff $a = 0$ (by 1b7,8). ‖
   (c) $a \leq 0$. *Proof:* Suppose $|a| = -a$. Then $-a \geq 0$ (by 1d9). $\therefore a \leq 0$ (by 1d5, with $c = -1$). Conversely, suppose $a \leq 0$. Then $-a \geq 0$ (by 1d5, with $c = -1$). $\therefore |a| = -a$ (by 1d9). ‖
   (e) By 1d9, $|a|$ is the unique nonnegative element of the set $\{a, -a\}$, and $|-a|$ is the unique nonnegative element of the set $\{-a, -(-a)\}$. But
   $$\{-a, -(-a)\} = \{-a, a\} = \{a, -a\}. \;\; ‖$$
   (g) If $a > 0$, then $a^2 > 0$ by 1d5, with $c = a$; If $a = 0$, then $a^2 = 0 \cdot 0 = 0$ (by a property of real numbers). If $a < 0$, then $a^2 > 0$ by 1d5, with $c = a$. By 1d7, there are no other cases to consider. Hence, in all cases, $a^2 \geq 0$. ‖
   (i) By 1d9, $|a|$ is nonnegative, and by P5d, $|a|^2 = a^2$. Hence, by definition of $\sqrt{\;}$, $\sqrt{a^2} = |a|$. ‖

219

(k) Suppose $a^2 > b^2$, but neither $a > b$ nor $a < -b$. Then $a \leq b$ and $a \geq -b$ (by 1d7). $\therefore$ $b - a \geq 0$ and $b + a \geq 0$ [by 1d2(ii)]. $\therefore$ $b^2 - a^2 \geq 0$ [by 1d4(ii)]. $\therefore$ $b^2 \geq a^2$ [by 1d2(ii)]. But this, together with our hypothesis $a^2 > b^2$, contradicts 1d7. Hence, either $a > b$ or $a < -b$ must be true.

Conversely, suppose $a > b$ or $a < -b$. If $a > b$, then since $b > 0$ (by hypothesis), $a > 0$ (by 1d6). $\therefore$ $a^2 > b^2$ (by P5j). If $a < -b$, then $-a > b$ (by 1d5). But again, $b > 0$ (by hypothesis). $\therefore$ $-a > 0$ (by 1d6). $\therefore$ $(-a)^2 > b^2$ (by P5j). $\therefore$ $a^2 > b^2$ [by 1c7(ii)].   ‖

1f.   (?) j has domain $\{0, 2\}$, $j(0) = 0$, $j(2) = 4$; k has domain $\{0, 2\}$, $k(0) = 0$, $k(2) = 4$. Hence, $j = k$ (by 1f1).   ‖

2a2. (?1) 2a1. (?2) 2a1. (?3) Hypothesis. (?4) 2a1. (?5) 2a1. (?6) Hypothesis. (?7) 2a1. (?8) 1e8. (?9) 1f1.

2a ILL. EX. (?) dir $t = \mathrm{dir}(A, t(A)) = \mathrm{dir}(A, B)$ (by 2a1 and hyp.). Similarly dir $u = \mathrm{dir}(D, C)$. $\therefore$ dir $t = $ dir u (by 1e11). Similarly $|t| = |u|$. $\therefore$ $t = u$ (by 2a2).   ‖

2a5. (?1) Hyp. (?2) 2a4. (?3) 1f1.

2a. PROBLEMS

1. dis(A, B).   2.   dir(A, B).

3. (a) $\overrightarrow{AA'} = \overrightarrow{BB'}$ iff dir $\overrightarrow{AA'} = $ dir $\overrightarrow{BB'}$ and $|\overrightarrow{AA'}| = |\overrightarrow{BB'}|$ (by 2a2). But dir $\overrightarrow{AA'} = \mathrm{dir}(A, A')$, dir $\overrightarrow{BB'} = \mathrm{dir}(B, B')$, $|\overrightarrow{AA'}| = \mathrm{dis}(A, A')$, and $|\overrightarrow{BB'}| = \mathrm{dis}(B, B')$ by P1 and 2. Hence, the desired result follows (by substitution).   ‖
    (c) By P2, $\mathrm{dir}(A, A') = \mathrm{dir}(B, B')$. $\therefore$ line AA' is parallel to line BB' (by 1e5).   ‖

5. By 1e10, B is the midpoint of line segment AC iff $\mathrm{dir}(A, B) = \mathrm{dir}(B, C)$, and $\mathrm{dis}(A, B) = \mathrm{dis}(B, C)$. But $\mathrm{dir}(A, B) = \mathrm{dir}(B, C)$, and $\mathrm{dis}(A, B) = \mathrm{dis}(B, C)$ iff $\overrightarrow{AB} = \overrightarrow{BC}$, by P3a.   ‖

2b3. (?1) Substitution. (?2) 2b1. (?3) 2b1. (?4) 2b1. (?5) 2b1. (?6) Sub.

2b4. (?1) 2aP3b. (?2) Sub. (?3) 2b1. (?4) 2b1. (?5) Sub. (?6) Sub.

2b5. (?1) Sub. (?2) 2b1. (?3) Sub. (?4) 2b4.

2b6. (?) $\overrightarrow{AB} + \overrightarrow{BA} = \overrightarrow{AA}$ (by 2b1), and $\overrightarrow{BA} + \overrightarrow{AB} = \overrightarrow{BB} = \overrightarrow{AA}$ (by 2b1, and 2aP3a).

2b. PROBLEMS

1. $|0_V| = |\overrightarrow{AA}| = \mathrm{dis}(A, A) = 0$ (by 2b8, 2aP1, and 1dP4a).   ‖

3. $|\overrightarrow{AB}| = 0$ (by P1). $\therefore$ $A = B$ (by P2).   ‖

5. (a) $\overrightarrow{AB} - \overrightarrow{AC} = \overrightarrow{AB} + \overrightarrow{CA}$ (by 1b13 and 2b9). But $\overrightarrow{AB} + \overrightarrow{CA} = \overrightarrow{CA} + \overrightarrow{AB} = \overrightarrow{CB}$ (by 2b4 and 2b1).   ‖

7. (a) Let $v = \overrightarrow{AB}$. Then $|-v| = |\overrightarrow{BA}| = \mathrm{dis}(B, A) = \mathrm{dis}(A, B) = |\overrightarrow{AB}| = |v|$ (by 2b9, 2aP1, 1dP4b, 2aP1, and sub.).   ‖

9. Let A, B, C lie on line 1. We wish to prove that D lies on 1 also. By 2b8 and 2bP3, $A = B$ iff $C = D$. Hence we may distinguish two cases:

CASE 1. $A = B$ and $C = D$. Then D lies on l (by sub.).

CASE 2. $A \neq B$ and $C \neq D$. Then $l =$ line AB is parallel to line CD (by 2aP3c). But C lies on l (by hyp.). Hence $l =$ line CD (parallel, intersecting lines are identical). Hence D lies on l (by sub.).   ‖

2c1.   (?1) 1e15 (with P, P', Q, Q' equal to A, B, A, C, respectively).   (?2) 1e15.

2c.   PROBLEMS

1. (a) CASE 1. $s > 0$. Suppose $sv = s \cdot \overrightarrow{AB} = \overrightarrow{AC}$. Then
$$|sv| = \text{dis}(A, C) = s \cdot \text{dis}(A, B) = |s|\,|v|,$$
(by 2a1, 2c1, P5b, and 2a1).   ‖

(d) Suppose $sv = 0_V$. Then $|s|\,|v| = |sv| = 0$ (by P1a, and 2bP1). $\therefore$ $|s| = 0$ or $|v| = 0$ (by a property of real numbers). But if $|s| = 0$, then $s = 0$ (by 1dP5a); and if $|v| = 0$, then $v = 0_V$ (by 2bP4).

Conversely, suppose $s = 0$ or $v = 0_V$. If $s = 0$, then $sv = 0_V$ (by 2c1). If $v = 0_V$, then $|sv| = |s|\,|v| = |s|\,0 = 0$ (by P1a, 2bP1, and a property of real numbers). $\therefore$ $sv = 0_V$ (by 2bP4).   ‖

2. (a) CASE 1. $|\overrightarrow{AB}| = 0$. Then $A = B$ (by 2bP2). $\therefore$ $A' = B'$ (by 1e1). $\therefore$ $\overrightarrow{A'B'} = 0_V = \overrightarrow{AB} = 1 \cdot \overrightarrow{AB}$ (by 2b8, 2bP4, and P1e); thus, $\overrightarrow{A'B'}$ is a positive scalar multiple of $\overrightarrow{AB}$.

CASE 2. $|\overrightarrow{AB}| \neq 0$. Let $s = |\overrightarrow{A'B'}|/|\overrightarrow{AB}|$. Then $s > 0$ (by 1d9, and a property of real numbers), and dir $s \cdot \overrightarrow{AB} =$ dir $\overrightarrow{AB} =$ dir$(A, B) =$ dir$(A',B') =$ dir $\overrightarrow{A'B'}$ (by P1b, 2aP2, hyp., and 2aP2). Furthermore, $|s \cdot \overrightarrow{AB}| = |s|\,|\overrightarrow{AB}| = s\,|\overrightarrow{AB}| = |\overrightarrow{A'B'}|$ (by P1a, 1dP5a, and sub.). $\therefore$ $\overrightarrow{A'B'} = s \cdot \overrightarrow{AB}$ (by 2a2).   ‖

(c) If line $A'B'$ is parallel to line AB, then
$$\text{dir}(A', B') = \text{dir}(A, B) \quad \text{or} \quad \text{dir}(A', B') = -\text{dir}(A, B),$$
(by 1e5). But then $\overrightarrow{A'B'}$ is a scalar multiple of $\overrightarrow{AB}$ (by P2a,b).

Conversely, suppose $\overrightarrow{A'B'} = s \cdot \overrightarrow{AB}$. If $s = 0$, then (by P1d and 2bP3), $A' = B'$, contrary to hyp. Hence $s \neq 0$, and dir$(A', B') =$ dir(A, B) or dir$(A', B') = -\text{dir}(A, B)$ (by P2b,c). Hence line $A'B'$ is parallel to line AB (by 1e5).   ‖

(e) Suppose A, B, C are collinear. If $A = B$, then $\overrightarrow{AB} = 0 \cdot \overrightarrow{AC}$ (by 2b8, and P1d). If $A \neq B$, then, since A, C lie on a line parallel to line AB (namely line AB itself), $\overrightarrow{AC}$ is a scalar multiple of $\overrightarrow{AB}$ (by P2d).

Conversely, suppose $\overrightarrow{AB}$ is a scalar multiple of $\overrightarrow{AC}$, or $\overrightarrow{AC}$ is a scalar multiple of $\overrightarrow{AB}$. If $A = B$ or $A = C$, then certainly A, B, C are collinear (since any two points are collinear). If $A \neq B$ and $A \neq C$, then line AB is parallel to line AC (by P2c). Hence, A, B, C are collinear (since parallel lines that intersect are identical).   ‖

2d6.   (vi)   (?) $(a - d)v + (b - e)w + (c - f)x = 0_V$,
$(a - d)v = (e - b)w + (f - c)x$, etc.

(viii) $w = (-b^{-1}a)v + (-b^{-1}c)x$.

2d. PROBLEMS

1. (a) $sv + s(-v) = s[v + (-v)] = s \cdot 0_V = 0_V$ (by 2d3, 2b6, and 2cP1d).
    (c) $2v + 3v = (2 + 3)v = 5v$ (by 2d2, and a property of real numbers).

2. (a) Suppose B is the midpoint of line segment AC. Then $\overrightarrow{AB} = \overrightarrow{BC}$ (by 2aP5).
    $\therefore \overrightarrow{AC} = \overrightarrow{AB} + \overrightarrow{BC} = \overrightarrow{AB} + \overrightarrow{AB} = 2 \cdot \overrightarrow{AB}$ (by 2b1, sub., and P1d).
    Conversely, suppose $\overrightarrow{AC} = 2 \cdot \overrightarrow{AB}$. Then $\overrightarrow{AB} + \overrightarrow{BC} = \overrightarrow{AB} + \overrightarrow{AB}$
    (by 2b1 and P1d). $\therefore \overrightarrow{BC} = \overrightarrow{AB}$ (by 1b9). $\therefore B$ is the midpoint of line
    segment AC (by 2aP5).

    Now suppose $\overrightarrow{AC} = 2 \cdot \overrightarrow{AB}$. Then $\frac{1}{2} \cdot \overrightarrow{AC} = \frac{1}{2} \cdot (2 \cdot \overrightarrow{AB}) =$
    $(\frac{1}{2} \cdot 2) \cdot \overrightarrow{AB} = 1 \cdot \overrightarrow{AB} = \overrightarrow{AB}$ (by sub., 2d1, 1c4, and 2cP1e).
    Finally, suppose $\overrightarrow{AB} = \frac{1}{2} \cdot \overrightarrow{AC}$. Then $2 \cdot \overrightarrow{AB} = 2 \cdot (\frac{1}{2} \cdot \overrightarrow{AC}) =$
    $(2 \cdot \frac{1}{2}) \cdot \overrightarrow{AC} = 1 \cdot \overrightarrow{AC} = \overrightarrow{AC}$ (by sub., 2d1, 1c4, and 2cP1e).

2e4. (?1) 2d6(v). (?2) 2d6, "etc." (?3) 2cP2e. (?4) 1b14. (?5) 2e3.

2e5. (?1) 2d6(vi). (?2) 2d6(vii). (?3) 2e2. (?4) 1b14. (?5) 2e3.

2g3. Suppose $i = \overrightarrow{OA}$ and $j = \overrightarrow{OB}$ were not linearly independent. Then $O, A,$
B would be collinear (by 2e4). However, since i, j are orthogonal (by 2g2), $O, A,$
B are not collinear (by 2g2). Hence i, j are linearly independent; similarly for $i,$
j, k, but with a slight difference. ‖

2g4 (preceding paragraph). (?1) 2b1. (?2) 2cP2d. (?3) Sub. (?4) 2g3 and 2e3.

2g. PROBLEMS

4. (a) $\overrightarrow{OP} + \overrightarrow{OQ} = 3i + 4j, \overrightarrow{PQ} = -i - 2j, \overrightarrow{QP} = i + 2j.$
5. (a) $\overrightarrow{OP} + \overrightarrow{OQ} = i + 4j + 3k, \overrightarrow{PQ} = -i - 3k, \overrightarrow{QP} = i + 3k.$

2h1 (preceding paragraphs). (?1) Lines parallel to perpendicular lines are perpendicular. (?2) 2b1. (?3) Pythagorean Theorem. (?4) 2gP3. (?5) 1dP5d. (?6) 2gP3. (?7) 1dP5i. (?8) Sub.

2h3. (?1) 2h2. (?2) 2b1. (?3) 2h2, 2gP3, and 1dP5d.

2h4. (?1) 2aP1. (?2) 2gP1a. (?3) 2h1. (?4) Property of real numbers.

2h. PROBLEMS

1. (a) 5. (c) 13. (e) 3.   3. (a) 7.   5. (4.5, 0).

2i1 (preceding paragraph). (?1) 2g5. (?2) Law of cosines. (?3) 2h4 and sub. (?4) Algebraic properties of real numbers.

2i6. In $E2'$, let $v = ai + bj, w = ci + dj$. Then $v \cdot w = ac + bd$, and $w \cdot v = ca + db$. However, $ac + bd = ca + db$ (by 1c5). Similarly for $E3'$. ‖

2i. PROBLEMS

1. (a) -7. (c) 0.
2. (a) Arccos$(-7/25)$. (c) $\pi/2$.
5. (a) π. (c) 0.
7. Arccos$(1/\sqrt{2}) = \pi/4$, Arccos$(\sqrt{3}/3)$, Arccos$(\sqrt{6}/3)$.

3a. (first paragraph).   (?1) 2cP2c.   (?2) 2d3, 2d1, and 2gP2.   (?3) Def. of equality of ordered pairs (2g, first paragraph).

3a3. (?)   Suppose $A \neq B$ are points in $E3'$, and $\overrightarrow{AB} = ai + bj + ck$. Then we refer to the ordered triple (a, b, c) as (a sequence of) *direction numbers* for line AB.

3a.   PROBLEMS

1. In $E2'$: Suppose $(0, 0)$ were direction numbers for a line. Then (by 3a3), there are points $A \neq B$ on the line such that $\overrightarrow{AB} = 0i + 0j = 0_V$ (by 2cP2d, and 2b8). Hence $A = B$ (by 2bP3). But this contradicts $A \neq B$. Hence $(0, 0)$ cannot be direction numbers for a line.
   Now suppose (a, b) is an ordered pair of real numbers, such that $a \neq 0$ or $b \neq 0$. In $E2'$, choose the point $P = (a, b)$. Then $O \neq P$, and line OP has direction numbers (a, b).   ‖

2. (a) In $E2'$: By 3a3, we may assume that if (a, b) are direction numbers for a line, then the line is line AB, where $\overrightarrow{AB} = ai + bj \neq 0_V$. Let $s \cdot \overrightarrow{AB} = sai + sbj = \overrightarrow{AC}$. By 2cP2e, A, B, C are collinear. Furthermore, since $s \neq 0$ and $\overrightarrow{AB} \neq 0_V$, $\overrightarrow{AC} \neq 0_V$ (by 2cP1d). Hence $A \neq C$ (by 2b8). Hence line AB = line AC (Two distinct points on a line determine the line.) But line AC has direction numbers (sa, sb) (by 3a3).   ‖

3. It will help to define a dot product for ordered pairs and triples of real numbers, analogous to the dot product of vectors: $(a, b) \cdot (c, d) = ac + bd$, and $(a, b, c) \cdot (d, e, f) = (ad + be + cf)$. One may then prove that two lines in E' with direction numbers D_1, D_2 are perpendicular iff $D_1 \cdot D_2 = 0$.

4. (a) Line AB is parallel to line CD.

5. Use direction number criteria.

7. A solution exists iff $a \neq 0$, and if a solution exists, it is not unique: either $(0, a)$, (a, a), or $(0, -a)$, $(a, -a)$ are, together with the given points, the vertices of a square.

10. (a) The line through $(0, 0, 1)$ and $(1, 2, 0)$.

11. (a) One sequence of direction numbers for the X axis in $E2'$: $(0, 0, 1)$.
    (b) All direction numbers for the X-axis in $E2'$: $\{(a, 0, 0) \mid a \text{ is a real number}\}$. (Read: "The set of all $(a, 0, 0)$ such that a is a real number.")

3b2. (?1) 2i3.   (?2) $v \cdot i = (ai + bj) \cdot (1i + 0j) = a$, and $|i| = 1$ (by 2g1).

3b4. (?1) 3b2.   (?2) 3a1.   (?3) 3a3.   (?4) 3aP2a.

3b5. (?1) 2gP2.   (?2) 3b2.   (?3) 2h1.

3b7. (?1) 3b4.   (?2) 3a10.   (?3) 3a1, and def. of equality of ordered pairs (2g, first paragraph).   (?4) 3b5.   (?5) Sub.

3b9. (?1) 2i3.   (?2) 2i2.   (?3) Properties of real numbers.   (?4) 3b2.

3b.   PROBLEMS

1. (a) $(1/\sqrt{2}, 1/\sqrt{2})$, $(\pi/4, \pi/4)$.
   (c) $(1/\sqrt{3}, 1/\sqrt{3}, 1/\sqrt{3})$, (α, β, γ), where $\alpha = \beta = \gamma = \text{Arccos}(\sqrt{3}/3)$.

2. (a) $(1, 0, 0)$, $(0, \pi/2, \pi/2)$.
   (d) $(1/\sqrt{2}, 1/\sqrt{2}, 0)$, $(\pi/4, \pi/4, \pi/2)$.
   (g) $(0, -1, 0)$, $(\pi/2, \pi, \pi/2)$.

3. $\{s(i + j) \mid s$ is a positive real number$\}$ (cf. answer to 3aP11b).
5. $(-1/3, 2/3, 2/3)$, $(4/5, 3/5, 0)$, Arccos$(2/15)$.

3c3. (?1) 3a10. (?2) 3a1. (?3) Def. of equality of ordered pairs (2g, first paragraph). (?4) Otherwise (by 2cP1d), $p = 0$, contradicting hyp. (?5) Sub. (?6) Property of real numbers.

3c7. (?1) $(p, q) - (0, 0) = (p, q)$. (?2) 3a10. (?3) 3c2. (?4) Sub.

3c ILL. Ex. (?1) 3a3. (?2) 3c4.

3c8. (?1) Exterior angle theorem. (?2) $(m_2 - m_1)/(1 + m_1 m_2)$ (by 3c7).

3c. PROBLEMS

1. (a) $\pi/4$, 0, Arctan$(-1/2)$, $\pi/3$.
3. (a) $m = 2$, $\overrightarrow{AB} = 2i + 4j$.
    (c) $m = 0$, $\overrightarrow{AB} = 5i + 0j$.
4. (a) Arctan$(1/3)$. (c) $\pi/2$. (e) Arctan$(1/2)$.

3d1. (?1) Hyp. (?2) 3a5. (?3) Sub. and 3a1. (?4) 3a10. (?5) Parallel lines that intersect are identical. (?6) Sub. (?7) 0. (?8) 3a5. (?9) 3a10. (?10) $x - x_A = sp, y - y_A = sq$; hence $x = x_A + sp, y = y_A + sq$. ‖

3d4. (?1) Properties of real numbers.

3d. PROBLEMS

1. (a) $x = 2 - s, y = 4 + 3s; 3x + y = 10$.
    (c) $x = 2s, y = -5s; 5x + 2y = 0$.
    (e) $x = 3 + s, y = 4; y = 4$.
3. (a) $x = -2 + 5s, y = 3 + s; x - 5y + 17 = 0$.
    (c) $x = 1 - 2s, y = 2, z = 3 + s; x + 2z = 7, y = 2$.
4. (c) $y = 0$. (e) $x = a$. (g) $x = y$.
    (i) $z = 0$. (l) $y = 2, z = 3$. (o) $x = y$.

3e (first two paragraphs). (?1) $C = (x, y) = (x_A + s(x_B - x_A)$, $y_A + s(y_B - y_A)) = (x_A, y_A) + s(x_B - x_A, y_B - y_A) = A + s(B - A)$. (?2) 2gP1a. (?3) Sub. (?4) 2d3. (?5) 2gP1a. (?6) 2bP3, 6.

3e. PROBLEMS

2. (a) $(1, 0)$; $(0, 1)$, $(2, -1)$.
    (c) $(3, -3, 6)$; $(2, -2, 4)$, $(4, -4, 8)$.
4. (a) $(0, 4/3, 2)$, $(2, 0, 0)$.
5. (a) $\sqrt{73}$, $\sqrt{85}$, $2\sqrt{26}$. (c) $\sqrt{305}/2$, $\sqrt{53}$, $\sqrt{269}/2$.
6. (a) $(-3, 4)$. (c) $(-1, 0)$. (e) $(-6, 8)$. (g) $(0, 5)$.
7. (a) $(4, -9)$. (c) $(-1, 1)$.
10. (a) $(4, 5)$. (c) $(-5, -1)$.

3f4. (?1) 3f3. (?2) 3f1. (?3) $y = mx + b$.

3f8. (?1) Hyp. (?2) 3a5. (?3) Hyp. (?4) Properties of real numbers, and hyp. (?5) 3aP3. (?6) Through a point, there exists one and only one line perpendicular to a given line. (?7) Sub. (?8) Sub. (?9) 3a5. (?10) Hyp. (?11) 3f7. (?12) 3aP3. (?13) $Ax + By = Aa + Bb$.

3f10. (?1) We may let $x = 0$ and solve for y. (?2) 3f8.

3f13. Continuing with the proof of 3f10, it follows from 3f8 and 3aP2a that (A, B) are direction numbers for any normal n to l. By 3aP3, 2a, $(-B, A)$ are direction numbers for any line perpendicular to n, hence for l. ‖

3f. PROBLEMS

1. (a) $y = 3x + 6$. (c) $y = (2/3)x - 4$. (e) $y = kx - ka + b$.
   (g) $x + 4y = 29$. (i) $y = 7$. (k) $3x + 4y = 11$.
6. (a) $-3/5, 6$. (c) $-1, 0$. (e) $\sqrt{3}, -3$. (g) $-2, 7$. (i) $-2, 11$.
   (k) $-1, 5$.
10. (a) $2x - 3y + 15 = 0$. (c) $x = 1$. (e) $y = 2$. (g) $x + y = 3$.

3g1. (?1) A point lies on a graph in E' iff the coordinates of the point satisfy the equation of the graph. (?2) 3f13 and 3a3. (?3) 2i5. (?4) 2i2. (?5) Properties of real numbers, sub., and 2h1. (?6) $|d| = |Ap + Bq + C|/\sqrt{A^2 + B^2}$, (by 1dP5m, b).

3g3. (?1) 3g1, Note. (?2) 1d5. (?3) Def. of graph.

3g. PROBLEMS

1. (a) $13/5$. (c) $4\sqrt{2}$. (e) $14/13$. (g) 6. (i) $|v + p|$. (k) $|a|$.
2. (a) $37\sqrt{26}$. 4. (a) $12/5$.

3h. PROBLEMS

1. (a) $(6, -3)$. (c) No intersection. (e) $(0, 2)$.

3i. (?1) 3fP3b. (?2) For $(p, q) = (0, 0)$, equation (3) is not a linear equation in x and y. (?3) All scalar multiples of $(2, -1)$.

3i. PROBLEMS

2. (a) $p(x - 7) + q(y - 11) = 0$. (c) $x - y = k$.

3j. PROBLEMS

1. (a) $(x,y) = (6, 1)$; minimum $C = 9$ cents.
   (c) $(x, y) = (0, 5)$ or $(6, 1)$ or any point on the line segment joining these two points; minimum $C = 15$ cents.
2. (a) 5 cards, 1 box.
3. (a) 27 skate keys, 1 can opener.
   (c) 5 skate keys, 45 can openers.
   (e) 0 skate keys, 50 can openers.
4. (a) k skate keys, $50 - k$ can openers, where k is any member of the set $\{0, 1, 2, 3, 4, 5\}$. (But note that $k = 0$ involves minimum use of machine time.)
5. (a) 0 gram of Dis, 8 grams of Dat.
   (c) 2 grams of Dis, 6 grams of Dat.
   (e) 8 grams of Dis, 4 grams of Dat.

3l2. (?1) Hyp. (?2) 3a10. (?3) Hyp. (?4) Hyp. and 3aP3. (?5) 3l1. (?6) 3l1. (?7) 3aP3.

3l. *PROBLEMS*

2. (a) $Ax + By + Az = 10A + 4B$.
  (b) $x - 3y + z = -2$.
  (e) $y = x + z$; intercepts: $x = 0$, $y = 0$, $z = 0$; traces: $y = x$, $z = -x$, $y = z$.
3. $x + y = 1$.   6. (a) $3x - 2y + 4z = 29$.   9. $2x + 3y + 4z = 72$.
11. $\pi/3$.   12. (c) $12\frac{1}{13}$, $5/13$.
13. $(36/169, 48/169, 144/169)$, $(154/169, 149/169, -60/169)$.
15. $x = 8 - 7t$, $y = 2t$, $z = 5t + 2$.
16. (a) $(8/3, -4/3, 4/3)$.   17. $x + z = 10$.
19. $x = 3 + at$, $y = -2 + bt$, $z = 7 - (a + b)t$.
20. (a) $(1, 1, 1)$.   (c) $x = 2$, $y = 1 - t$, $z = t$.   21. $2x + 3y + z = 37$.

3n4. (?1) If $b = c = 0$, then $i \times (ai + bj + ck) = i \times ai = a(i \times i) = a0_V = 0_V = -cj + bk$ [by 2cP1d, 2b8, 3n3(iii), 3n2, 2cP1d, and 2b8]. (?2) 2i8. (?3) 2i3. (?4) Trigonometric formula. (?5) Sub. (?6) 3n1(i).

3n6. (?1) 2b3, 2n5, and 3n3(iv). (?2) 3n2. (?3) 3m. (?4) 3m.

3n ILL. EX. (?1) 2gP1b. (?2) 3aP2a. (?3) 3l2.

3n. *PROBLEMS*

1. (a) $4k$. (c) $-2k$. (e) $5(i + j - k)$.
3. (a) $15\sqrt{5}$. (c) $(3/2)\sqrt{269}$.
8. (a) 120. (c) 180.

4c. *PROBLEMS*

2. (a) A constant polynomial of no degree, whose graph is a straight line, the X axis.
  (e) A second-degree, or quadratic, polynomial whose graph only rises, both to the right and to the left of the origin. The graph is symmetric to the Y axis, has one extremum (a minimum), and intercepts the axes only at the origin.
  (g) A fourth-degree, or quartic, polynomial; the rest of our discussion is as for (e) above. How, then, do the graphs differ?
  (j) The discussion in this case is exactly as in (e) above. How do the graphs differ?
  (l) A third-degree, or cubic, polynomial whose graph only rises to the left and only falls to the right of the origin. The graph has 0 or 2 extrema (it turns out to be 0) and intercepts the axes only at the origin.
  (n) A second-degree, or quadratic, polynomial whose graph eventually only rises on both right and left. It has one extremum (a minimum), no x-intercepts, and y-intercept 5.
  (p) A third-degree, or cubic, polynomial whose graph eventually only rises on the right and falls on the left. The graph has 0 or 2 extrema (it turns out to be 2), an x-intercept between 2 and 3, and a y-intercept of -5.
  (r) A cubic polynomial whose graph eventually only rises on the right and falls on the left. The graph has 0 or 2 extrema, and intercepts at the origin and $x = 3$.
  (t) A cubic polynomial whose graph eventually only rises on the right and falls on the left. The graph has 0 or 2 extrema, x-intercepts 2, -1, -3, and y-intercept -6.

4e. PROBLEMS

1. (a) Domain: All real numbers except 0; symmetric with respect to the origin; asymptotes: $x = 0, y = 0$.

(d) Domain: All real numbers except $x = 0$; symmetric with respect to the Y axis; asymptotes: $x = 0, y = 0$.

(f) Domain: All real numbers except 1 and -1. Intercept: The origin; symmetric with respect to the origin; asymptotes: $x = \pm 1, y = 0$.

(i) Domain: All real numbers; y-intercept: 1; symmetric with respect to the Y axis; asymptote: $y = 0$.

(m) Domain: All real numbers except 0; x-intercept: -1; asymptote: $x = 0$.

(o) Domain: All real numbers; x-intercepts: 1, -2; y-intercept: -2; asymptote: $y = 1/2$.

(r) Domain: All real numbers except 1 and -1. Intercepts $x = -3, y = -3$; asymptotes: $x = \pm 1, y = 0$.

(u) Domain: All real numbers except -2; y-intercept: 2; asymptotes: $x = -2, y = x - 2$.

4f. PROBLEMS

1. (a) Intercepts: $x = 2, y = 2$; solutions for x and y: $x = (2 - y)/(1 + y)$, $y = (2 - x)/(1 + x)$; asymptotes: $y = -1, x = -1$.

(c) Intercepts: The origin, $x = -1$; symmetry with respect to the X axis; solutions for x and y: $y = \pm \sqrt{x(x + 1)}$, $x = (-1 \pm \sqrt{1 + 4y^2})/2$; excluded values: $-1 < x < 0$.

(f) Intercept: The origin; symmetry with respect to the X axis; solution for y: $y = \pm x\sqrt{x/(4 - x)}$; asymptote: $x = 4$; excluded values: $x < 0$, $x > 4$.

(h) Intercept: The origin; symmetry with respect to the X axis; solutions for x and y: $y = \pm \sqrt{x/(x - 2)}$, $x = 2y^2/(y^2 - 1) = 2 + [2/(y^2 - 1)]$; asymptotes: $x = 2, y = \pm 1$; excluded values: $0 < x < 2$.

(k) Intercept: The origin; symmetry with respect to the Y axis; solutions for x and y: $x = \pm 4\sqrt{y/(y - 2)}$, $y = 2x^2/(x^2 - 16)$; asymptotes: $y = 2$, $x = 4, x = -4$; excluded values: $0 < y < 2$.

5b. PROBLEMS

1. (a) $(x - 1)^2 + (y - 2)^2 = 9$.

(c) $(x - 1)^2 + (y + 2)^2 = 9$.

(e) $(x - 3)^2 + (y - 4)^2 = 25$.

(g) $(x - 3)^2 + (y + 4)^2 = 25$.

(i) $x^2 + y^2 = 49$.   (k) $x^2 + y^2 = 0$.

2. (a) Circle, center at the origin, radius 3.

(c) "Point" circle: $(0, 0)$.

(e) Equation equivalent to: $x^2 + y^2 = 25$.

(g) Semicircle consisting of those points of the graph of $x^2 + y^2 = 25$ for which $y \geq 0$.

(k) Circle, center $(2, 3)$, radius 5.

(m) Circle, center $(-2, 3)$, radius 4.

(o) Circle, center $(1, -5)$, radius 5.

(q) Circle, center $(4, 4)$, radius $4\sqrt{2}$.

(s) Circle, center $(-3.5, -1.5)$, radius $3.5\sqrt{2}$.

(u) Circle, center $(7.5, 2.5)$, radius 2.5.

5c. PROBLEMS

1. Equation, center, and radius are:
   (a) $x^2 + y^2 - 6x - 4y = 0$; (3, 2); $\sqrt{13}$.
   (c) $x^2 + y^2 - 6x + 4 = 0$; (3, 0); $\sqrt{5}$.
   (e) $x^2 + y^2 - 2x + 4y - 20 = 0$; (1, −2); 5.
   (g) $3x^2 + 3y^2 - 4x - 14y - 4 = 0$; (2/3, 7/3); $\sqrt{65}/3$.
2. (a) $(x + 2)^2 + (y - 1)^2 = 52$.
   (c) $(x - 2)^2 + (y + 3)^2 = 4$.
3. (a) (1, −2); (2, 1).   (c) (3/2, $\pm\sqrt{35}/2$).
4. (a) $(x - h)^2 + (y - k)^2 = h^2 + k^2$.
   (c) $(x - h)^2 + (y - k)^2 = h^2$.
   (e) $x^2 + (y - k)^2 = r^2$.
   (g) $(x - h)^2 + y^2 = h^2$.

5e. PROBLEMS

1. Foci and eccentricity are:
   (a) (0, ±4); 0.8.   (c) (0, ±2$\sqrt{3}$); $\sqrt{3}/2$.
   (e) (±$\sqrt{3}$, 0); $\sqrt{3}/2$.   (g) (±1, 0); $\sqrt{2}/2$.
2. (a) $3x^2 + 4y^2 = 91$.   (c) $x^2 + y^2 = 25$.
3. $x^2 + 4y^2 = 16$; $4x^2 + y^2 = 16$.
5. $16x^2 + 25y^2 = 400$.   7. $e = 0.5$.

5h. PROBLEMS

1. The type of curve, foci, eccentricity [approximate, except in (a)], and asymptotes
   are:
   (a) Hyperbola; (±5, 0); 1.25; $y = \pm\frac{3}{4}x$.
   (c) Hyperbola; (0, ±5); 1.67; $y = \pm\frac{3}{4}x$.
   (e) Ellipse; (0, ±4$\sqrt{3}$); 0.87.
   (g) Hyperbola; (0, ±4$\sqrt{5}$); 1.12; $y = \pm2x$.
   (i) Hyperbola; (±$\sqrt{34}$, 0); 1.94; $y = \pm\frac{5}{3}x$.
   (k) Hyperbola; (±2$\sqrt{5}$, 0); 2.24; $y = \pm2x$.
   (m) Rectangular hyperbola; (±5$\sqrt{2}$, 0); 1.41; $y = \pm x$.
   (o) Rectangular hyperbola; (6, 6), (−6, −6); 1.41; $x = 0, y = 0$
   (p) Rectangular hyperbola; (6, −6), (−6, 6); 1.41; $x = 0, y = 0$.
2. (a) $2y^2 - 3x^2 = 5$.   (c) $xy = 6$.
3. (a) $9x^2 - 16y^2 = 144$ or $9y^2 - 16x^2 = 144$.
   (c) $9x^2 - y^2 = 36$ or $y^2 - 9x^2 = 4$.

5i. PROBLEMS

1. (a) Parabola; symmetric to the Y axis; y is never negative; $V = (0, 0)$;
      $F = (0, \frac{1}{4})$; directrix: $y = -\frac{1}{4}$.
   (d) Parabola; symmetric to the X axis; x is never positive; $V = (0, 0)$;
      $F = (-\frac{1}{4}, 0)$; directrix: $x = \frac{1}{4}$.
   (f) Parabola; symmetric to the X axis; x is never negative; $V = (0, 0)$;
      $F = (\frac{1}{12}, 0)$; directrix: $x = -\frac{1}{12}$.
   (i) Parabola; symmetric to the Y axis; y is never negative; $V = (0, 0)$;
      $F = (0, 4)$; directrix: $y = -4$.

(l) Parabola; symmetric to the Y axis; y is never positive; $V = (0, 0)$; $F = (0, -4)$; directrix: $y = 4$.
2. (a) $12x = y^2$. (c) $12x + y^2 = 0$. (e) $49y = 11x^2$, or $121x = 7y^2$.
3. (a) $(0, 0)$, $(1, 1)$. (c) $(0, 0)$, $(1, 1)$.
 (e) $(-3, 9)$, $(2, 4)$.

5j1 (preceding paragraph). (?1) 2bP5a. (?2) 2g5. (?3) 2d6(iii), 2b4, etc. (?4) 2g5.

5k. PROBLEMS

1. The type of curve, and foci are:
 (a) Ellipse $(1 \pm \sqrt{3}, -2)$. (c) Circle; $(1, -2)$.
 (e) Hyperbola; $(-4, 2)$, $(6, 2)$.
 (g) Hyperbola; $(0, 0)$, $(0, 10)$.
 (i) Parabola; $(2.5, -3)$. (k) Parabola; $(2, 0)$.
 (m) Hyperbola; $(1 \pm 2\sqrt{13}, -2)$.
3. $3(x - 2)^2 + (y - 1)^2 = 12$.
5. $(x - 1)^2 - 3(y - 11)^2 = 12$.
7. $x^2 - 2x + 20y + 41 = 0$.
9. $16(x - 1)^2 + 25(y - 3)^2 = 400$.

6b. PROBLEMS

1. $2\pi/3$; 2.   3. π; 2.   5. $\pi/2$; 2.   7. 4π; 5.   9. $2\pi/3$; 2.

6c. PROBLEMS

2. (a) $\sin x$, $\sin 2x$ represent equally loud sounds, $\sin x + \sin 2x$ a sound louder than either; $\sin x$ and $\sin x + \sin 2x$ represent sounds of the same pitch, $\sin 2x$ a sound of higher pitch. (In fact, an *octave* higher—sounds whose periods are in the ratio $2:1$ are said to be an *octave* apart.)
 (c) Ranked from softest to loudest: $\sin 3x$, $2 \sin x$, $2 \sin x + \sin 3x$; the last two are of the same pitch, the first of higher pitch.
 (e) Ranked from softest to loudest: $\sin 3x$, $2 \sin 2x$, $2 \sin 2x + \sin 3x$; this is also their ranking going from highest to lowest pitch.

6d. PROBLEMS

The maximum ordinates and the abscissas at which they occur are, respectively:
1. (a) 1; $\frac{1}{2} + 2k$. (c) 3; $\frac{1}{4} + k$.
 (e) 4; k. (g) 2; $\frac{1}{2} + 2k$.
2. (a) 1; $(-\pi/2) + 2\pi k = -1.6 + 6.3k$ (approximately).
 (c) 2; $x = 0.3 + 3.1k$ (approximately).
3. (a) 1; $2k\pi$. (c) 3; $\frac{1}{2} + 2k$. (e) 2; $2 + 4k$.

6f. PROBLEMS

1. (a) -3. (c) -1. (e) 1. (g) 3.
 (i) Nonexistent. (k) -2. (m) 0. (o) 2.
2. (a) $x = \log_{10} 5$. (c) $\log_{10} 2 = 0.3010$ (approx.).
3. (a) $10^{0.4771} = 3$ (approx.). (c) $10^y = x$.
4. Maximal domain and range:
 (a) 10^x: R, R^+; $\log_{10} x$: R^+, R.

(c) 4^x: R, R^+; $\log_4 x$: R^+, R.
(e) $(1/2)^x$: R, R^+; $\log_4 x$: R^+, R.
(g) R, R^+ (i) R, R^+.
(k) R, the set of all negative real numbers.
(m) $R, (0, 1]$. (o) R, R.
(q) R^+, R. (s) R^+, R.
(u) R^+, the set of all nonnegative real numbers.
6. (a) 2^{x+1}. (c) $4^x - 4^{-x}$.
    (e) $4^x + 4^{-x} - 2$. (g) 4.

6g. PROBLEMS

1. (b) $y = (x - 1)^2$. (c) $x^2 + y^2 = 100$.
    (e) $x^2 - 2xy + 2y^2 = 1$. (g) $x^4 - 100x^2 + 25y^2 = 0$.
    (i) $x^{2/3} + y^{2/3} = 1$. (m) $25x^3y^2 = (4 - x)(2 - x)^2$.

6i. PROBLEMS

1. (a) $(3\sqrt{3}/2, 3/2)$. (c) $(0, 0)$. (e) $(0, -4)$.
    (g) $(5\cos 20°, -5\sin 20°)$. (i) $(0, 2)$.
3. (a) $x^2 + y^2 = 25$. (c) $y = 5$. (e) $x = y$.
    (g) $x^2 + y^2 - 10y = 0$. (i) $x^2 + 8y - 16 = 0$.
4. (a) $(x^2 + y^2)^3 = 4a^2x^2y^2$. (c) $(x^2 + y^2)^3 = a^2(x^2 - y^2)^2$.
    (e) $(x^2 + y^2 - ax)^2 = b^2(x^2 + y^2)$.
    (g) $(x^2 + y^2)^2 = 2a^2xy$.

7c. PROBLEMS

2. (a) $(x - 1)^2 + (y - 2)^2 + (z + 3)^2 = 16$.
    (c) $x^2 + z^2 = 25$.

7d. PROBLEMS

1. Ellipsoid of revolution.   3. Hyperboloid of two sheets.
5. Paraboloid of revolution.   7. Elliptic cylinder.   9. Cone.
11. Hyperbolic paraboloid.   13. Ellipsoid of revolution.
15. Ellipsoid of revolution.   17. Cone of revolution.   19. Sphere.

7e. PROBLEMS

1. (a) $(2, \pi/3, 0), (2, \pi/3, \pi/2)$.
    (c) $(\sqrt{2}, \pi/4, \sqrt{2}), (2, \pi/4, \pi/4)$.
2. (a) $(3\sqrt{3}/2, 3/2, 7), (\sqrt{58}, \pi/6, \text{Arccos } 7/\sqrt{58})$.
    (c) $(-\pi, 0, \pi), (\pi\sqrt{2}, \pi, \pi/4)$.
3. (a) $(5, 5, 5\sqrt{2}), (5\sqrt{2}, \pi/4, 5\sqrt{2})$.
    (c) $(-3\sqrt{3}/2, 3\sqrt{3}/2, 3), (3\sqrt{3}, 3\pi/4, 3)$.
4. (a) $\rho = a$. (c) $\rho = 2a \cos\theta \sin\phi$. (e) $\phi = 0$. (g) $\theta = \pi/2$.
5. (a) $x^2 + y^2 = z^2$. (c) $x = y$.
    (e) $x^2 + y^2 = 100$. (g) $(x^2 + y^2 + z^2)^2 = 100(x^2 + y^2)$.
6. (a) $x^2 + y^2 = 25$. (c) $z = 5$.
    (e) $x^2 + y^2 = 10y$. (g) $x^2 + y^2 = 4z^2$.
7. (a) $\rho = 3, r^2 + z^2 = 9$. (c) $\rho \cos\theta \sin\phi = 9, r \cos\theta = 9$.
    (e) $\rho \sin^2\phi = 8 \cos\phi, r^2 = 8z$.
    (g) $\theta = \pi/4, \theta = \pi/4$.

Index

La   The